The World Guide to Combat Planes

VOLUME I

Compiled by William Green

The World Guide to COMBAT PLANES ONE

Illustrated by Dennis Punnett and John Weal

With contributions by Roy Braybrook, John Fricker
Kenneth Fulton and Philip Robins

DOUBLEDAY AND COMPANY INC.
Garden City, New York

DOUBLEDAY EDITION 1967

PRINTED IN GREAT BRITAIN

Introduction

On November 8, 1950, a new era opened in military aviation history—the first jet air combat took place South of the Yalu between the MiG-15 and the F-80C Shooting Star; the aircraft, with their simple lead pursuit optical gunsights, pitting a trio of slow-firing cannon against a sextet of machine guns. Some fifteen years later, on April 26, 1966, their Mach 2.0 successors, the MiG-21 and the F-4C Phantom II, met for the first time in combat 65 miles N.N.E. of Hanoi, the capital of North Vietnam. They had been fifteen years of dramatic change in combat aircraft, and in none more so than the fighter, the primary subject of this volume.

The MiG-15s and F-80Cs endeavouring to establish superiority over each other in the skies above the Yalu were very basic aircraft by standards appertaining even a few short years later, and today the various "black boxes" making up the autopilot, radio, radar, fire control and navigation systems of an aircraft such as the Phantom II cost, in themselves, more than two complete F-80Cs such as participated in that first historic jet combat. Indeed, the modern warplane has become one of the most complex weapons in the world's armouries which, without its quota of "black boxes", could not leave its runway, let alone find its target or release its weapons.

The near-mystical faith that had developed, particularly in the West, in the electronic-brained, fully-automated weapon that virtually rejected man in any other role than that of a button pusher, has been largely dispelled by the Vietnamese air war, however, for human skill and courage have, as in previous wars, proved to be key elements. Like the Korean war before it, the Vietnamese conflict has exploded its share of cherished theories, and the acid test of combat has demanded some reassessment of the computerized peacetime analyses on which so much reliance had been placed. The prophets of the doctrine that the missile's birth had sounded the death knell for the manned combat aircraft have been confounded, and deficiencies have revealed themselves in the most lauded of warplanes and other weapons, attestations to their efficacy made by both East and West proving spurious.

Mach 2.0 fighters are no longer confined to the air arms of the "Big League", as a cursory glance through the first section of this volume will reveal. This survey also reveals the numerical growth of individual air forces and naval air arms which now exceed 120—among the first acts of the many new states that have emerged in recent years has been the establishment of national arms, such being considered *de rigueur* for prestige purposes, and many of these countries having found the Soviet Union far more accommodating than the western nations in the indiscriminate supply of combat aircraft. In the pages that follow, an attempt has been made to describe not only the development of all current fighter and attack aircraft, but to detail their equipment, and provide the reader, where possible, with some idea of their capabilities and shortcomings. The various types of electronic equipment that now form so indispensable a part of all types of modern warplane are surveyed, and fighter requirements and the various aircraft currently under development to provide the next generation of warplanes in this category are reviewed.

London, September 1966 — WILLIAM GREEN

Contents

Acknowledgements

The sources of some of the photographs appearing in this volume are as follows: Aireview (pages 68, 115, 122, 192, 193, 214 and 216); Amilpress (page 158); B-R Photo (page 82); G. Bignozzi (page 147); Flight International (page 77); K. Hinata (pages 144, 153 and 161); Karel Kliment (page 128); F. A. Giro (page 8); Alfredo B. Linder (page 30); Letectvi & Kosmonautika (pages 136 and 172); M. W. Miranda (page 13); Neil A. MacDougall (page 19); P. R. March (104 & 106); S. P. Peltz (pages 9, 28, 62, 97 lower, 120 and 152); R. E. A. Taylor (page 80); Giuseppe Tosolini (page 160); Robert Watt (page 29).

GUIDE TO AIR FORCE COMBAT EQUIPMENT

A summary of the combat equipment of the world's air arms and their equipment procurement plans. Aircraft quantities indicated are those originally acquired by the air arm concerned, and make no allowance for subsequent attrition, and where such quantities are approximations this fact is indicated by an asterisk.

AFGHANISTAN

Royal Afghan Air Force: Small interceptor fighter force operating some 60 of the 100* **MiG-17s** acquired from the Soviet Union in the late 'fifties, and based at Pagram and Mazar-i-Sharif. A token force of 10–12 **Il-28** tactical light bombers also supplied by the Soviet Union, but flying is relatively limited. Most Afghan jet pilots have received advanced training in India or the Soviet Union.

ALBANIA

Albanian People's Army Air Force: Small defensive force administered and controlled by the Army Command and possessing the equivalent of four interceptor squadrons. Two operate the survivors of 40* **MiG-15s** supplied by the Soviet Union 1955–57, the others operating **MiG-17s** of which 30* were received from the Soviet Union prior to the discontinuation of Soviet military aid resulting from political differences between the two countries. Serviceability was extremely low until 1964 owing to spares shortages, only a token strength being maintained by cannibalization, but in that year China commenced delivery of spares for the **MiG-15s** and **-17s** and, in 1965, supplied 30 Chinese-built **MiG-17s** to supplement the surviving aircraft of Russian origin. The Albanian interceptor squadrons operate from Berat/Kucove, Durazzo/Shijak, Tirana and Valona.

ALGERIA

Algerian Air Force: Established in 1962, this small air arm is receiving aid from both the Soviet Union and the United Arab Republic, but by mid-1966 its operational elements were still in an embryo state. A small number of **MiG-15** fighters surplus to the requirements of the Air Force of the United Arab Republic have been supplied to Algeria from Egypt, and the Soviet Union has furnished 12 **Il-28** light tactical bombers. An initial quantity of six **MiG-21** interceptors was delivered from the Soviet Union during 1965, and additional quantities of aircraft of this type were delivered in 1966. A strong Soviet training contingent is based in Algeria, and a number of Algerian pilots have undergone training in Egypt.

ARGENTINA

Fuerza Aérea Argentina: The principal operational elements of the F.A.A. are concentrated within the IV and VII Air Brigades with Headquarters at El Plumerillo Air Force Base, Mendoza, and the Moron Air Force Base, Buenos Aires, respectively. The only combat element included in the IV Air Brigade is the I Fighter-Bomber Group equipped with the **F-86F Sabre** of which 28 examples were acquired from the U.S.A. in 1960. The VII Air Brigade has two combat units, the II and III Fighter-Bomber Groups which, primarily equipped with the 28 surviving examples of the 100 **Meteor F.Mk.4** fighters acquired 1946–48, began re-equipping with reconditioned ex-U.S. Navy **A-4B Skyhawk** light attack aircraft in the summer of 1966. Fifty **A-4Bs** are being supplied to Argentina, and the U.S. government is to supply spares and support for the aircraft for five years. The F.A.A. has a long-standing requirement for modern interceptor fighters, but foreign currency limitations have restricted military aircraft purchases to training and transport aircraft and helicopters.

Serving as first-line equipment with Argentina's Aviación Naval *only, the Grumman F9F-2 Panther was delivered to the U.S. Navy from November* 1948, *a total of* 437 *being built. Powered by a* 5,750 *lb.s.t. Pratt & Whitney J42-P-*8, *it has a maximum speed of* 526 *m.p.h. at* 22,000 *ft., and carries an armament of four* 20-*mm. cannon and six* 5-*in. HVARs or two* 500-*lb. bombs.*

Aviación Naval: The operational elements of Argentina's Naval Aviation are divided between *Escuadras Aeronavales* 1 and 2 at the Commandante Espora and Puerto Belgrano naval air bases, and *Escuadras Aeronavales* 3 and 4 at the Punta de Indio base. Attack Squadron I, a component of *EA* 3, operates the survivors of 20 **F9F-2 Panther** shipboard fighter-bombers acquired from U.S. Navy surplus, together with two **TF-9J Cougar** tandem two-seat operational trainers. Attack Squadron II recently retired its last **F4U-5 Corsairs** which it operated from the 14,000-ton light fleet carrier A.R.A. *Independencia*, and is currently awaiting re-equipment with 45 **Fennecs** (French conversions of the **T-28A** equivalent to the **T-28D**), and Attack Squadron III is equipped with **SNJ-5C** trainers. Patrol Squadron I of *EA* 2 operates six ex-R.A.F. **P-2E Neptunes** in the maritime patrol role, and six **S-2A Trackers** in the ASW role, the former being based at Puerto Belgrano and the latter aboard the *Independencia*. The *Aviación Naval* hopes to acquire **Skyhawks** for the re-equipment of Attack Squadron II, and has requested **Sikorsky S-61** helicopters for the ASW role, but budget limitations had prevented procurement of aircraft of these types at the time of closing for press.

AUSTRALIA

Royal Australian Air Force: Immersed in a major re-equipment programme, the R.A.A.F.'s combat elements based in Australia are controlled by the Operational Command, and those based outside Australia are administratively controlled directly by the Department of Air in Canberra, and operationally by the forces to which they are attached. Combat strength comprises two jet fighter wings with a total of five squadrons, one jet bomber wing with three squadrons, and two maritime reconnaissance squadrons. One of the two fighter wings, No. 81, includes Nos. 75 and 76 Squadrons which operate **Mirage IIIOF** interceptors and each of which will eventually have 21 aircraft on strength. The remaining three fighter squadrons, those of No. 78 Wing, each operate 16 **CA-27 Sabre Mks. 31** and **32** from Butterworth, Malaya, Ubon, Thailand, and Darwin. These units, Nos. 3, 77, and 79 Squadrons, are being progessively re-equipped, current plans calling for the phasing out of the **Sabres** in 1969–70. Two will re-equip with the **Mirage IIIOA,** the first of these being No. 3 Squadron scheduled to convert during the summer of 1967, current R.A.A.F. orders calling for 48 **Mirage IIIOFs** and 52 **Mirage IIIOAs** with deliveries scheduled for completion by late 1968. The remaining squadron is likely to convert to the light ground attack role with an armed version of the licence-built **Macchi MB.326H,** 108 examples of which for the basic training role are called for under the initial contracts. No. 82 Wing comprises Nos. 1 and 6 Squadrons at Amberley, Brisbane, and No. 2 Squadron at Butterworth, Malaya, equipped with the **Canberra B.Mk.20.** These units will re-equip with the **F-111A** from 1969, current orders calling for 24 aircraft of this type, six of which will be returned to the U.S.A. two years after delivery for conversion to **RF-111A** standards. The remaining R.A.A.F. combat units fulfil the maritime reconnaissance role, these being No. 10 Squadron at Townsville with 12 **P-2H Neptunes** and No.11 Squadron at Richmond with 12 **P-2E Neptunes.** Current plans call for the re-equipment of the latter unit with the **P-3B Orion,** a letter of intent existing for 10 aircraft of this type for mid-1968 delivery.

Royal Australian Navy: The Australian Fleet Air Arm is currently a one-carrier, one air-station force which, from mid-1963, was to have been reduced to a wholly anti-submarine force equipped with rotocraft, but took a new lease on life with the reversal of the decision to retire fixed-wing combat aircraft. This change of heart, which resulted from the situation in S.E. Asia, has led to the retention in service of the R.A.N.'s two operational fixed-wing units, No. 805 Squadron with 10 **Sea Venom F.A.W.Mk.53** all-weather interceptors, and No. 816 Squadron with a similar number of **Gannet A.S.Mk.4** ASW aircraft which are deployed aboard H.M.A.S. *Melbourne*, together with No. 817 Squadron which operates 10 of the 27 **Wessex H.A.S.Mk.31** ASW helicopters acquired by the R.A.N. The Sea Venoms and Gannets are to be phased out at the end of 1967 when No. 805 Squadron will re-equip with the **A-4E Skyhawk** light shipboard attack aircraft, and No. 816 Squadron will re-equip with the **S-2A Tracker** ASW aircraft, eight **A-4Es,** together with two **TA-4E** trainers, and 14 **S-2A Trackers** having been ordered in 1964–65.

AUSTRIA

Österreichische Luftstreitkräfte: Austria's air arm, the *Luftstreitkräfte*, possesses only two combat units, No. 1 *Jagdbomber-Staffel* at Linz-Hörsching, and No. 2 *Jagdbomber-Staffel* which shares the same base. Both *Staffeln* operate 15 surplus Swedish Air Force **Saab 29F** fighter-bombers acquired 1961–62 and now in urgent need of replacement, and there is a current requirement for some 45 aircraft. The *Luftstreitkräfte* has been offered the **Saab 35X,** the **MiG-21,** the **Mirage III,** the **Lockheed F-104G** and the **Northrop F-5A,** but no choice had been announced at the time of closing for press.

BELGIUM

Force Aérienne Belge: Possessing both N.A.T.O. and national tactical and air defence commitments, the F.Aé.B. has been the recipient of 100 **F-104G Starfighters** which now equip one interceptor wing and one fighter-bomber wing, the latter, the 10*ème Wing de Chasseurs-Bombardiers* comprising the 23*ème* and 31*ème Escadrilles* at Kleine Brogel, being committed to N.A.T.O.'s 2nd ATAF, together with the 2*ème Wing* which, comprising the 1*ère* and 2*ème Escadrilles*, currently operates from Florennes with **F-84F Thunderstreaks,** and the 42*ème Escadrille de Reconnaissance-Photographique* which operates the **RF-84F Thunderflash** from Bierset. The remaining combat formation is the 1*ère Wing Chasse Tous-Temps*, the **F-104G**-equipped all-weather interceptor unit comprising the 349*ème* and 350*ème Escadrilles* based at Beauvechain. A decision is imminent concerning the choice of a fighter-bomber to replace the **F-84F Thunderstreak** in F.Aé.B. service

The sole remaining version of the de Havilland Sea Venom in first-line service is the F.A.W.Mk.53 serving with the Royal Australian Navy's No.816 Squadron aboard H.M.A.S. Melbourne. *To be phased out at the end of 1967, the Sea Venom F.A.W.Mk.53 two-seat interceptor has a 4,850 lb.s.t. de Havilland Ghost 104 turbojet with which it attains 563 m.p.h. at sea level.*

The Gloster Meteor remains in first-line service with three Latin-American air arms, and is illustrated above in its F.Mk.8 version serving with the Fôrça Aérea Brasileira. *Powered by two* 3,600 *lb.s.t. Rolls-Royce Derwent R.D.8 turbojets, the Meteor F.Mk.8 attains* 592 *m.p.h. at sea level, and has an armament of four* 20-*mm. cannon.*

from 1969–70. The choice is being made jointly with the *Koninklijke Luchtmacht* of the Netherlands, the F.Aé.B. requirement being for 104 aircraft, 27 of which will be equipped for photo-reconnaissance, plus 12 of a trainer version.

BOLIVIA

Fuerza Aérea Boliviano: The F.A.B., in receipt of Military Assistance Programme supplies since the overthrow of the Marxist revolutionary government of Bolivia in November 1964, is little more than a token force, its operational strength comprising six **F-51D Mustang** fighter-bombers, and two **T-28A** and two **T-28D** armed trainers which are employed primarily for internal security purposes.

BRAZIL

Fôrça Aérea Brasileira: Brazil possesses one of the largest air arms in Latin America, but the F.A.B. has little modern combat equipment, and funding difficulties render any large-scale purchase of modern warplanes unlikely in the immediate future despite the urgency of the re-equipment problem. The operational combat elements of the F.A.B. comprise the 1° *Grupo de Caça* and the 14° *Grupo de Caça*, with a statutory strength of two and one squadrons respectively and operating the survivors of 60 **Meteor F.Mk.8s** and 10 **Meteor T.Mk.7s,** acquired in 1953–55, from the Santa Cruz and Canoas Air Force Bases; the 4° *Grupo de Caça* with two squadrons equipped with the **F-80C Shooting Star** and **T-33A,** 30 of the Lockheed aircraft being delivered to Brazil in 1958–59, these being supplemented by a further six **T-33As** in 1965; the 7° *Grupo de Aviação* with 14 **P-2E Neptunes** for maritime reconnaissance operating from Salvador, Bahia, and the 1° *Grupo de Aviação Embarcada* which, equipped with 13 **S-2A** and **CS2F-1 Trackers,** is deployed aboard the carrier *Minas Gerais* in the ASW role.

Marinha do Brasil: The Aeronautical Department of the Brazilian Navy is responsible for all military rotorcraft operations as a result of a presidential directive of 1965 which also allocated the F.A.B. responsibility for all fixed-wing aircraft operations, including those from the carrier *Minas Gerais*. The combat elements of Brazilian naval aviation are confined to the ASW task for which six **Sikorsky S-58** and five **Westland Whirlwinds** are available for operation from the *Minas Gerais*, and three **Westland Wasps** have been acquired for operation from platforms on destroyers and frigates. A supplementary order for **Wasps** was anticipated at the time of closing for press, and governmental approval had been requested for the purchase of 10* **Sikorsky S-61** helicopters.

BULGARIA

Bulgarian Air Force: A small defensive air arm comprising two interceptor fighter regiments each with a statutory strength of three squadrons, a fighter-bomber regiment and an independent reconnaissance squadron, Bulgaria's air force is totally dependent on the Soviet Union for its equipment. A token number of **MiG-21** interceptors has been supplied since 1964 and equips one squadron, but the other interceptor squadrons and the reconnaissance squadron are equipped with the **MiG-17,** the fighter-bomber squadrons operating a mixture of **MiG-15s** and **-17s,** and first-line operational strength reportedly barely exceeds 100 aircraft.

BURMA

Union of Burma Air Force: Concerned primarily with the policing of Burmese territory and the support of Burmese field forces in operations against Communist guerillas in the North and North-East, the U.B.A.F. has one fighter-bomber squadron equipped with the **Vampire T.Mk.55,** eight examples of which were originally purchased for the dual operational-instructional role, and another equipped with the survivors of eighteen reconditioned **Sea Fury F.B.** and **T.T.Mk.11s** and three **T.Mk.20s** acquired in 1957. Two other squadrons operate **Provost T.Mk.53s** which are used in both the light ground attack and training roles, 40 aircraft of this type having been purchased between 1954 and 1960, but there has been no more recent procurement of operational equipment.

CAMEROUN

Cameroun Air Force: An embryo air arm established primarily for transport and communications duties, the Cameroun Air Force, like those of other newly independent territories formerly administered by France, has received some aid from the *Armée de l'Air* but possesses no combat element and has no plans for the acquisition of combat aircraft.

CAMBODIA

Royal Khmer Aviation: Cambodia, sandwiched between South Vietnam, Laos and Thailand, professes neutrality, but its air arm, Royal Khmer Aviation, currently possesses the services of a Chinese mission which acts in a advisory capacity and provides advanced instruction for Cambodian pilots, and has received 20* **MiG-15s** and **-17s** of Chinese manufacture to equip one interceptor and one fighter-bomber squadron. Other operational equipment has been provided by France in the form of ex-*Armée de l'Air* **A-1D Skyraider** attack bombers, the Royal Khmer Aviation inventory of this type now totalling 30, these supplanting the **M.S.733 Alcyons** previously used in the dual operational-instructional role, and equipping two squadrons.

*The A-1D Skyraiders with Cambodia's Royal Khmer Aviation are ex-*Armée de l'Air *aircraft, this version of the Skyraider having been manufactured* 1949–53. *Later variants of the Skyraider are described and illustrated on pages* 164–168, *Vol. II.*

CANADA

Royal Canadian Air Force: The R.C.A.F. currently possesses three operational components, the Air Defence Command, the No. 1 Air Division in Europe committed to N.A.T.O., and the Maritime Air Command which forms a part of the N.A.T.O. Atlantic Command. The manned aircraft elements of the A.D.C. comprise three all-weather interceptor units, Nos. 409, 416 and 426 Squadrons at Comox, Bagotville, Chatham and Val d'Or, these being equipped with the **CF-101 Voodoo**, the R.C.A.F. having received 54 **CF-101Bs** and 10 **CF-101Fs,** the latter variant being intended for the dual operational-instructional role. No. 1 Air Division in Europe comprises eight **CF-104** squadrons (Nos. 421, 422, 427, 430, 434, 439, 441, and 444) fulfilling strike and tactical reconnaissance roles, each with 18 aircraft, and the Maritime Air Command has four maritime reconnaissance squadrons, Nos. 404 and 405 Squadrons at Greenwood, and No. 415 Squadron at Summerside with the **CL-28 Argus**, and No. 407 Squadron based at Comox with **P-2H Neptunes**. One hundred and twenty-five Canadair-built **CF-5** fighter-bombers are currently programmed for the newly formed Mobile Command, about 20 two-seat **CF-5Bs** being included in this total, with deliveries to the R.C.A.F. being scheduled to commence in 1967. As the **CF-104** squadrons of the No. 1 Air Division in Europe run down through normal attrition they will be disbanded, no replacement for the **CF-104** being envisaged, and plans for a successor to the **CF-101 Voodoo** in the A.D.C. depend largely on U.S. Defence Department policy.

Royal Canadian Navy: The R.C.N. possesses one ASW aircraft carrier, H.M.C.S. *Bonaventure*, with one fixed-wing operational squadron, VS 880, operating 12-14 **CS2F-2 Tracker** ASW aircraft, and one operational rotorcraft squadron, HS 50 equipped with the **CHSS-2 Sea King** which also operates in the ASW role. A total of 36 **CHSS-2** helicopters has been ordered, and these will be operated in the ASW role from a number of R.C.N. vessels, including four new destroyer escorts, and eight *St. Laurent* and seven *Restigouche* class ASROC destroyers. The *Bonaventure* will undergo a major refit during 1967 which will extend its life for a further five years, and the R.C.N. will undoubtedly have to consider new ASW aircraft for operation from this carrier after 1970.

CEYLON

Royal Ceylon Air Force: The R.Cy.A.F. is a small air arm primarily concerned with internal security and light transport tasks, and its operational element is confined to **Jet Provost T.Mk. 51** armed trainers, the R.Cy.A.F. having received 11 aircraft of this type. No combat aircraft procurement plans have been announced.

CHILE

Fuerza Aérea de Chile: The F.A.Ch. is one of the most efficient of South American air forces. It has been trained with U.S. assistance under a mutual aid pact, but budgetary restrictions have limited the procurement of modern combat aircraft, and most first-line F.A.Ch. equipment is obsolescent. The F.A.Ch. possesses several *Grupos de Combate*, these comprising one or more *Escuadrillas* of varying strength and not necessarily fulfilling similar roles. For example, *Grupo* 6 at Punta Arenas possesses one fighter *escuadrilla* equipped with the **F-80C Shooting Star**, plus transport and rescue *escuadrillas*. The principle operational *Grupos* are: *Grupo* 2 which fulfils the maritime reconnaissance and ASW roles from Quintero with **HU-16B Albatross** amphibians, a total of 14 aircraft of this type having been obtained by the F.A.Ch.; *Grupo* 7 which, based at Los Cerrillos, Santiago, includes both an **F-80C**-equipped fighter *escuadrilla* and jet training *escuadrillas* operating the **F-80C,** the **T-33A** and the **Vampire T.Mk.55,** and *Grupo* 8 with **Douglas B-26 Invaders** and **North American B-25 Mitchells.** The F.A.Ch. has received 30 **F-80C Shooting Stars,** 15 **B-26 In-**

vaders and five **T-33As,** and was scheduled to receive 25 ex-U.S.A.F. **F-86F Sabres** during the course of 1966. Combat aircraft procurement in the immediate future is likely to be confined to additional ASW aircraft as the F.A.Ch. is anxious to expand its anti-submarine force.

CHINA (People's Republic)

Air Force of the People's Liberation Army: Numerically the fourth largest of the world's air arms, with a first-line strength of some 1,800 combat aircraft, all but some 300 of which are interceptor fighters and fighter-bombers, the A.F.P.L.A. is a "large but ageing" force, according to the U.S. Defense Secretary, Robert S. McNamara, the bulk of its equipment being obsolescent. This state of affairs has resulted directly from the ideological differences between Peking and Moscow which led to the discontinuation of Russian aid in 1960. However, improved Chinese industrial capabilities are attested to by domestic production of modern supersonic jet fighters based on the design of the **MiG-19** and **MiG-21,** small numbers of which had been delivered to China from the Soviet Union immediately prior to the breach in relations between the Sino-Communists and Russia, and a progressive improvement in A.F.P.L.A. potency may be expected in consequence. The major formation of the A.F.P.L.A. is the Air Division which comprises three Regiments each of three squadrons, and there are currently some 14 Air Divisions possessing a ratio of approximately five interceptor fighter and fighter-bomber squadrons to one light tactical bomber squadron. At the present time, the bulk of the interceptor squadrons are equipped with **MiG-17s** that have been built at the Government Aircraft Manufacturing Centre at Shen Yang, near Mukden, but these are being transferred to the fighter-bomber elements, many of which still operate the **MiG-15,** with the availability of increasing numbers of the Chinese version of the **MiG-21.** Other **MiG-17s** are being transferred to such countries as Albania, Cambodia and North Vietnam, and early in 1966 several Chinese-built **MiG-19s** were delivered to Pakistan. All light tactical bomber squadrons are equipped with the **Il-28,** some 400 of which were originally acquired from the Soviet Union, and there is a small heavy bomber element equipped with the obsolete piston-engined **Tu-4** (B-29 copy).

The Lockheed F-80C Shooting Star has been supplied under the MAP to the air arms of Brazil, Chile, Ecuador, Peru and Uruguay, and is illustrated here in service with the Fuerza Aérea de Chile. *The F-80C has a* 4,600 *lb.s.t. Allison J35-A-38 turbojet and attains* 594 *m.p.h. at sea level. Armament comprises six* 0.5-*in. machine guns, and two* 1,000-*lb. bombs may be carried. The F-80C was manufactured during* 1948–50.

CHINA (Nationalist)

Chinese Nationalist Air Force: Based on the island of Taiwan (Formosa), the C.N.A.F. has enjoyed for a number of years and continues to enjoy substantial U.S. aid. Organised along U.S.A.F. lines into wings of three squadrons, each wing having a statutory strength of 75 aircraft, the C.N.A.F. still operates two day fighter wings, the 2nd and 3rd, with the **F-86F Sabre,** 320 of which were supplied to the Nationalist government during 1954–58, but the main C.N.A.F. fighter strength is provided by 50* **F-104G Starfighters,** and in December 1965 the first squadron of

Northrop F-5 fighter-bombers was handed over to the 1st Fighter Wing at the Tainan Air Base, this type being the intended successor to the **F-86F** in C.N.A.F. service. The 4th Fighter Wing operates about 45 surviving **F-100 Super Sabres** from the 80 ex-U.S.A.F. **F-100As** (brought up to later **F-100D** standards) obtained in 1960, and there is one all-weather interceptor squadron equipped with the **F-86D Sabre.** There are two tactical reconnaissance squadrons, one equipped with the **RF-101C Voodoo** and the other with the **RF-104G Starfighter,** and a few **RB-57B** reconnaissance-bombers remain on strength.

COLOMBIA

Fuerza Aérea Colombiana: A signatory to the 1947 Rio Pact, Colombia possesses a small but efficient air arm with the primary task of internal security. All operational aircraft of the F.A.Col. are of U.S. or Canadian origin. The combat Group is equipped with small numbers of MAP-supplied **F-86F Sabres** and **Lockheed T-33A** armed trainers, plus a few **Canadair CL-13B Sabre Mk.6s,** the F.A.Col. having acquired six fighters of this type in 1956. There is a Bomber Group at the Luis F. Gomez Nino Air Force Base equipped with the **B-26B Invader**, small reconnaissance elements operating the **RB-26C Invader** and **RT-33A,** and a special unit for COIN-type operations equipped with **UH-1B Iroquois** helicopters and based at the F.A.Col's Combat Centre at the Germán Olano Air Force Base. Additional **T-33A** armed trainers are being acquired from the U.S.A., but no other combat aircraft procurement plans have been announced.

CONGO

Forces Aériennes Congolaises: Recently expanded and reorganised with U.S. and Italian aid, the Congolese air arm is concerned primarily with internal security tasks, and its combat element is provided by the *Deuxieme Groupement Aérien Tactique* comprising the 12*ème Wing Tactique* with the 120*ème* and 121*ème Escadrilles* each with 12 armed **T-6 Texans** and the 21*ème Wing Tactique* with the 210*ème Escadrille* with 16 **T-28Ds** and the 211*ème Escadrille* with nine **B-26K Invaders.**

CUBA

Fuerza Aérea Revolucionaria: Now equipped entirely with combat aircraft of Russian origin, the F.A.R.'s operational element comprises three squadrons of **MiG-21s,** a squadron of **MiG-19s** and two squadrons of **MiG-17s.** A Soviet training and advisory mission assists the F.A.R., many Cuban personnel having received training in the Soviet Union and other Communist states.

CZECHOSLOVAKIA

Ceskoslovenské letectvo: A tactical force with strong defensive capabilities, the *letectvo* has undergone extensive modernisation and re-equipment over the past two years, both combat and training elements converting to more modern aircraft types, and this air arm now possesses between 500 and 600 first-line combat aircraft. The basic formation of the *letectvo* is the *Letecký pluk*, or Air Regiment, which normally comprises three *letky* (a *letka* being roughly equivalent to a squadron), these being sub-divided into units of three or four aircraft known as *roje* (a *roj* being equivalent to a flight), and there are currently some six interceptor fighter *pluku*, one of which is equipped with the **MiG-19** day interceptor, one with the limited all-weather **MiG-21** interceptor, and the remainder are either equipped with the Czechoslovak-built **MiG-21** day interceptor or are in process of converting to this type from the **MiG-17** which was produced in Czechoslovakia as the **S-105.** The four fighter-bomber and ground attack *pluky* are equally divided in equipment between the **Sukhoi Su-7MB** and the **MiG-17,** and there are reportedly two light bomber *pluky* with the obsolescent **Il-28.**

DAHOMEY

Force Aérienne du Dahomey: The Republic of Dahomey possesses a small air arm, which like those of other newly independent territories formerly administered by France, has been established with the aid of the *Armée de l'Air*, and is concerned solely with transport and communications tasks. It currently possesses no plans for the acquisition of combat aircraft.

DENMARK

Kongelige Danske Flyvevåben: The Royal Danish Air Force, generally known as *Flyvevåbnet*, is a small tactical force, all combat units of which come within the control of the *Flyvertaktisk Kommando*, or Air Tactical Command, at Karup. The Defence Act of 1960 fixed the size of the *Flyvevåben* at seven combat *Eskadrillerne* fully committed to Allied Air Forces Baltic Approaches of N.A.T.O., and with the disbandment of No. 728 *Eskadrille* in March 1966, first-line strength was reduced to this figure, comprising Nos. 723 and 726 *Eskadrillerne* equipped with 12 **F-104G Starfighters** each and serving in the all-weather interceptor role, No. 724 *Eskadrille* operating 16 **Hunter F.Mk.51s** in the low-level intercept role, Nos. 725, 727 and 730 *Eskadrillerne* each with 16 **F-100D Super Sabre** fighter-bombers, and No. 729 *Eskadrille* with 16 **RF-84F Thunderflashes** for tactical reconnaissance. The *Flyvevåben* has received 26 **F-104G Starfighters** (plus three two-seat **TF-104Gs**) to re-equip the two interceptor units formerly operating the **F-86D Sabre,** and it is expected that the **Northrop F-5** will eventually be acquired to replace the **F-100D** in two of the fighter-bomber *Eskadrillerne* and the **RF-84F** in No. 729 *Eskadrille*. The **Hunters** of No. 724 *Eskadrille* are expected to be phased out of service in 1968.

DOMINICA

El Cuerpo de Aviación Militar Dominicana: The Dominican Military Aviation Corps, the A.M.D., has declined in operational efficiency in recent years owing to the Dominican Republic's inability to procure new combat equipment from abroad, the bulk of its current combat aircraft having been procured from surplus Swedish *Flygvapen* stocks in the early and mid 'fifties. The organisation of the A.M.D. is based on two combat *escuadrones*, these being similar in strength to a U.S.A.F. squadron with 25 aircraft plus reserves. The *Escuadron de Caza* is equipped with the **F-51D Mustang,** 42 examples of which were purchased from Sweden in 1952, and the 30* survivors of these being overhauled and updated by Florida Aviation in 1965, and the *Escuadron de Caza-Bombardero* operates **Vampire F.B.Mk.50s** and a few **Vampire F.Mk.1s,** also originally acquired from Sweden, 25 **F.Mk.1s** having been purchased in 1955 and 17 **F.B.Mk.50s** in 1956. Negotiations with Hawker Siddeley for the purchase of reconditioned **Hunters** to replace the **Vampires** were broken off in 1964.

Small numbers of de Havilland Vampire fighters remain in service, one operator being El Cuerpo de Aviación Militar Dominicana *which has both Vampire F.Mk.*1*s and F.B.Mk.*50*s, an example of the former being illustrated above. The Vampire F.Mk.*1 *first flew on April* 20, 1945, *and is powered by a* 3,100 *lb.s.t. de Havilland Goblin D.Gn.*2, *maximum speed being* 538 *m.p.h. at* 17,500 *ft.*

ECUADOR

Fuerza Aérea Ecuatoriana: A small tactical air arm with an operational element comprising three *escuadrillas*, the F.A.E.

has, in recent years, received all its equipment from the U.S.A., but recent deliveries under the Military Assistance Programme have been limited to transports, trainers and helicopters. There is one interceptor *escuadrilla* equipped with the **F-80C Shooting Star,** one fighter-reconnaissance *escuadrilla* operating the **Meteor F.R.Mk.9,** and one light tactical bomber *escuadrilla* with the **Canberra B.Mk.6.** The F.A.E. purchased 12 **Meteor F.R.Mk.9s** and six **Canberra B.Mk.6s** in the mid 'fifties, but no details of future combat aircraft procurements have been announced.

ETHIOPIA

Imperial Ethiopian Air Force: The I.E.A.F. possesses little more than a token combat element at the present time, its most modern operational aircraft being the **F-86F Sabre,** an initial batch of 12 examples of which was delivered in 1960 to equip the first I.E.A.F. interceptor squadron. The I.E.A.F. now possesses three **F-86F**-equipped squadrons, and two light tactical bomber squadrons operating the survivors of 66 **Saab 17As** acquired from Sweden in the late 'forties but scheduled to re-equip with the **Northrop F-5A** during the next two years.

FINLAND

Ilmavoimat: A small defensive force currently restricted by the Peace Treaty of February 1947 to a maximum of 60 combat aircraft, Finland's air arm, the *Ilmavoimat*, currently possesses only two combat squadrons at operational status with plans for a third to be based at Rissala, Kuopio. The basic formation of the *Ilmavoimat* is the *Lennosto*, or Wing, of which there are three. One of these, the *Satakunnan Lennosto* at Pori, is concerned with flying training and possesses no operational element, but the *Hämeen Lennosto* has one fighter-bomber squadron equipped with the **Gnat Mk.1,** *Havittäjälaivue* (HävLv) 21 at Luonetjärvi, and the *Karjalan Lennosto* at Rissala, Kuopio also has one combat unit, HävLv 31, a day interceptor squadron equipped with the **MiG-21.** The *Ilmavoimat* acquired 13 **Gnats** between 1958 and 1960, and placed an initial order with the Soviet Union for 21 **MiG-21s** (including two two-seat **MiG-21UTI** conversion trainers), the first 10 of these arriving at Kuopio in April 1963, the last being delivered early in 1965. Some *Ilmavoimat* personnel have received training on the **MiG-21** in the Soviet Union, and an additional quantity of fighters of this type has now allegedly been delivered to Finland, unconfirmed reports suggesting that a total of 40* having now been received. No other procurement of combat aircraft is currently envisaged, the **MiG-21** having been selected as the standard interceptor for the operational elements of the *Lennostot*, and HävLv 21 is expected to convert from the **Gnat** to this type when sufficient numbers of the Russian fighter are available. Four **Il-28** bombers acquired from the Soviet Union serve in the target-towing role.

FRANCE

Armée de l'Air: The *Armée de l'Air* possesses three Commands controlling the combat elements of the service: the *Commandement 'Air' des Forces de Défense Aérienne* (CAFDA) responsible for the air defence of France in conjunction with the other services; the *Commandement des Forces Aériennes Tactiques* (FATac), and the *Commandement des Forces Aériennes Stratégiques* which respectively control the tactical operational elements and the strategic bomber force, the so-called '*force de frappe*'. The CAFDA currently possesses three *Escadres de Chasse* each of two *escadrons* of **Super-Mystère B.2** day interceptors (5e, 10e, and 12e), the 8e *Escadre* with two *escadrons* of **Mystère IVA**s, and the 30e *Escadre de Chasse Tous-Temps* with three *escadrons* of **Vautour IIN** all-weather interceptors. Certain of these *Escadres* are expected to be disbanded in the near future, those retained each eventually comprising three *escadrons*. The FATac's principal component, the 1er CATac (*Commandement Aérien Tactique*), formed a considerable proportion of the 4th Allied Tactical Air

Force until France's decision to withdraw from N.A.T.O., and its operational manned aircraft units comprise the 2e *Escadre* with three *escadrons* of **Mirage IIIC** interceptors, the 3e and 13e *Escadres* each with two *escadrons* of **Mirage IIIE** strike fighters, the 4e *Escadre* with two *escadrons* of **F-84F Thunderstreaks,** the 7e *Escadre* with two *escadrons* of **Mystère IVAs,** and the 11e *Escadre* with two *escadrons* of **F-100D Super Sabres**, plus the 33e *Escadre de Reconnaissance* with two **Mirage IIIR**-equipped *escadrons.* The strategic bombing force consists of the 91e *Escadre de Bombardement* with three *escadrons* of **Mirage IVAs** plus one *escadron* of **C-135F** flight-refuelling tankers, and the 92e *Escadre* with two *escadrons* of **Vautour IIBs.** The 93e and 94e *Escadres* are in process of formation and will be equipped with the **Mirage IVA.** Overseas organisation of the *Armée de l'Air* within the *Zones d'Outre Mer* comprises mostly transport and communications units, the only overseas combat elements being the *Escadrons d'Avions d'Appui* 1/21 and 2/21 equipped with the **A-1D Skyraider,** and the *Escadron d'Outre-Mer* 85 with **Vautour IINs.** Future procurement of combat aircraft so far announced includes additional **Mirage IIIEs** (increasing current orders from 120 to 200) and, from 1972, the single-seat tactical strike version of the **SEPECAT Jaguar.** From 1975, the *Armée de l'Air* anticipates receiving a variable-geometry aircraft with nuclear capability and greater penetration range than the **Jaguar,** and which will fulfil both the strike and intercept roles.

Aéronautique Navale: France's naval air arm, usually known by the abbreviation *Aéronavale*, is a small but efficient carrier-borne strike and anti-submarine force built around the 27,300-ton carriers *Clémenceau* and *Foch*, and the 11,000-ton helicopter carrier *La Résolue*, plus shore-based maritime reconnaissance units. For shipboard duties, *Flottilles* 4F, 6F and 9F operate the **Breguet 1050 Alizé,** *Flottilles* 11F, 15F and 17F are equipped with **Etendard IVM** strike fighters, *Flottilles* 12F and 14F serve in the interceptor role with the **F-8E (FN) Crusader,** and *Flottille* 16F has **Etendard IVP** reconnaissance aircraft. Helicopter units for ASW tasks are *Flottilles* 31F, 32F and 33F with **Sikorsky S-58s,** replacement of which with the **Super Frelon** was scheduled to commence during the course of 1966, and apart from the *Section P2V-6 du Pacifique* operating **P-2F Neptunes** from New Caledonia, there are five shore-based *Aéronavale* maritime reconnaissance units: *Flottille* 21F which is the first unit to convert to the **Br.1150 Atlantic,** *Flottille* 22F equipped with the **P-2F Neptune,** and *Flottilles* 23F, 24F and 25F operating the **P-2H Neptune.** Future *Aéronavale* combat aircraft procurement is currently restricted to the **Atlantic** and the **Super Frelon,** initial orders, which call for 20 and 23 aircraft respectively, probably being supplemented over the next two years.

GERMANY (Democratic Republic)

Luftstreitkräfte der DDR: A tactical force based closely on the pattern of the Russian *Voenno-Vozdushnye Sily*, the *Luftstreitkräfte* possesses a strong defensive element embodied in two Fighter Divisions which provide the backbone of this air arm. The 1st Fighter Division comprises three *Geschwader* at Cottbus, Jocksdorf, and Neubrandenburg, with *Staffeln* on detachment to various other airfields, and the 3rd Fighter Division has *Geschwader* at Drewitz, Marxwalde and Peenemünde. These Divisions, together with several semi-autonomous *Geschwader*, have some 300 interceptor fighters and fighter-bombers. Most interceptor *Geschwader* are now equipped with the **MiG-19** or **MiG-21** day fighters and limited all-weather **MiG-21,** the fighter-bomber elements operating the obsolescent **MiG-17.** There is one Bomber Division with two *Geschwader* of **Ilyushin Il-28** light tactical bombers totalling 70–75 aircraft.

GERMANY (Federal Republic)

Luftwaffe der Deutschen Bundesrepublik: The *Luftwaffe*, whose original target strength of 20 operational *Geschwader* has been somewhat pruned over the past two years, is, nevertheless, the most powerful tactical air arm in West Europe. Its combat *Geschwader* each comprise 52 aircraft, including two *Staffeln* each of 18 operational aircraft (six aircraft being in the immediate reserve and the remaining 10 normally being under maintenance), and the bulk of its interceptor, strike fighter and reconnaissance units are N.A.T.O.-integrated and committed to the 2nd and 4th Allied Tactical Air Forces. There are currently two interceptor *Geschwader* equipped with the **F-104G Starfighter**, JG 71 '*Richthofen*' at Wittmundhaven and JG 74 at Neuburg, and similarly-equipped strike fighter *Geschwader* are Jabo G 31 '*Boelcke*' at Norvenich, Jabo G 32 at Lechfeld, Jabo G 33 at Buchel, Jabo G 34 at Memmingen, and Jabo G 36 at Rheine. Jabo G 35 at Husum is currently scheduled to re-equip from the **F-84F Thunderstreak.** There are two **Starfighter**-equipped tactical reconnaissance *Geschwader*, Aufkl G 51 '*Immelmann*' at Ingolstadt and Aufkl G 52 at Leck, and there are two Light Ground Attack Wings, or *Leichte Kampfgeschwader*, which, equipped with the **G.91R.3,** fulfil both tactical reconnaissance and fighter-bomber tasks, these being LeKG 41 at Husum and LeKG 44 at Leipheim. The two remaining *Luftwaffe* combat units are Jabo G 42 at Pferdsfeld and Jabo G. 43 at Oldenburg, both of which operate the **G.91R.3** fighter-bomber.

Marineflieger der Bundeswehr: The shore-based Federal German naval air arm's combat element comprises both strike fighter and maritime reconnaissance units and, apart from its **Br.1150 Atlantics,** its aircraft are similar to those operated by the *Luftwaffe*. The *Marineflieger* has received 100 of the 700 **F-104G Starfighter** strike fighters acquired by Germany, and this type now equips *Marinefliegergeschwader* 1 and 2 at Eggebeck and Schleswig-Jagel respectively. Fulfilling the maritime reconnaissance role and currently working up to operational status, *Marinefliegergeschwader* 3 at Nordholz will operate all 20 **Atlantics** so far ordered by Federal Germany. *Marinefliegergeschwader* 5 at Kiel-Holtenau operates one *Staffel* of ASW **Sikorsky SH-34s.** With the acquisition of **Sikorsky SH-3Ds** this unit will be expanded to *Geschwader* strength.

GHANA

Ghana Air Force: The Gh.A.F.'s main tasks since its formation in 1959 have been those of communications, aerial survey and light transport, but in 1965 an initial batch of seven Macchi **MB.326F** armed trainers was acquired, these aircraft being suitable for both training and operational roles. Plans exist for the establishment of a light ground attack squadron, but Ghana's financial difficulties have prevented the purchase of additional **MB.326F** aircraft to equip this unit.

GREECE

Royal Hellenic Air Force: Integrated within N.A.T.O.'s Allied Air Forces Southern Europe, the R.H.A.F. currently possesses 11 tactical combat squadrons within the 28th Tactical Air Force, the operational command of all combat units. There are four fighter-bomber squadrons of which two have now re-equipped with the **Northrop F-5,** an initial quantity of 40 aircraft of this type having been supplied to the R.H.A.F. to re-equip the 341st and 343rd Squadrons of the 111th Combat Wing, one of the four combat wings included in the R.H.A.F. operational organisation. The remaining two fighter-bomber squadrons are equipped with the **F-84F Thunderstreak,** but these are scheduled to re-equip with the **F-5** with the arrival in Greece of the second batch of MAP-supplied aircraft. Two all-weather interceptor squadrons re-equipped with **F-104G Starfighters** during 1964–65, and two interceptor squadrons still operate the **F-86D Sabre.** The remaining combat squadron is equipped with the **RF-84F Thunderflash** for tactical reconnaissance. The R.H.A.F. hopes to acquire eventually sufficient **F-5**'s to equip a total of seven squadrons.

GUATEMALA

Fuerza Aérea de Guatemala: Guatemala maintains a small air arm, the operational element of which comprises one squadron of **F-51D Mustang** fighter-bombers and one squadron of **B-26 Invader** light bombers. All combat equipment is supplied by the U.S.A. under the Military Assistance Programme.

GUINEA

Force Aérienne de Guinée: The West African Republic of Guinea established a small air arm with the aid of Communist bloc countries shortly after the territory was proclaimed independent in October 1958. Some personnel have since received instruction in East European countries, but the embryo *Force Aérienne de Guinée* has so far confined itself to communications and light transport tasks. Plans exist for the establishment of a combat squadron with **MiG-17s** promised by the Soviet Union, but these plans are not believed to have yet achieved fruition.

Now virtually extinct, the Chance Vought Corsair is still operated in small numbers by the Fuerza Aérea Hondureña *in its F4U-4, -5 and -5N versions, and one of this service's F4U-5s is illustrated below. Powered by a* 2,300 *h.p. Pratt & Whitney* R-2800-32*W engine, the F4U-5 has a maximum speed of* 462 *m.p.h. at* 31,400 *ft. Armament comprises four* 20-*mm. cannon and up to* 4,000 *lb. underwing.*

*The North American F-*51*D Mustang remains in service with several air arms, primarily in Latin America, and that illustrated above belongs to the* Fuerza Aérea de Guatemala. *The F-*51*D has a Packard V-*1650-7 *Merlin rated at* 1,450 *h.p. dry and* 1,695 *h.p. with water injection, and attains* 437 *m.p.h. at* 25,000 *ft. Armament comprises six* 0.5-*in. guns and a pair of* 500-*lb. or* 1,000-*lb. bombs.*

HAITI

Corps d'Aviation d'Haiti: The Haitian Air Corps is a component of the *Garde d'Haiti*, and six **F-51D Mustang** fighter-bombers are included in a composite squadron together with training aircraft of various types.

HONDURAS

Fuerza Aérea Hondureña: Administered by the *Jefatura de las Fuerzas Armadas*, or Armed Forces Command, the F.A.H. possesses a small combat element comprising several squadrons, each of four aircraft, equipped with **F4U-4, F4U-5** and **F4U-5N Corsairs** which have been in service since the late 'fifties. There has been no recent combat aircraft procurement.

HUNGARY

Magyar Légierö: Reconstituted after the abortive uprising of 1956, the Hungarian Air Force, or *Magyar Légierö*, is now considerably smaller than the air arm that existed at the time of the revolution, although its first-line combat strength is still virtually double that allowed under the 1947 Peace Treaty, comprising 120–130 aircraft, most of which are interceptors and fighter-bombers with a token force of light tactical bombers. The largest formation of the *Légierö* is the *Repülö Hadosztály*, or Air Division, of which there are two, each with a statutory strength of three Fighter Regiments (*Vadasz Ezred*) of from three to six squadrons (*század*). However, neither Division is currently at full operational strength, and there are 60–80 **MiG-21** point-defence day interceptors, and 50–60 **MiG-17s,** detached squadrons from each Regiment being stationed in various parts of Hungary. A *Könnyü Repülö Ezred*, or Light Air Regiment, fulfils the tactical bombing role with **Il-28** light bombers, but this formation is reportedly well below statutory strength. All combat equipment is furnished by the Soviet Union, and changes in the immediate future are likely to be confined to replacing the obsolescent **MiG-17s** with more modern fighter-bombers such as the **Su-7.**

INDIA

Indian Air Force: Currently in process of building up to a 45-squadron air arm, the Indian Air Force achieved equal status with the Indian Army on January 15, 1966, having been blooded in action against Pakistan in September of the previous year; a 23-day conflict in which the I.A.F. lost between 35 (according to official Indian sources) and 110 (according to official Pakistani sources) aircraft. The basic formation of the I.A.F. is the Wing which normally comprises three squadrons of 16 aircraft, and all combat wings, stations and sub-formations are controlled by the Operational Command with Headquarters in Delhi. At the present time, the I.A.F. possesses one day interceptor wing of three squadrons of **MiG-21s,** 48* fighters of this type having been purchased from the Soviet Union. Licence manufacture of the **MiG-21** is being undertaken in India, initial deliveries of fighters assembled from Russian-supplied components being scheduled for 1967 with the first deliveries of **MiG-21s** produced from components of entirely indigenous manufacture being scheduled for 1969, current plans calling for the acquisition of 450* **MiG-21s** by 1972 to equip seven–nine wings. Four wings of **Gnat Mk.1** lightweight fighters now form a major component of the I.A.F.'s day interceptor element. Twenty-five complete **Gnats** plus components for the assembly of a further fifteen were supplied to India by the U.K. during 1957–58, and licence manufacture has since been undertaken, the I.A.F. having now received more than 200 fighters of this type. **Gnat** production was in process of phasing out in 1965, but its successes during the September conflict, together with delays in the commencement of large-scale production of the indigenous **HF-24 Marut,** have resulted in further procurement of this type which will carry production into 1967. The third standard I.A.F. fighter is the **Hunter F.Mk.56,** a total of 160 examples of which was acquired from the U.K. during 1957–61, attrition since being made up by the delivery of some refurbished **Hunters** brought up to F.Mk.56 standards. Serving primarily in the ground attack fighter role, the **Hunter** equips three wings which share this task with one wing equipped with the survivors of the 110 **Mystère IVAs** purchased by India in the mid 'fifties. One or two squadrons equipped with the **Vampire F.B.Mk.9**—HAL having assembled 52 aircraft of this type in the 'fifties—are currently awaiting re-equipment, and a tactical bomber component is provided by squadrons of **Canberra B.(I). Mk.58s,** the 66 aircraft of this type, plus eight **P.R.Mk.7s** to equip one photo-reconnaissance squadron, having been supplemented by small numbers of re-furbished ex-R.A.F. machines, and making up a total of more than 30 combat squadrons. Apart from the **MiG-21,** current combat aircraft procurement is confined to the indigenous **HF-24 Marut Mk.1** strike and reconnaissance fighter, the first squadron of which was expected to be working up to operational status before the end of 1966.

Indian Naval Aviation: Built up around the Indian Navy's single carrier, the I.N.S. *Vikrant*, Indian Naval Aviation possesses three combat squadrons, two equipped with the **Sea Hawk F.G.A.Mk.6** fighter-bomber and one equipped with the **Br.1050 Alizé** for the ASW role. The first of 24 **Sea Hawks,** which included both new aircraft and refurbished ex-R.N. machines, reached India early in 1960, entering service with No. 300 Squadron, and in the following year 15 **Alizés** were purchased for No. 310 Squadron.

*The Indian Navy is now the sole remaining air arm to retain the Armstrong Whitworth Sea Hawk in its operational aircraft inventory, this fighter-bomber serving in its F.G.A.Mk.*6 *version with No.*300 *Squadron aboard the I.N.S.* Vikrant. *The Sea Hawk F.G.A.Mk.*6 *has a* 5,400 *lb.s.t. Rolls-Royce Nene* 103 *turbojet with which it attains* 590 *m.p.h. at sea level. Armament comprises four* 20-*mm. cannon.*

INDONESIA

Angkatan Udara Republik Indonesia: The Indonesian Republican Air Force, the A.U.R.I., is now largely equipped with combat aircraft supplied by the Soviet Union, but political changes have resulted in difficulties in acquiring spares and support equipment, and serviceability is reportedly extremely low. For an air arm of its size, the A.U.R.I. operates a considerable variety of combat aircraft types, and prior to its present difficulties, most of the service's squadrons were operating at half strength. The principal combat units of the A.U.R.I. are two strategic bomber squadrons, two tactical light bomber squadrons, and four fighter squadrons. Following the May 1965 agreement signed between Indonesia and the Soviet Union for the supply of additional military equipment for the Indonesian forces, additional **MiG-21** jet fighters and **Il-28** bombers reached the A.U.R.I., but as previously-supplied Russian combat aircraft had lacked comprehensive spares backing and attrition had been high, these only served to bring the squadrons already equipped with these types temporarily up to strength. The strategic bomber squadrons, Nos. 41 and 42, both have nine **Tu-16** medium bombers which, equipped with "Kennel" ASMs, also fulfil the anti-shipping role, and the tactical bomber squadrons, Nos. 1 and 21, are respectively equipped with the **B-26B Invader** and **Ilyushin Il-28.** The fighter complement of the A.U.R.I. consists of No. 3 Squadron which operates primarily in the counter-insurgency role with **F-51D Mustangs,** No. 11 Squadron with **MiG-17s**, No 12 Squadron with **MiG-19s** and No. 14 Squadron with **MiG-21s.** No. 12 Squadron was reportedly in process of re-equipping with the **MiG-21** late in 1965.

Angkatan Laut Republik Indonesia: Possessing no carriers, Indonesia's naval air arm is a small shore-based force, the only operational element of which is an ASW squadron equipped with **Gannet A.S.Mk.4s.** Sixteen aircraft of this type were purchased from the U.K. in 1961–62, but lack of spares backing has reduced these to a negligible quantity. In mid-1964, it was announced that the A.L.R.I. was to receive fixed-wing ASW aircraft and turbine-powered ASW helicopters from the Soviet Union, but there has been no evidence of any deliveries of such aircraft to Indonesia.

IRAN

Imperial Iranian Air Force: At the present time the combat elements of the I.I.A.F. are undergoing long-overdue re-equipment and expansion. Its sole combat formation, the Fighter Wing comprising three squadrons each of 25 aircraft, was equipped solely with the **F-84G Thunderjet** from the mid 'fifties until January 1965 when the first 13 **Northrop F-5s** of an initial batch of 26 aircraft of this type arrived at the 1st Fighter Air Base at Mehrabad to re-equip one of the I.I.A.F.'s three fighter squadrons. A further 60–70 **F-5s** are scheduled to be delivered to the I.I.A.F. over the next two years to complete the re-equipment of the Fighter Wing, and a second I.I.A.F. combat wing is to be formed although it subsequently became known that the 90 **Canadair Sabre Mk.6s** surplus to *Luftwaffe* requirements, purchased from Federal Germany, ostensibly for this purpose were destined for Pakistan.

IRAQ

Iraqi Air Force: Despite the ravages of revolution and counter-revolution, the Ir.A.F. forms a substantial combat force with 10 first-line combat squadrons operating relatively modern equipment of both British and Russian origin, the latter predominating. All but one of the combat units operate fighters, the exception being a light tactical bomber squadron equipped with the **Ilyushin Il-28.** Four squadrons are equipped with the **Hunter,** the Ir.A.F. having received 15 **F.Mk.6s** during 1957–58, and 18 **F.Mk.59s** (refurbished Belgian **F.Mk.6s** brought up to **F.G.A.Mk.9** standards) in 1964. Additional reconditioned **Hunters** delivered during 1965–66 brought the total of single-seat **F.Mk.59s** to 44, and two-seat **T.Mk.69s** to six. The Ir.A.F. has also acquired four **Hunter F.R.Mk.10s.** Two squadrons are equipped with the **MiG-21,** one with the **MiG-19,** and two with the **MiG-17**. Some assembly of **MiG-21s** has reportedly taken place in Iraq under Russian supervision, and the Iraqi Air Force was scheduled to receive three squadrons of all-weather **MiG-21s** during 1966. Until recently a small number of piston-engined Hawker Furies were retained in service for the counter-insurgency role, but it is likely that this task has been assumed by the 20 **Jet Provost T.Mk.52s** which are suitable for both training and operational roles.

IRELAND (EIRE)

Irish Air Corps: Organised as an Army Command, the Air Corps possesses no combat units, being a small force concerned primarily with light transport, communications and training tasks. No plans exist for the establishment of a combat element.

ISRAEL

Heil Avir Le Israel: The Israeli Defence Force/Air Force (I.D.F./A.F.), the *Heil Avir Le Israel*, is a small but extremely well-trained and well-equipped arm maintained at a constant state of readiness owing to the hostility of the Arab states surrounding Israel. The backbone of the combat element is provided by three squadrons of **Mirage IIICJ** interceptors, 72 aircraft of this type having been acquired by the I.D.F./A.F. since 1963, the first squadron having become operational in May of that year. A fourth interceptor squadron is equipped with the **Super-Mystère B.2,** 24 examples of which were purchased. There are now two fighter-bomber squadrons operating the survivors of the 60 **Mystère IVAs** obtained in 1956, one attack bomber squadron with the single-seat **Vautour IIA,** 25 of which were originally purchased, and several light close-support squadrons equipped with an armed version of the licence-built **Magister** trainer. Most future procurement of combat aircraft is likely to be from France, and the most urgent requirement is a modern strike fighter to supplant the ageing **Mystère IVA,** a version of the **Mirage IIIE** being a likely choice. The ordnance-lifting capability of the **Magister** is generally considered to be inadequate for the close-support task, and attempts have been made to acquire refurbished ex-U.S. Navy **A-4A Skyhawks** to fulfil this role, these finally meeting with success in 1966.

ITALY

Aeronautica Militare Italiana: The combat elements of the A.M.I. are controlled by the *Ispettorato per la Difesa Aerea* through the *Comando Operativo di Regione* in co-ordination with the 5th Allied Tactical Air Force. The largest A.M.I. formation is the *Aerobrigata;* each of the *Aerobrigate* possesses two or three *Gruppi* at two or more air bases, the *Gruppo* thus forming a semi-autonomous unit. The combat *Aerobrigate* are as follows: 3ª *Aerobrigata Ricognizione Tattica* comprising the 18° and 132° *Gruppi* operating **RF-84F Thunderflash** tactical reconnaissance aircraft; 4ª *Aerobrigata* comprising the 12° *Gruppo* with **F-86K** all-weather interceptors, and the 9° and 10° *Gruppi* with **F-104G Starfighters** operating in the all-weather interceptor role; 5ª *Aerobrigata* comprising the 101° and 102° fighter-bomber *Gruppi* equipped respectively with the **F-104G Starfighter** and **F-84F Thunderstreak,** and the 103° *Gruppo* with **RF-104G Starfighters** for tactical reconnaissance; 6ª *Aerobrigata* consisting of the 154° *Gruppo* with **F-104Gs** and the 156° and 155° *Gruppi* with **F-84Fs,** all operating in the fighter-bomber role, and the 51ª *Aerobrigata* with three *Gruppi* of all-weather interceptors, the 21° with **F-104Gs,** and the 22° and 23° with **F-86K Sabres.** One other combat unit is the 2° *Stormo Caccia Tattici/Ricognitori Leggeri* comprising the 13° and 14° *Gruppi* operating **Fiat G.91R.1s** in both fighter-bomber and tactical reconnaissance roles. The A.M.I. thus possesses six *Gruppi* with **F-104Gs,** three *Gruppi* with **F-84Fs,** two *Gruppi* with **RF-84Fs,** three *Gruppi* with **F-86Ks** and two *Gruppi* with **G.91Rs.** An **F-104G**-equipped *Gruppo* normally has 16 aircraft on strength, most other *Gruppi* having a statutory strength of 25 aircraft, and the A.M.I. thus possesses some 350 first-line combat aircraft plus reserves. The most recent combat aircraft procurement has consisted of 125 **F-104G Starfighters** and 98 **Fiat G.91R.1s,** and orders have been placed for 165 **F-104S Starfighters** for 1968–70 delivery. These will supplant the **F-104Gs** and **F-86Ks** currently employed by the A.M.I. for the intercept role, the **F-104Gs** being passed to the fighter-bomber *Gruppi* now flying the **F-84F Thunderstreak,** and these and the **F-86K Sabres** will be withdrawn. The **Fiat G.91Y** is currently envisaged as the successor to the **G.91R,** two prototypes being under construction with production deliveries envisaged for 1968–69.

Aviazione per la Marina Militare: Italian naval aviation, generally known as the *Marinavia* and controlled by the *Ispettorato per l'Aviazione per la Marina*, possesses a substantial ASW force of fixed-wing aircraft and helicopters. The *Marinavia's* fixed-wing ASW element comprises three *Gruppi Antisommergibill*, the 86°, 87° and 88°, each with some 12 **S-2A Trackers,** and deploys four **Sikorsky SH-34** ASW helicopters aboard each of the cruisers *Andrea Doria* and *Caio Duilio*, and when it joins the *Marina* the new cruiser *Vittorio Veneto* will carry nine of the ASW version of the Agusta-built **AB-204B** helicopter. Each of the frigates *Rizzo*, *Fasan*, *Margottini* and *Bergamini* carries a single *Marinavia* **Agusta AB-47J-3,** although this helicopter performs only the attack role. Agusta is shortly to commence manufacture of the **Sikorsky SH-3D Sea King** ASW helicopter for the *Marinavia*.

IVORY COAST

Force Aérienne de Côte d'Ivoire: Founded in 1962 with the assistance of the *Armée de l'Air*, the diminutive air arm of the Ivory Coast Republic is concerned solely with transport, communications and air ambulance tasks, and possesses no combat element. No procurement plans exist for combat aircraft.

JAPAN

Japanese Air Self-Defence Force: The J.A.S.D.F. is primarily a defensive arm, all combat units fulfilling intercept or tactical reconnaissance roles. The J.A.S.D.F. currently possesses six interceptor wings with a seventh forming, plus two interceptor groups and one tactical reconnaissance group. Deployment is as follows: Northern Air Command with Headquarters at Misawa comprises the **F-86D**-equipped 103rd Squadron and the **F-104J**-equipped 201st and 203rd squadrons based at Chitose and forming the 2nd Wing, plus the 81st Group consisting of the **F-86F**-equipped 3rd Squadron at Hachinoe; Central Air Command with Headquarters at Iruma comprising the 3rd Wing with the 101st, 102nd, and 105th **F-86D**-equipped squadrons at Komaki, the 4th Wing with the 5th and 7th **F-86F**-equipped squadrons at Matsushima, and the 6th Wing with the **F-86F**-equipped 4th Squadron and the **F-104J**-equipped 205th Squadron at Komatsu; Western Air Command with Headquarters at Kasuga and comprising the 5th Wing with the 202nd and 204th squadrons operating the **F-104J** from Nyutabaru, the 8th Wing with the 6th and 10th squadrons of **F-86Fs** operating from Tsuiki, and the 82nd Group consisting of the 8th Squadron with **F-86Fs** at Iwakuni. The 7th Wing comprising the 206th and 207th Squadrons with **F-104Js** is in process of formation at Hayakuri, giving the J.A.S.D.F. a first line strength of seven **F-104J Starfighter** squadrons, four **F-86D Sabre** squadrons and seven **F-86F Sabre** squadrons. There is also the 501st Squadron at Iruma with **RF-86F Sabres** for tactical reconnaissance, bringing the total number of combat squadrons to 19 and first-line operational strength to some 470 combat aircraft plus reserves, a J.A.S.D.F. squadron normally comprising 25 aircraft, an exception being the 501st Squadron with 18 **RF-86Fs.** The J.A.S.D.F. has received 508 **F-86F Sabres,** 300 of these being assembled in Japan by Mitsubishi, 106 **F-86D Sabres,** and 180 **F-104J Starfighters.** The **F-86D Sabre** will be phased out of service during 1967, and 30 additional **F-104J Starfighters** are to be delivered in that year. The J.A.S.D.F. is considering the purchase of 50 advanced interceptors to supplement the **Starfighters** from 1968, and is considering such types as the **F-111A,** the **Phantom II** and the **YF-12A.** The service also plans to acquire a number of **T-38 Talons** which will have both a training and a secondary attack role.

Japanese Maritime Self-Defence Force: Primarily concerned with ASW and maritime reconnaissance tasks, the J.M.S.D.F. possesses four Air Groups with fixed-wing aircraft, and three Air Groups with ASW helicopters. The operational units are controlled by the J.M.S.D.F.'s Air Command with Headquarters at Shimofusa, and comprise the 1st Air Group which consists solely of the 1st Squadron with **P-2H Neptunes** at Kanoya; the 2nd Air Group with the 2nd and 4th Squadrons with **P-2H Neptunes** and the 13th Squadron with **S-2A Trackers** at Hachinoe; the 3rd Air Group comprising the 11th and 12th Squadrons with **S-2A Trackers** at Tokushima, and the 4th Air Group with the **P-2H Neptune**-equipped 3rd Squadron and the **S-2A Tracker**-equipped 14th Squadron at Shimofusa. The ASW helicopter Air Groups each possess one squadron, and are the 21st Air Group at Tateyama with the 101st Squadron which operates **Sikorsky SH-34** and **SH-3A** helicopters; the similarly-equipped 22nd Air Group with the 102nd Squadron at Komatsijima, and the Ohminato Air Group with the **SH-34**-equipped Ohminato Squadron. The J.M.S.D.F. has received 64 **P-2H Neptunes,** 58 **S-2A Trackers,** 14 **SH-34s** and 19 **SH-3As,** and plans to acquire four additional examples of the last-mentioned type. The service envisages acquiring 90 new maritime reconnaissance aircraft of which 68 will be the **Kawasaki GK-210** derivative of the **P-2H** for service from 1968, the remaining 22 being **Shin Meiwa PX-S** flying boats for service from 1971, and 60 of the former and 20 of the latter are expected to be in J.M.S.D.F. service by the end of 1973.

JORDAN

Royal Arab Air Force: A small defensive arm with an operational element comprising one day interceptor squadron equipped with the **Hunter F.Mk.6,** and two fighter-bomber squadrons equipped with **Vampires** (both **F.B.Mk.9s** and

F.B.Mk.52s). The R.Ar.A.F. has received 14 **Hunters,** including one **F.R.Mk.6** tactical reconnaissance aircraft and two **T.Mk.66B** armed trainers, but both these and the **Vampires** are in urgent need of replacement and, having rejected U.A.R. offers of surplus **MiG-17s** and **-19s,** the Jordan government reached agreement with the U.S. government in March 1966 for the supply of 24* refurbished **F-104C Starfighters** with which two R.Ar.A.F. squadrons are to re-equip.

Jordan's Royal Arab Air Force is one of seven air arms that still include single-seat de Havilland Vampires in their first-line operational inventories, that illustrated above being a Vampire F.B.Mk.9, which type, together with the F.B.Mk.52 version, equips two Jordanian fighter-bomber squadrons. Powered by the 3,350 lb.s.t. de Havilland Goblin D.Gn.3 turbojet, the F.B.Mks.9 and 52 are essentially similar, attain a maximum speed of 548 m.p.h. at 30,000 ft. and carry a four 20-mm. cannon armament.

KENYA

Kenya Air Force: Currently in the embryo stage, the K.A.F. has existed for only three years and, at the present time, is concerned with training, communications and transport tasks. The acquisition of armed jet trainers for the dual instructional-operational role is planned.

KOREA (Democratic People's Republic)

Korean People's Armed Forces Air Force: Organised on the Chinese pattern and enjoying considerable Sino-Communist aid, the K.P.A.F.A.F. now possesses a first-line combat strength of nearly 500 aircraft, plus reserves. These are divided between three fighter-equipped Air Divisions each comprising two Air Regiments of 30–35 aircraft, one Air Regiment with light tactical bombers, and one Air Regiment with tactical reconnaissance aircraft. The bulk of K.P.A.F.A.F. combat equipment is obsolescent and includes 380* Chinese-built **MiG-17s** which equip all but one of the six fighter regiments, the remaining fighter regiment having recently converted to the **MiG-21.** Both the tactical bomber and reconnaissance regiments operate the **Il-28,** some 70–80 being in service.

KOREA (Republic)

Republic of Korea Air Force: Patterned on the lines of the U.S.A.F. and equipped with aircraft supplied under the Military Assistance Programme, the R.O.K. Air Force has a purely defensive role, and its principal combat units are the 10th and 11th Fighter Wings each with a statutory strength of three squadrons. The 10th Fighter Wing at Suwon A.F.B. comprises two fighter-bomber squadrons, the 102nd and 105th, equipped with the **Northrop F-5A,** an initial batch of 30 **F-5As** and four **F-5Bs** having been received in 1965 to replace the **F-86F Sabres** previously operated by these squadrons, and one all-weather interceptor squadron operating the **F-86D Sabre**. The 11th Fighter Wing has three squadrons of **F-86F Sabres,** 112 fighters of this type having been supplied to the R.O.K.A.F., together with 10 **RF-86F Sabres** which equip an independent tactical reconnaissance squadron. There is also a second **F-86D Sabre**-equipped squadron which, currently independent, will probably be incorporated within the proposed 12th Fighter Wing. All operational squadrons are controlled by the Combat Air Command, but operationally the R.O.K.A.F. is subordinate to the Commander of the U.S.A.F. 314th Air Division.

KUWAIT

Kuwait Air Force: An extension of the Security Department of the Government of Kuwait, the Ku.A.F. is aided and advised by a British mission, and many of its personnel have been trained with the R.A.F. in the United Kingdom. Current combat equipment comprises **Hunter F.Mk.57** ground attack fighters, an initial batch of four of which was supplied to the Ku.A.F. in 1964, together with two **T.Mk.67** armed trainers, and limited expansion of the combat element is anticipated with the acquisition of some 20–24 new fighters, the choice resting, at the time of closing for press, between the **Lightning F.Mk.53** and the **Mirage III.** The Ku.A.F. has also received six **Jet Provost T.Mk.51** armed trainers for the dual instructional-operational role.

LAOS

Royal Lao Air Force: Concerned primarily with operations against the Hanoi-controlled Pathet Lao forces in support of the Royal Lao Army, the Royal Lao Air Force has received 50–60 **North American T-28D** light close-support aircraft which equip some three squadrons. The **T-28Ds** are flown by Lao, Thai and U.S. mercenary pilots, and the Royal Lao Air Force is receiving considerable U.S. support which, in deference to the 1962 Geneva Agreement barring U.S. military personnel from Laos, is provided by two civilian organisations employed by the Central Intelligence Agency, Air America being responsible for training and strikes against the Pathet Lao, and Continental Air Services furnishing logistic support with transport aircraft. In 1966, the Royal Lao Air Force was in process of receiving additional **T-28Ds** and a small number of **B-26K Invader** bombers.

LEBANON

Force Aérienne Libanaise: Possessing a combat element of one day interceptor and fighter-bomber squadron equipped with the **Hunter,** the F.Aé.L. having received five **F.Mk.6s,** five **F.G.A.Mk.9s** and two **T.Mk.69s,** the small Lebanese air arm selected the **Mirage III** early in 1966 as its future standard fighter, and a French mission will assist the F.Aé.L. in converting to the new type for which an initial order for 12 has been placed by the Lebanese government, the total requirement being for 25.

LIBYA

Libyan Air Force: The Federal Kingdom of Libya formed the nucleus of an air arm in 1959, and some assistance in training and the supply of equipment has been provided by the U.S.A. A small number of **Lockheed T-33A** armed trainers serve in the dual instructional-operational role.

MALAGASY

Armée de l'Air Malgache: Malagasy, the former French colony of Madagascar, has established a small air arm with French assistance. Its principal formation, the 1*ère Escadrille*, is concerned primarily with transport and communications tasks, and possesses no combat element.

MAURITANIA

Force Aérienne Islamique de Mauritanie: Since gaining independence in November 1960, the Islamic Republic of Mauritania has established a small air arm equipped with transports and utility aircraft presented as a gift from France and currently manned by *Armée de l'Air* personnel. There is no combat element.

MALAYSIA

Tentera Udara Diraja Malaysia: Steadily expanded over the past three years, the *Tentera Udara Diraja Malaysia*, or Royal Malaysian Air Force, is currently in process of forming a combat element, and the first light strike squadron equipped with the **Canadair CL-41,** an armed version of the **CL-41A Tutor** basic trainer, is expected to be operational late in 1967 at Kuantan, an initial quantity of 20 **CL-41** aircraft having been ordered early in 1966. A second similarly-equipped strike squadron is scheduled to be formed early in 1968. Prior to the acquisition of the **CL-41,** the R.Mal.A.F. was concerned primarily with training, transport, communications and rescue roles.

MALI

Force Aérienne du Mali: Currently in the embryo stage, the F.Aé.M. is believed to have received some assistance from Eastern Europe, and unconfirmed reports have stated that a combat element is to be formed with **MiG-15** fighters.

MEXICO

Fuerza Aérea Mexicana: The F.A.M.'s main functions are policing and training, and seven units operating armed piston-engined trainers and two operating jet aircraft are considered to be *combat* squadrons. The two jet units are *Escuadron Aéreo* 200 with ex-R.C.A.F. **Vampire F.Mk.3s** and **Vampire T.Mk.11s,** of which 15 and two examples were acquired respectively, and *Escuadron Aéreo* 202 with 15 **Lockheed T-33Bs.** *Escuadron Aéreo* 101 serves in the reconnaissance role with **Beech T-11s,** *Escuadrones* 201 and 205 have received the majority of the 32 **North American T-28As** supplied to the F.A.M., and *Escuadrons* 203, 204, 206 and 207 operate the **T-6 Texan.**

Armada de Mexico: The Mexican Navy operates a small air component which is primarily concerned with training, transport, communications and rescue tasks, and possesses no combat element.

MONGOLIA

Mongolian People's Air Force: The Mongolian People's Republic possesses a token air arm concerned primarily with internal transport and communications tasks, and some flying training, and it is not believed that any combat element has been formed.

MOROCCO

Aviation Royale Chérifienne: The Kingdom of Morocco has possessed a small air arm for ten years which has received desultory aid from France, the Soviet Union and the U.S.A. Its combat element was established with the gift of four **Hawker Furies** from Iraq and twelve **MiG-17** fighters and two **MiG-15UTI** trainers from the Soviet Union, the Russian fighters being accompanied by a training mission. Small additional quantities of **MiG-17s** and two **Il-28** light bombers followed, but these aircraft are reportedly flown rarely, suffering inadequate spares backing, and most operational missions flown by the *Aviation Royale Chérifienne* against insurgents are conducted with armed **T-6G Texans,** a small number of ex-*Armée de l'Air* aircraft of this type having been donated by France. Mid-1966 Moroccan personnel began training in the U.S.A. on the **Northrop F-5** and 12–18 aircraft of this type were in process of delivery to the *Aviation Royale Chérifienne*.

MUSCAT AND OMAN

Sultan of Oman's Air Force: Formed in 1959 to provide support for the Army in operations against insurgents, the Sultan of Oman's Air Force is largely manned by seconded R.A.F. personnel, and the service possesses five **Hunting Provost T.Mk.52** armed trainers for the counter-insurgency role. Expansion of the combat element is unlikely in the immediate future.

NETHERLANDS

Koninklijke Nederlandse Luchtmacht: Possessing 10 first-line combat squadrons, the K.N.L.'s main strike element is the *Commando Taktische Luchtstrijdkrachten*, or Tactical Air Command integrated with the No. 1 Tactical Operations Centre of

The North American T-6 Texan (alias Harvard) is widely used for the combined training and operational counter-insurgency task. The T-6G of Morocco's Aviation Royale Chérifienne, *illustrated above, is one of a number of ex-*Armée de l'Air *aircraft of this type serving with Morocco for light attack and COIN tasks.*

N.A.T.O.'s 2nd Allied Tactical Air Force, and comprising four fighter-bomber squadrons, Nos. 311 and 312 at Volkel each with 18 **F-104G Starfighters,** and Nos. 314 and 315 at Eindhoven with **F-84F Thunderstreaks,** and one tactical reconnaissance squadron, No. 306, with **RF-104G Starfighters** at Twente. The *Commando Luchtverdediging*, or Air Defence Command, controls three interceptor squadrons, Nos. 322 and 323 with a total of 36 **F-104G Starfighters** at Leeuwarden, and No. 325 Squadron which, the last K.N.L. combat unit to retain the **Hunter F.Mk.6,** operates in the low-level intercept role, and is expected to retain its present equipment until at least 1968. The K.N.L. has received 120 **F-104G** and **RF-104G Starfighters,** and has a joint requirement with the *Force Aérienne Belge* for a fighter-bomber replacement for the surviving **F-84F Thunderstreaks** (the K.N.L. and F.Aé.B. having received 184 and 197 **F-84Fs** respectively under the M.D.A.P.) which are expected to remain in service until 1969–70, and a choice of type was believed imminent at the time of closing for press, the requirement being for 75 single-seaters and 30 two-seaters.

Koninklijke Marine Luchtvaartdienst: The Dutch naval air arm, the K.M.L., has the primary operational roles of maritime reconnaissance and anti-submarine warfare, and its combat element comprises No. 1 Squadron with **CS2F-1A Trackers** operating in the ASW role from Curaçao in the Netherlands West Indies, and Nos. 2 and 4 Squadrons each with 12 **S-2A Trackers** for service aboard the light fleet carrier *Karel Doorman*. No. 8 Squadron operates eight **Sikorsky SH-34J** ASW helicopters from Valkenburg when not embarked aboard the *Karel Doorman*, and twelve **Westland Wasps** are in process of delivery as ASW weapons carriers for platform operation from the six new frigates of the *Van Speyk* class. The remaining operational unit serves in the maritime reconnaissance role, this being No. 320 Squadron operating **P-2H Neptunes** in N.A.T.O. Channel Command. The *Karel Doorman* is scheduled to be retired from active service in 1970.

NEW ZEALAND

Royal New Zealand Air Force: The combat components of the R.N.Z.A.F. currently comprise a single light bomber unit, No. 14 Squadron, with 10 **Canberra B.(I).12s** at Ohakea, the Vampire Operational Flight with six **Vampire F.B.Mk.6s** for close-support duties, also at Ohakea, and No. 5 Squadron for maritime reconnaissance which is operating a few **Sunderland M.R.Mk.5** flying boats from Lauthala Bay, Fiji, pending the delivery of five **P-3B Orion** land-based maritime reconnaissance aircraft from August 1966. A strike and reconnaissance fighter replacement for both the **Canberras** and **Vampires** is currently sought for service from 1968–69, and the Phantom II is currently favoured although such a purchase will not further the common policy with the R.A.A.F. towards re-equipment.

Royal New Zealand Navy: The R.N.Z.N. will operate aircraft for the first time when it receives the two **Westland Wasp** helicopters that it has ordered for the ASW weapons-carrying role from the Leander-class frigate *Waikato* currently being built in the U.K.

NICARAGUA

Fuerza Aérea, Guardia Nacional de Nicaragua: The air component of the Nicaraguan National Guard is a small force equipped, for the most part, with obsolete aircraft, although limited U.S. assistance has been received in recent years, resulting in a jet component of six **Lockheed T-33B** armed trainers which are operated by one squadron in the fighter-bomber role. A light bomber flight operates six **B-26 Invaders,** and there is one counter-insurgency squadron with a secondary training role with six **T-28s,** and four **T-6s** remain on strength.

NIGER

Force Aérienne du Niger: The Republic of Niger has established a small air arm with French assistance and personnel seconded from the *Armée de l'Air*, and its tasks are confined to transport and communications, no plans existing for the establishment of a combat element.

NIGERIA

Nigerian Air Force: The Nigerian Air Force is enjoying the services of a Federal German advisory and training mission, and is equipped almost entirely with ex-*Luftwaffe* training, communications and transport aircraft. A combat element is being established with **Fiat G.91R** fighter-bombers, but this is not expected to attain operational status before 1968.

NORWAY

Kongelige Norske Flyvåpen: The Royal Norwegian Air Force, usually known as *Luftforsvaret*, is divided between two Air Commands, the *Luftkommando Sör-Norge* and the *Luftkommando Nord-Norge*, each with its own Headquarters and operational control, and is currently immersed in a re-equipment programme which began in 1964 with the conversion of Nr.331 *Skvadron* to the **F-104G Starfighter** at Bodø, this unit previously operating the **F-86F Sabre.** A second *Luftforsvaret* **F-86F Sabre** unit, Nr.336 *Skvadron* at Rygge, began converting to the **Northrop F-5** in March 1966, and a third, Nr.332, was to convert from the **F-86F Sabre** to the **F-5** during the course of 1966. The last **F-86F Sabre** unit, Nr.338 *Skvadron*, will convert to the **F-5** in 1967 at Orlandet, followed by Nr.334 *Skvadron* at Bodø which is currently one of three *Luftforsvaret* squadrons operating the **F-86K Sabre** in the all-weather intercept role, the others being Nr.337 and Nr.339. Sixty-eight **F-5s** have been ordered by the Norwegian government, and it is anticipated that a supplementary order for a further 16–20 **F-5s** will be placed in order to permit the four *Luftforsvaret* **F-5** squadrons to attain a statutory strength of 20 aircraft each. The remaining *Luftforsvaret* combat elements are

An ASW version of the Grumman HU-16B Albatross amphibian, the G-111, has been supplied under the MAP to the Norwegian and Spanish air arms, and is illustrated below in service with the Kongelige Norske Flyvåpen. *Powered by two 1,425 h.p. Wright R-1820-76A radial engines, the G-111 Albatross has sonobuoy receiver and ECM antennae in the wingtips, ASW search radar in an enlarged nose radome, a retractable MAD boom in the rear fuselage, a searchlight under the starboard wing, and underwing pylons for torpedoes, HVAR missiles, or depth bombs.*

Nr.717 *Skvadron* operating **RF-84F Thunderflash** aircraft in the tactical reconnaissance role, and two maritime reconnaissance and ASW squadrons, Nr.330 and Nr.333, each equipped with eight ASW versions of the **HU-16B Albatross** amphibian.

PAKISTAN

Pakistan Air Force: Although a signatory to the original Baghdad Pact and, at least, at the time of closing for press, ostensibly a U.S. ally as a participant in C.E.N.T.O. and S.E.A.T.O., Pakistan is now obtaining combat aircraft from China as a result of the U.S. decision to furnish the Pakistani armed forces with only non-lethal aid since the 23-day conflict between Pakistan and India. As virtually all first-line P.A.F. equipment is of U.S. origin, the refusal of further spares could result in a steady decline.

The Republic F-47D Thunderbolt now survives in first-line operational service with only one air arm, the Fuerza Aérea del Peru, *and is illustrated below in service with that air arm's* Escuadron de Caza 13. *The F-47D has a Pratt & Whitney R-2800-59 radial rated at 2,000 h.p. dry and 2,300 h.p. with water injection, and has a maximum speed of 429 m.p.h. at 30,000 ft.*

During the conflict with India in 1965, the P.A.F. was officially stated to have lost two **B-57s** and 14 **Sabres** (although India officially claimed the destruction of 73 Pakistani aircraft in the air and on the ground), and of the 120 **F-86F Sabre** fighter-bombers supplied to the P.A.F. during 1956–58, more than 80 remain in service, equipping some six squadrons. One interceptor squadron operates the **F-104A Starfighter** and two light bomber squadrons are equipped with the **B-57B,** 12 **Starfighters** and 30 **B-57Bs** having been delivered to the P.A.F. There is also a tactical reconnaissance squadron equipped with the **Lockheed RT-33A.** Early in 1966, some P.A.F. personnel undertook conversion courses in China, and shortly afterwards an agreement was signed with China for the supply of 125 **MiG-17s** and **-19s**, but it is unlikely that any extensive re-equipment with Chinese-supplied combat aircraft has yet taken place at squadron level. Ninety surplus *Luftwaffe* **Canadair Sabre Mk. 6s** were purchased in 1966.

PARAGUAY

Fuerza Aérea del Paraguay: Paraguay possesses a small air arm concerned primarily with transport and communications tasks. There is no organised combat element, although a small number of **T-6 Texans** have been used in the attack role against insurgent forces. The economic situation of Paraguay renders any major expansion of the *Fuerza Aérea* unlikely.

PERU

Fuerza Aérea del Peru: Perhaps the best equipped and most efficient of Latin-American air arms, Peru's air arm possesses three combat groups each with three squadrons. *Gruppo* 12 comprises three *Escuadrones de Caza*, one equipped with the **Hunter F.Mk.52** (16 fighters of this type being acquired in 1956 to equip *Escuadron* 14), one with **F-80C Shooting Stars,** and the other with **F-86F Sabres;** *Gruppo* 13 possesses the *Fuerza Aérea's* last piston-engined fighters in the shape of *Escuadrones* 12 and 13 which operate the **F-47D Thunderbolt,** and one *escuadron* equipped with the **F-80C Shooting Star,** and *Gruppo* 21 provides the bomber component of the service with two *escuadrones* of eight **B-26C Invaders** and one *escuadron* of eight **Canberra B.(I).Mk.8s.**

PHILIPPINES

Philippine Air Force: Organised on U.S.A.F. lines, the Philippine Air Force possesses four combat squadrons, three of these forming the 5th Fighter Wing for which 40 **F-86F Sabres** were acquired in 1957–58. One squadron of the 5th Wing began conversion from the **F-86F** to the **Northrop F-5** early in 1966, and all three squadrons will eventually convert to this type. The fourth combat squadron serves in the all-weather intercept role with the **F-86D Sabre,** 18 aircraft of this type having been supplied under the Military Assistance Programme.

POLAND

Polskie Lotnictwo Wojskowe: A tactical air arm based broadly on the pattern of the *Voenno-Vozdushnye Sily* of the Soviet Union and operating combat aircraft of Russian design, the P.L.W. is the largest air arm of any of the countries allied to the Soviet Union. The main combat strength of the P.L.W. is provided by three Air Defence Corps the basic formation of which is the *Pulk Lotnictwa Mysliwskiege*, or Fighter Air Regiment, each of which is divided into two or three *Eskadra* of 10–12 aircraft. There are currently some 700 interceptor fighters and fighter-bombers. It is believed that four Regiments are now equipped with day and limited all-weather point defence interceptors of the **MiG-21** type, and roughly a similar number are equipped with **MiG-19s.** A few units still operate the **LIM-5** (Polish-built **MiG-17**) for the intercept role but these are presumably in process of converting to the **MiG-21.** The majority of the remaining fighter squadrons serve in the fighter-bomber role with the **SU-7** and **LIM-5,** some *Eskadra* operating a modified version of the latter for use from grass strips. There are two Bomber Air Regiments (*Pulk Lotnictwa Bombardujace*) operating the **Ilyushin Il-28,** several tactical reconnaissance *Eskadra* equipped with both this type and the **LIM-5,** and a small naval air arm, the *Morskie Wojskowe Lotnictwo*, which, manned by naval personnel and intended for naval co-operation duties in the Baltic, operate similar types to the P.L.W., bringing Polish first-line combat aircraft strength to 900–950.

PORTUGAL

Forca Aérea Portuguesa: The smallest of N.A.T.O.'s air arms, the F.A.P. possesses only five combat squadrons. There are two fighter-bomber units, Nos. 20 and 21 Squadrons equipped with **Fiat G.91Rs** to which they converted from **F-84G Thunderjets** early in 1966, a batch of 40 **G.91Rs** surplus to the *Luftwaffe's* requirements being acquired from Federal Germany; two day interceptor units, Nos. 10 and 11 Squadrons equipped with **F-86F Sabres,** a total of 50 aircraft of this type having been delivered to the F.A.P. under the Military Assistance Programme, and one maritime reconnaissance squadron for which 12 **P-2E Neptunes** (originally operated by the R.A.F. and subsequently by the Dutch naval air arm) were supplied. No major expansion or extensive re-equipment of the F.A.P. is currently envisaged.

RHODESIA

Royal Rhodesian Air Force: A small but highly trained and efficient force, the R.R.A.F. possesses a combat element of three squadrons comprising No. 1 (Fighter) Squadron with **Hunter F.G.A.Mk.9s,** No. 2 (Fighter) Squadron with **Vampire F.B.Mk.9s,** and No. 5 (Bomber) Squadron with **Canberra B.Mk.2s.** The R.R.A.F. has received 12 **Hunter F.G.A.Mk.9s,** 12 **Vampire F.B.Mk.9s** and 15 **Canberra B.Mk.2s,** but with the dissolution of the Federation in 1963, a small number of the **Canberras** and **Vampires** were placed in storage. Since the Unilateral Declaration of

Independence a ban has been imposed on the supply of spares from the U.K. for R.R.A.F. aircraft, but it is likely to be some time before this seriously affects serviceability.

RUMANIA

Aviatia Română: Possessing approximately 200 first-line combat aircraft, Rumania's air arm, which is simply known as *Aviatia Română*, or Rumanian Aviation, is a tactical air arm with a strong interceptor fighter element. Administered by the *Ministerul Fortelor Armate*, or Armed Forces Ministry, it is equal in status to the Infantry and Tank Corps, and is organised on Russian lines. Its largest formation is the *Divizie Aeriană* (Air Division) which is sub-divided into *Corpuri Aeriene* (Air Corps), each of which consists of two or more *Regimente de Aviatie* (Air Regiments) of 50–80 aircraft. Although equipped largely with obsolescent combat aircraft types, some modernity has been provided since 1964 in the shape of the **MiG-21** point defence interceptor which is now believed to equip one complete *regiment de aviatie* comprising two groups of three squadrons. There are two other *regimente de aviatie* which, equipped with the **MiG-17,** fulfil both intercept and fighter-bomber roles, and there is another with three *escadrile* of **Il-28** light tactical bombers.

SALVADOR

Fuerza Aerea Salvadoreña: The diminutive Salvadorean air arm has an operational element comprising one flight of **F4U-4 Corsair** fighter-bombers. Re-equipment of this flight is envisaged in the near future, but no expansion of this sole combat unit is foreseen.

SAUDI ARABIA

Royal Saudi Air Force: The complete revision of the Saudi-Arabian air defence system and the Royal Saudi Air Force will commence in 1967 following the decision, in January 1966, to acquire 34 **Lightning F.Mk.53s,** six **Lightning T.Mk.55s,** and 25 **BAC 167 Jet Provosts,** associated ground radar, and surface-to-air missile batteries. The **Lightning F.Mk.53s,** which will equip two R.S.A.F. squadrons, will be employed in the intercept, strike and reconnaissance roles, and there is a strong likelihood that the initial order for fighters of this type will be supplemented by an order for a sufficient additional quantity to equip two further squadrons. Four refurbished ex-R.A.F. single-seat **Hunter F.Mk.6s** and two two-seat **Hunter T.Mk.66s** were acquired from the U.K. during 1966 for pilot and ground attack training, and it is possible that 12 more **Hunters** will be acquired. Four **Lightning F.Mk.52s** and two **T.Mk.54s** have also been obtained from R.A.F. stocks. The R.S.A.F. received nine **B-26 Invader** light bombers and 16 **F-86F Sabre** fighters under the Military Assistance Programme during 1955–58, and was also presented with four surplus **Vampire F.B.Mk.52** fighter-bombers by the U.A.R., but the the **B-26s** have remained unflown owing to lack of trained R.S.A.F. personnel and inadequate spares backing, and the **Sabres** (which were provided without armament) have been grounded for long periods as a result of spares shortages and the need for overhaul. However, most of the **Sabres** have undergone IRAN overhauls in Federal Germany recently, and the 30 U.S.-trained R.S.A.F. jet pilots will be supplemented over the next two years by British-trained pilots.

SENEGAL

Armée de l'Air du Sénégal: Established with French assistance for transport and communications tasks, and currently manned primarily by French personnel, the Senegalese air arm has no combat element, and no plans currently exist for the acquisition of armed aircraft.

SOMALIA

Cuerpo Aeronautica della Somalia: Somalia's Air Corps,

originally established as an Italian-controlled force, has, since 1963, received aid from both Italy and the Soviet Union, the latter supplying a small number of **MiG-15** fighter-bombers to supplement the piston-engined **F-51D Mustang** fighter-bombers that had previously provided the sole operational equipment of the Air Corps. Some personnel have been trained in Italy and others in the Soviet Union and the U.A.R., but the Air Corps' primary tasks are transport, communications and policing, and the combat element is reportedly confined to the equivalent of two squadrons, neither of which is at full strength.

SOUTH AFRICA

Suid-Afrikaanse Lugmag: Steadily expanded in recent years to provide well-balanced tactical and maritime combat elements against threats of military action from emergent African states, the *Suid-Afrikaanse Lugmag*, or South African Air Force, has two main units embodying all combat formations. These are the Tactical Group with Headquarters in Pretoria which controls the transport squadrons as well as the fighter and light bomber elements, and the Maritime Group with Headquarters at Langebaanweg Cape which, primarily concerned with naval co-operation, controls the maritime strike and reconnaissance elements. The combat units controlled by the Tactical Group include Nos. 1 and 2 Squadrons which operate the **Mirage IIIEZ**, the 16 **Mirage IIICZ** fighters formerly operated by No. 2 Squadron from Waterkloof being transferred to a third fighter squadron formation of which began in early 1966, and a light bomber and reconnaissance component is provided by the six **Canberra B.(I).Mk.12** and six **B.(I).Mk.58** aircraft of No. 12 Squadron. A number of light attack squadrons will be formed within the Tactical Group during 1968–70 with the **Impala,** an armed version of the **MB.326** basic trainer which is to enter production in South Africa in 1967, current plans calling for the manufacture of 234 **Impalas** for issue to both light attack and training elements. The Maritime Group controls No. 24 Squadron with 15 **Buccaneer S.Mk.50** strike aircraft, and the seven **Shackleton M.R.Mk.3** maritime reconnaissance aircraft for which a replacement is currently being sought. Sixteen ASW Sud-Aviation **SA-321 Super Frelon** helicopters have been ordered to equip a new squadron. Two reserve squadrons, Nos. 71 and 72, which form part of the Active Citizen Force, are equipped with the **Vampire F.B.Mk.5,** and the survivors of the 34 **Canadair Sabre Mk.6** fighters acquired in 1956 are being transferred to reserve squadrons.

Suid-Afrikaanse Marine: The South African Navy operates a number of helicopters, and has purchased eight **Westland Wasps** for the ASW weapons-carrying role from platforms aboard the destroyers *Van der Stel* and *Van Riebeeck*.

SPAIN

Ejercito del Aire Español: The recipient of large-scale U.S. aid, the E.d.A. is a comparatively large force although much of its current combat equipment is obsolete. There are two E.d.A. operational commands, the *Mando de la Defensa* and the *Aviacion Táctica*, the former being concerned primarily with the intercept role and the latter with army support. The *Mando de la Defensa* comprises *Alas de Caza-Bombardeo* Nos. 11, 12, and 15 at Valencia (Manises), Zaragoza and Seville (Moron) respectively, each with one *Escuadron* (Nos. 112, 121 and 151) of 25 **F-86F Sabres,** *Ala de Caza-Bombardeo No. 16* consisting of *Escuadron* 161 equipped with **F-104G Starfighters** at Torrejon, and, at the same base, the *Unidad Cuertel Gral* with the **F-86F Sabre**-equipped *Escuadron* No. 981. The *Aviacion Táctica* has two fighter-bomber units, *Escuadrones Caza-Bombardeo* Nos. 101 and 102 at Valencia (Manises) and Madrid (Torrejon) respectively with **F-86F Sabres,** *Ala de Bombardeo Ligero* No. 27 equipped with aged piston-engined **C.A.S.A. 2.111-D** (Merlin-engined **Heinkel He 111H**) light bombers and comprising *Escuadrones* Nos. 271 and 272 at Malaga, *Escuadron* 431 with **T-6 Texans** at Valladolid (Villanubla),

A licence-built version of the Heinkel He 111*H*-16 *with* 1,600 *h.p. Rolls-Royce Merlin* 500/29 *engines, the C.A.S.A.* 2.111-*D reconnaissance-bomber equips the* Ala de Bombardeo Ligero *No.* 27 *of the* Ejercito del Aire Español. *Carrying a* 2,200-*lb. bomb load and a defensive armament of one* 12.7-*mm. and two* 7.92-*mm. machine guns, the C.A.S.A.* 2.111-*D has a maximum speed of* 260 *m.p.h.*

and *Ala de Cooperacion Aeronaval* No. 61 at Jerez-Rota with the ASW version of the **HU-16B Albatross.** The re-equipment of the bulk of the E.d.A. combat units is becoming a matter of some urgency. The E.d.A. received 244 **F-86F Sabres** during 1956–58 in exchange for U.S. use of Spanish bases, and the only additional combat aircraft received since that time are 21 **F-104G Starfighters** supplied under the Military Assistance Programme, and seven examples of the ASW **Albatross.** However, the U.S. government is partly financing an E.d.A. order for 70 **Northrop F-5s,** some component manufacture for which, together with local assembly is planned. Deliveries of the **F-5** to the E.d.A. are scheduled to begin in 1967, and the **Sabre**-equipped units of the *Mando de la Defensa* will begin conversion in 1968, their existing equipment being handed over to the *Aviacion Táctica* after IRAN inspection.

Aviacion Naval Español: The Spanish Navy has an extensive ASW task and, currently operating three flights of helicopters, the service has ordered specialised ASW rotorcraft, including a small number of the ASW version of the **Agusta-Bell AB-204B,** the first of which entered service late in 1965, and six **Sikorsky SH-3D** helicopters, deliveries of which began in June 1966. The Spanish Navy is to receive on loan for a period of five years a former U.S. escort carrier, the 11,000-ton *Thetis Bay*, for use as an ASW helicopter carrier. Also ordered are a number of **Gyrodyne QH-50C** anti-submarine drone helicopters for operation from several destroyers, commencing with the *Roger de Lauria* and the *Marques de la Ensenada*.

SUDAN

Sudanese Air Force: A small force concerned entirely with internal policing, training, transport and communications tasks, Sudan's air arm possesses no combat aircraft, but its **Provost** and **Jet Provost** trainers are equipped to carry armament, and seven **Provost T.Mk.53s,** four **Jet Provost T.Mk.51s** and four **Jet Provost T.Mk.52s** are on strength. Plans reputedly exist for the establishment of a light tactical squadron with armed jet trainers.

SWEDEN

Svenska Flygvapnet: Superior to the air forces of many larger nations in both size and efficiency, *Flygvapnet* is essentially a defensive force, the combat elements of which are equipped almost entirely with aircraft of indigenous design. The *Flygvapen* is organised in four *Eskaders*, or Groups, to each of which a number of *Flottiljer*, or Wings, are assigned, these each having a statutory strength of three *Divisions*, or squadrons, of 12–15 aircraft. Out of *Flygvapnet's* current first-line strength of 46 combat squadrons with a total of some 700 aircraft, 27 are interceptor squadrons and 12 are all-weather attack squadrons. The *Eskaders* are as follows: *Flygeskadern* 1 with Headquarters at Göteborg and embodying the four attack Wings (F 6, F 7, F 15 and F 17) all of which are equipped with the **A 32A Lansen**; *Flygeskadern* 2 with Headquarters at Ängelholm and embodying F 3 and F 10 equipped with the **J 35D Draken,** F 9 which is still equipped with the **Hunter F.Mk.50** but will re-equip with the **Draken** in 1967, and F 12 with the **J 32B Lansen**; *Flygeskadern* 3 with Headquarters in Stockholm comprising F 1 equipped with the **J 32B Lansen,** F. 13 equipped with the **J 35F Draken,** F 16 with the **J 35A Draken** and F 18 with the **J 35B Draken**, and *Flygeskadern* 4 with Headquarters at Luleå and comprising F4 with the **J 29F,** and two tactical reconnaissance units, F 11 with the **S 32C Lansen** and the **S 35E Draken,** and F 21 with the **S 29C** and **S 35E** plus one all-weather interceptor squadron with the **J 32B Lansen.** For light air support of naval and military forces, *Flygvapnet* had ordered 20 armed versions of the **Saab 105** jet trainer which will be known as the **A 60,** but the entire **Saab 105 (Sk 60)** trainer fleet of 130 aircraft will have light strike potential for emergency use. The multi-mission **Saab 37 Viggen** is expected to begin replacing the **A 32A Lansen** in its **AJ 37** version from 1970, **JA 37** and **S 37** versions of the **Viggen** subsequently supplanting the **Draken** and **Lansen** in the intercept and reconnaissance roles.

Kungl. Svenska Marinen: The Royal Swedish Navy currently operates two helicopter squadrons whose principal roles are ASW and mine-sweeping. No. 1 Helicopter Squadron at Berga has four **Vertol 44** and three **Boeing-Vertol 107-II-15** helicopters equipped for ASW and mine-countermeasures tasks, plus seven **Alouette IIs** which may be equipped for submarine detection, and No. 2 Helicopter Squadron at Torslanda has six **Vertol 44s** and three **Alouette IIs,** but under "Navy Plan 60", the total Navy helicopter force is to be increased to eight heavy, 12 medium and 14 light helicopters.

SWITZERLAND

Schweizerische Flugwaffe: A purely defensive force, the *Flugwaffe* currently possesses 21 *Flieger-Staffeln* each possessing a statutory strength of 18 aircraft and equipped with single-seat ground-attack fighters and fighter-bombers, giving a first-line strength of 378 combat aircraft plus reserves. Controlled by the *Kommando Flieger- und Fliegerabwehrtruppen*, the combat elements of the *Flugwaffe* are divided between three *Flieger-Regimenten* which, in turn, are sub-divided into *Geschwader* of from two to four *Staffeln*. At the present time, five *Flieger-Staffeln* are equipped with **Hunter F.Mk.58** ground attack fighters, 100 aircraft of this type having been purchased for the *Flugwaffe* during 1958–60; 13 *Flieger-Staffeln* have **Venom F.B.Mk.50** fighter-bombers, 250 of which were manufactured under licence during 1953–56, and the remaining three *Flieger-Staffeln* still operate the **Vampire F.B.Mk.6.** Only four of the *Flieger-Staffeln* are manned by full-time personnel and at constant readiness, the remaining units being manned by short-service and reserve personnel. The first-line strength of the *Flugwaffe* will be progressively reduced over the next few years, current proposals calling for the phasing out of all 16 **Venom** and

Shortly to be finally phased out of first-line Flygvapnet *service, the Saab 29 single-seat fighter currently remains in use with the F 4 wing in whose service it is seen below. Powered by an RM 2B (Ghost 50) turbojet rated at 4,750 lb.s.t. and 6,170 lb.s.t. with after-burning, the J 29F has an armament of two Rb 24 infra-red homing AAMs and four 20-mm. Hispano cannon. Maximum speed is 658 m.p.h. and initial climb rate is 11,810 ft./min.*

Vampire *staffeln* by 1970, although the five **Hunter** *Staffeln* will be retained beyond 1970. Current procurement for the combat elements comprises only 36 licence-built **Mirage IIIS** interceptors and 18 **Mirage IIIRS** tactical reconnaissance aircraft to equip three *Staffeln*, deliveries of the former commencing mid-1966 with completion at the beginning of 1968, deliveries of the latter following from mid-1968 until mid-1969. Unless additional combat aircraft procurement is authorised in the interim, by 1970 the first-line strength of the *Flugwaffe* will have fallen to 144 combat aircraft.

SYRIA

Syrian Air Force: No fewer than eight *coups d'état* in Syria in 17 years have largely frustrated attempts to increase the effectiveness and efficiency of the Syrian Air Force. Extensive assistance has been given to Syria by both the Soviet Union and Czechoslovakia in the form of training missions and facilities, and combat aircraft, but serviceability in the five first-line combat squadrons is reportedly extremely low owing to a deficiency of trained personnel and inadequate spares backing, and less than half of the 140–150 combat aircraft supplied to the Syrian Air Force in the past ten years are allegedly airworthy. Few of the original batch of 40 **MiG-15s** remain serviceable but about half the 60 **MiG-17s** supplied to Syria remain on strength, and two squadrons, each with a nominal strength of 18 aircraft, are equipped with the **MiG-21.**

TANZANIA

Tanzanian Air Force: Following the federation of Tanganyika and Zanzibar into the single state of Tanzania, Federal German assistance was obtained in the establishment of an air arm, but this assistance was withdrawn in February 1965 with the recognition of the German Democratic Republic by Tanzania, and an R.C.A.F. mission has since taken over the German commitments. At the present time, the Tanzanian Air Force's activities are confined to training, transport and communications tasks, although the Tanzanian government hopes to establish an operational element for policing and support of the Tanzanian ground forces.

THAILAND

Royal Thai Air Force: Reorganised by a U.S. Military Air Advisory Group in the early 'fifties, the Royal Thai Air Force has since enjoyed the services of a substantial U.S. advisory team and supplies of aircraft under the Military Assistance Programme. Current operational strength comprises three combat wings each with two-three squadrons with a 16-aircraft establishment. One wing comprises two squadrons of **F-86F Sabres** and one squadron of **F-86L Sabres** for which 47 **F-86F** and 17 **F-86L Sabres** have been supplied since 1961. The other two combat wings operate in the counter-insurgency role with **T-28Ds** and armed **T-6G Texans.** Under a new agreement reached with the U.S. government in 1965, the Royal Thai Air Force is to be re-equipped and modernised. Some Thai personnel are undergoing training in the U.S.A., and the delivery of **Northrop F-5** fighter-bombers to Thailand commenced in April 1966.

TOGO

Force Aérienne Togolaise: The Republic of Togo has established a small air arm with French assistance and manned by *Armée de l'Air* personnel seconded to the Togo government. The activities of the *Force Aérienne Togolaise* are confined to transport and communications tasks, and no plans exist for the formation of a combat element.

TUNISIA

Armée de l'Air Tunisienne: The nucleus of a small air arm was established by the Republic of Tunisia in 1960, and some technical and financial assistance has since been received from France. The first step towards establishing an operational element was taken with the delivery of eight **Macchi MB.326B** armed trainers for the dual training-operational role in 1965–66.

TURKEY

Türk Hava Kuvvetleri: Forming a component of the 6th Allied Tactical Air Force Southern Europe, the *Türk Hava Kuvvetleri* (T.H.K.), or Turkish Air Force, commits its 1st and 3rd Tactical Air Forces to N.A.T.O., although these remain under Turkish operational control except during N.A.T.O. exercises or during an emergency. The T.H.K.'s 1st Tactical Air Force with Headquarters at Eskisehir possesses eleven squadrons, two of these each having an establishment of 18 **F-104G Starfighters,** six each operating 20–25 **F-100C Super Sabres,** two having similar establishments of **F-84F Thunderstreaks,** and one being equipped with the **RF-84F Thunderflash** for tactical reconnaissance. The 3rd Tactical Air Force with Headquarters at Diyarbakir has seven fighter-bomber squadrons, four being equipped with the **F-100C Super Sabre** and three with the **F-84F Thunderstreak.** Re-equipment of the **F-84F** squadrons with the **Northrop F-5** began early in 1966, and 140* aircraft will have been delivered to the T.H.K. by 1968–69, the first **F-5** squadron, the 161st, being assigned to the 1st T.A.F. and the second to the 3rd T.A.F. The third operational component of the T.H.K. is the 2nd Tactical Air Force which forms, with missile batteries, the Air Defence Command, and comprises one wing of three squadrons of **F-86E(M) Sabre** day fighters, and two wings each of two squadrons of all-weather interceptors, one equipped with the **F-86D Sabre** and the other operating the **F-86K.** The T.H.K. originally received 105 **F-86E(M) Sabres** and 50 **F-86D Sabres**, the latter being supplemented by 50* former-Dutch **F-86K Sabres**. Other combat aircraft deliveries to the T.H.K. under the Military Assistance Programme over the past ten years have included 260 **F-100C Super Sabres,** 30 **RF-84F Thunderflashes** and 150* **F-84F Thunderstreaks.**

UGANDA

Uganda Army Air Force: Currently concerned primarily with light transport, communications and rescue roles, and the logistic support of the Uganda Rifles. Proposals exist for the expansion of the Uganda Army Air Force which will absorb some elements of the Police Air Wing, and Uganda student pilots have undergone jet training in Israel. An operational element is allegedly being provided by the Soviet Union with an initial batch of 12 **MiG-21s** to be based at Gulu.

UNION OF SOVIET SOCIALIST REPUBLICS

Voenno-Vozdushny Sily: The Soviet Military Aviation Forces, or *Voenno-Vozdushny Sily* (V.-V.S.), form together one of the world's two largest air arms, with a first-line operational aircraft strength currently estimated at 10,000* machines of which 1,400* are medium bombers and 200* are long-range strategic bombers, the remainder being interceptor fighters, light bombers and reconnaissance and strike fighters. The combat elements of the V.-V.S. are divided between three major components, the I.A.P.-V.O., or *(Istrebitilnaya) Aviatsiya Protivo-vozdushnoi Oborony Strany*, the (Fighter) Aviation of the Air Defence of the Country; the F.A., or *Frontovaya Aviatsiya* (Frontal Aviation), the Tactical Air Force, and the A.D.D., or *Aviatsiya Dalnovo Deistviya*, the Long-range Air Force, sometimes known as the *Dalnaya Raketonosnaya Aviatsiya*, or Long-range Rocket-carrying Aviation. In addition, there is a shore-based naval air arm known as the *Morskaya Aviatsiya* (Naval Aviation), or *Voenno-Vozdushny Sily Morskovo Flota* (Air Forces of the Navy), for the direct support of the Soviet Navy and for maritime reconnaissance and patrol.

The I.A.P.-V.O. with Headquarters in Moscow includes two P.-V.O. *Okrugs*, or Districts, at Baku and Moscow, but elsewhere in the Soviet Union air defence is the responsibility of the local Military District Air Commander who acts in liaison with the P.-V.O. *Strany*, all reporting being tied in to the P.-V.O. Headquarters. The basic formations are the *Divisiya* (Division) and the *Polk* (Regiment), and a large proportion of the P.-V.O. Divisions are equipped with the **MiG-21** day interceptor and the all-weather **MiG-21** and **Su-7** all-weather interceptors, together with the third-generation all-weather interceptor development of the **Yak-25** known in the West as *Firebar*, but some Divisions attached to the less important Military Districts are still equipped with the obsolescent **Yak-25**, and day and limited all-weather versions of the **MiG-17F** and **MiG-19**, and numerical strength is of the order of 3,000 aircraft, the interceptor elements of the *Morskaya Aviatsiya* having been transferred to the P.-V.O. since 1962.

The F.A., or *Frontovaya Aviatsiya*, is the largest component of the V.-V.S., and is divided between Frontal Air Armies which, possessing no fixed establishment and varying in size with the importance attached to the particular Army District, come under the direct command of the local Military District Air Commander. An F.A. Division normally comprises three Regiments, a Fighter Regiment having a statutory strength of 36 aircraft and a Bomber or Attack Regiment having 32 aircraft. The interceptor elements, responsible for defending the zone surrounding the entire U.S.S.R., possess generally similar equipment to P.-V.O. units. Some attack bomber elements still operate the obsolescent **Il-28**, but this has now been largely replaced in the tactical strike and reconnaissance role by the **Yak-28** and its derivative, the *Brewer*, and by the single-seat **Su-7** close-support fighter.

The A.D.D. has progressively diminished in importance with the growth of the ICBM forces, and its long-range heavy bomber force has now been reduced to less than 200* machines of which about half have been adapted to carry stand-off missiles, and the remainder modified for tanker and strategic reconnaissance tasks, these being primarily **Tu-20s** with a small proportion of **Mya-4s.** The principal strength of the A.D.D. lies in its ageing but still substantial force of **Tu-16** medium bombers which it also employs extensively in the photo- and electronic-reconnaissance roles. The long-range medium and heavy bombers, reconnaissance aircraft and aerial refuelling tankers plus supporting transport are divided into Long-range Air Armies of varying size, these being sub-divided into Divisions, and some two-thirds of the V.-V.S.'s **Tu-16s,** or some 900-950 aircraft, are included on the A.D.D. strength. The so-called *Blinder* is believed to have been developed as a potential successor to the **Tu-16** but has apparently been manufactured in relatively small numbers.

The *Morskaya Aviatsiya* operates the remainder of the **Tu-16s** in the long-range anti-shipping role with *Kipper* missiles, and for maritime reconnaissance and patrol, this task being shared by the elderly piston-engined **Be-6** flying boat and, to a lesser extent, the **Be-10** flying boat. There are some light bomber elements in the *Morskaya Aviatsiya* equipped with the **Il-28,** but most such units have been transferred to the F.A., and there are a substantial number of ASW units equipped for the most part with an ASW version of the **Mi-4** helicopter. *Morskaya Aviatsiya* units are distributed between the four Soviet Fleets—Baltic, Northern, Black Sea and Pacific.

UNITED ARAB REPUBLIC

Air Force of the United Arab Republic: The air arm of the United Arab Republic, as Egypt continues to be called despite the termination of the union between this country, Syria and Yemen, possesses combat elements equipped virtually entirely with aircraft supplied by the Soviet Union, although small numbers of licence-built **HA-200B Saeta** basic trainers are intended for both training and operational roles. The efficiency of the combat units is limited by inadequate spares backing, and relatively few of the operational squadrons are reputedly at full statutory strength. First-line strength is nominally 350* combat aircraft. There are currently two interceptor wings respectively equipped with **MiG-21s** and **MiG-19s,** 52 examples of the former fighter and 80 of the latter having been delivered to Egypt, two fighter-bomber wings each with a statutory strength of three squadrons, one with **MiG-17s,** and the other with **MiG-15s**, although only the first of these wings is reportedly active, one light bomber wing with three squadrons for which 32 **Il-28s** were received, and one heavy bomber wing with two squadrons of **Tu-16s.** Plans to re-equip the interceptor elements with the indigenous **HA-300** from 1967–68 no longer appear likely to see fruition, and it is probable that the United Arab Republic will continue to rely on Soviet-supplied combat aircraft in the foreseeable future. Factual first-line operational strength is believed to be 180–200 aircraft.

UNITED KINGDOM

Royal Air Force: The combat elements of the R.A.F. are organised within Fighter, Bomber and Coastal Commands in the U.K., the 2nd Tactical Air Force in Germany, Air Headquarters Malta, R.A.F. Gibraltar, the Near East Air Force, Air Forces Middle East, and the Far East Air Force, and comprise more than 60 first-line operational squadrons. Fighter Command, comprising No. 11 Group with Headquarters at Leconfield and No. 12 Group with Headquarters at Horsham St. Faith, has been, numerically, a declining force for several years, and is now purely **Lightning**-equipped, Nos. 5, 23, 56, 64, 74 and 111 Squadrons operating the **Lightning F.Mks.3** and **6** which have a planned operational life of at least a further seven years. Bomber Command possesses two Groups controlling about a dozen V-bomber squadrons, the majority of which are **Vulcan**-equipped. No. 1 Group with Headquarters at Bawtry controls some nine squadrons, including Nos. 9, 12, 27, 35, 50, 83 and 617 with **Vulcan B.Mk.2s** and Nos. 44 and 101 with **Vulcan B.Mk.1Bs,** while No. 3 Group with Headquarters at Mildenhall supervises a substantially smaller force of **Victor B.Mk.2** squadrons (Nos. 100 and 139), and No. 58 Squadron with **Canberra P.R.Mk.7s** and **9s** and No. 543 Squadron with **Victor B. (S.R.) Mk.2s** for reconnaissance. Flight refuelling facilities are provided by the **Victor B.K.Mk.1As** of Nos. 55 and 57 Squadrons. The V-bombers are to be phased out in the early 'seventies, this being linked with the planned introduction of the proposed Anglo-French variable-geometry aircraft, although it is acknowledged that this is envisaged primarily as a tactical strike type. Coastal Command with Nos. 18 and 19 Groups possesses eight **Shackleton**-equipped maritime reconnaissance squadrons. Those equipped with the **Shackleton M.R.Mk.3,** which include Nos. 120, 201 and 206 Squadrons, are having their aircraft progressively updated to enable them to operate well into the 'seventies, but the **Shackleton M.R.Mk.2,** which equips Nos. 37, 38, 42, 205 and 224 Squadrons, will be progressively withdrawn from 1969 when it is anticipated that the **HS.801** will begin to enter service for the maritime role, the delivery of 38* aircraft of this type to Coastal Command being anticipated. Coastal Command also includes R.A.F. Gibraltar with part of the **Shackleton** force.

The 2nd Tactical Air Force, which provides the main component of N.A.T.O. 2nd Allied Tactical Air Force in Germany, comprises Nos. 19 and 92 Squadrons with **Lightning F.Mk.2s,** Nos. 3, 14, 16 and 213 Squadrons with **Canberra B.(I).Mk.8s** and **B.Mk.16s,** Nos. 17, 31 and 80 Squadrons with **Canberra P.R.Mk.7s,** and Nos. 2 and 4 Squadrons with **Hunter F.R.Mk.10s.** The other overseas commands are Air Headquarters Malta with the **Shackleton M.R.Mk.2**-equipped No. 38 Squadron and the **Canberra P.R.Mk.9s** of No. 39 Squadron; the Near East Air Force (Cyprus) embodies Nos. 32, 73 and 249 Squadrons with **Canberra B.Mk.15s,** No. 6 Squadron with **Canberra B.Mk.16s,** No. 13 Squadron with **Canberra P.R.Mks.7** and **9,** and No. 29 Squadron with **Javelin F.A.W.Mk.9s;** Air Forces Middle East deploys Nos. 8, 43 and 208 Squadrons with **Hunter F.G.A.Mk.9s,** and the Far East Air Force centred on Malaysia and Singapore includes Nos. 20 and 28 Squadrons with **Hunter F.G.A.Mk.9s,** No. 45 Squadron with

Canberra B.Mk.15s, No. 60 Squadron with **Javelin F.A.W.Mk.9s** and No. 81 Squadron with **Canberra P.R.Mk.7s.** R.A.F. Transport Command possesses a self-contained tactical task force, No. 38 Group, with its own ground attack fighter support provided by Nos. 1 and 54 Squadrons with **Hunter F.G.A.Mk.9s.** During the next few years, the **Hunter** which currently equips nine R.A.F. squadrons, will be progressively supplanted by the **F-4M Phantom II** and the **P.1127 Kestrel,** the acquisition of 150* of the former and 110* of the latter being planned, with the **F-4M** also taking over some of the roles currently performed by the **Canberra.** The remaining **Canberra** tasks, particularly in the Far East, are to be fulfilled by the **F-111K**, 50* aircraft of this type being planned to equip three–four squadrons.

Fleet Air Arm: The Fleet Air Arm of the Royal Navy currently provides mobile tactical air power in limited war, with additional nuclear strike capability, operating from shore bases and the 44,100-ton *Eagle*, the 43,340-ton *Ark Royal*, the 30,000-ton *Victorious*, and the 22,000-ton *Centaur*, while the 23,000-ton *Hermes* rejoined the Fleet in 1966 after refitting. However, the carrier force is scheduled to be phased out in 1975, and all fixed-wing Fleet Air Arm aircraft will subsequently be operated from shore bases. There are currently eight fixed-wing F.A.A. combat squadrons, three of these, Nos. 800, 801 and 809, having **Buccaneer S. Mk. 2s** for the strike role, four having **Sea Vixen F.A.W.Mks.1** and **2** for the all-weather intercept role, these being Nos. 890, 892, 893 and 899 Squadrons, and No. 849 Squadron operating **Gannet A.E.W.Mk.3** in the early warning role. The ASW role is now undertaken exclusively by helicopters, Nos. 814, 815, 819 and 845 Squadrons being equipped with the **Wessex H.A.S.Mk.1** which, together with the **H.A.S.Mk.3** version of the **Wessex,** is supplanting the **Whirlwind H.A.S.Mk.7s** of Nos. 824, 846 and 847 Squadrons. The **Wasp A.S.Mk.1** helicopters of No. 829 Squadron operate in the ASW weapons-carrying role on detachment aboard the first of the Royal Navy's 14 *Leander* and *Tribal* class frigates, and the five guided-weapon destroyers for the Royal Navy will carry **Wessex** ASW helicopters on stern platforms. The **Wessex H.A.S. Mk.3** will begin to give place in the ASW squadrons to an anglicised version of the **Sikorsky SH-3D** towards the end of the 'sixties. The **Sea Vixens** are to be progressively replaced by **F-4K Phantom IIs** during the late 'sixties, 70* aircraft of this type having been ordered.

UNITED STATES OF AMERICA

United States Air Force: With an active aircraft inventory of 14,000* of which about half comprises first-line combat types, the U.S.A.F. is in process of transferring emphasis from manned aircraft strategic and defensive to limited-war capability as a result of its commitment in Vietnam coupled with the diminishing likelihood of global nuclear war. Increased reliance on ICBM and IRBM capability as the principal nuclear deterrent is being accompanied by the steady numerical decline of the strategic bomber force, and the reduced threat of Soviet manned bomber attack on the North American Continent is resulting in a commensurate reduction in the U.S.A.F.'s interceptor fighter force. The U.S.A.F.'s major operational commands embodying combat elements which are divided between 16 Air Forces and a number of Air Divisions, are the Air Defence Command (A.D.C.); the Strategic Air Command (S.A.C.); the Tactical Air Command (T.A.C.); U.S.A.F. Europe (U.S.A.F.E.); Pacific Air Force (Pac.A.F.), and Alaskan Air Command (A.A.C.).

The Air Defence Command controls 35 of the 42 active U.S.A.F. interceptor fighter squadrons (four being assigned to U.S.A.F.E., two to Pac.A.F., and one to the A.A.C.), these being deployed at bases throughout the continental U.S.A., integrated with the R.C.A.F. in NORAD (North American Air Defense Command), and controlled through five geographically oriented SAGE (Semi-Automatic Ground Environment) Air Divisions. Now equipped almost exclusively with the **F-101B Voodoo** (16 squadrons) and the **F-106A Delta Dart** (13 squadrons), the A.D.C.'s interceptor fighter strength is currently being reduced to 31 squadrons which level is scheduled to be attained by June 30, 1967. Future manned interceptor procurement for the A.D.C. is uncertain, but both the **Lockheed YF-12** and an air defence interceptor variant of the **General Dynamics F-111** have been proposed. The Strategic Air Command's manned aircraft force, which is still responsible for the bulk of the U.S.A.F.'s nuclear striking power, comprises two wings equipped with the **B-58A Hustler** and 38 equipped with the **B-52 Stratofortress.** Three of the latter are scheduled to be phased out by June 30, 1967, and a further 17 **Stratofortress** wings together with the two **Hustler** wings will be phased out during 1968–70, their place in the S.A.C. being filled by 210 **FB-111s,** these entering the operational inventory in 1969 and all being deployed by 1971 when 18 wings of **B-52G** and **B-52H Stratofortresses** will remain on strength. Current proposals call for the development of an Advanced Manned Strategic Aircraft (AMSA) for deployment in the mid 'seventies as successor to the late-model **Stratofortresses.** The Strategic Air Command also possesses a reconnaissance commitment, units assigned to this task being the 9th Strategic Reconnaissance Wing equipped with 16 **Lockheed SR-71s** and a Wing in process of converting to the **RC-135.** The S.A.C. bomber and reconnaissance forces are sub-divided between the 2nd Air Force (Central U.S.A.), the 8th Air Force (Eastern U.S.A.), the 15th Air Force (Western U.S.A.), the 16th Air Force (Spain), and the 3rd Air Division (Guam).

The U.S.A.F.'s tactical combat forces, currently being increased in strength from 125 to 128 squadrons, are divided roughly equally between the Tactical Air Command and overseas commands. The T.A.C., which possesses some 2,500 combat and support aircraft, its 15 Tactical Fighter Wings possessing about 1,400 fighter-bombers, is currently committing more than a fifth of its strength to Vietnam. It comprises the 9th, 12th, and 19th Air Forces, the last-mentioned Air Force, known as the Composite Air Strike Force, possessing no combat elements of its own and drawing its aircraft from the other two Air Forces as required. The fighter-bomber mainstay of T.A.C. for a number of years, the **F-100D Super Sabre,** is being progressively phased out in favour of the **F-4C Phantom II** which is to equip 14 wings each of 75 aircraft, three wings operate the **F-105D Thunderchief,** and from 1967 the Command will begin to receive the **F-111A** followed, in 1969, by the **Ling-Temco-Vought A-7.** The U.S.A.F.'s other tactical combat elements are assigned to U.S.A.F. Europe and the Pacific Air Forces. U.S.A.F.E., which comprises the 3rd Air Force in the U.K. and the 17th Air Force in Germany assigned to N.A.T.O.'s 4th Allied Tactical Air Force, deploys six Tactical Fighter Wings equipped with the **F-100D Super Sabre** (2), the **F-105D Thunderchief** (1) and the **F-4C Phantom II** (3), and two Tactical Reconnaissance Wings now operating from the United Kingdom with the **RF-4C** and **RF-101C.** One Air Division of four squadrons of **F-102A Delta Daggers** is also assigned to U.S.A.F.E. Pac.A.F., which consists of the 5th Air Force in Japan, the 13th Air Force in the Philippines, and the 7th Air Force in Vietnam to which much of the Pac.A.F. strength is currently assigned, includes a Fighter Interceptor Wing of **F-102A Delta Daggers,** and nine Tactical Fighter Wings with **F-100D Super Sabres, F-105D Thunderchiefs,** and **F-4C Phantom IIs.** There is also one Tactical Bomber Wing with **B-57s** and two Tactical Reconnaissance Wings with **RF-101 Voodoos** and **RF-4C Phantom IIs.**

For all practical purposes a part of the U.S.A.F. itself, the Air National Guard, comprising the flying element of the territorial force raised by each U.S. state, provides a substantial reserve force, and its combat units are frequently deployed overseas. The A.N.G. possesses five Tactical Fighter Wings, five Tactical Reconnaissance Wings and 21 Fighter Interceptor Squadrons. **F-100 Super Sabres** and **F-105B Thunderchiefs** are the principal equipment of the tactical fighter elements, the **RF-84F Thunderflash** and **RB-57** serving in the tactical reconnaissance role, while 16 of the 21 A.N.G. interceptor squadrons are now equipped with the **F-102A Delta Dagger.**

United States Navy and Marine Corps: Operating from 15 attack carriers, including seven displacing more than 75,000 tons, plus eight anti-submarine carriers and numerous shore bases, the U.S. Navy's 28 Attack and ASW Carrier Air Groups and the U.S. Marine Corps' three Aircraft Wings together comprise the third largest of the world's air arms. The U.S.N. and U.S.M.C. possess an active aircraft inventory of some 8,300 machines of all types, and the carriers are distributed among the 1st and 7th Fleets (Pacific) and 2nd and 6th Fleets (Atlantic), one Carrier Air Group being assigned to each of the attack carriers. A Carrier Air Group usually comprises two fighter, two or three attack and (on *Forrestal* or *Midway* class carriers) one heavy attack squadron, and there are 30* fleet fighter squadrons each with 14 aircraft and equipped with the **F-4B** or (one squadron) **F-4G Phantom II** and the **F-8D** or **F-8E Crusader,** 46* attack squadrons, approximately one-third of which still operate the piston-engined **A-1H** and **A-1J Skyraider,** three being equipped with the **A-6B Intruder** and the remainder operating the **A-4C** and **A-4E Skyhawk,** and 12 heavy attack squadrons, six of these now being equipped with the **RA-5C Vigilante** with which they also perform the reconnaissance role, the remainder having the **A-3B Skywarrior.** There are four photo-reconnaissance squadrons equipped with the **RA-3B Skywarrior,** and the **RF-8A** and **RF-8G Crusader,** and four airborne early warning squadrons with the **E-1B** and **E-2A,** these deploying detachments with the various Carrier Air Wings. There are eight Fleet Air Wings with 30 patrol squadrons for the maritime reconnaissance role, about a dozen of these operating the **P-3A Orion**, three having the **SP-5B Marlin,** and the remainder having **SP-2H Neptunes**, and nine Anti-Submarine Air Groups each with two squadrons of **S-2 Trackers** and a squadron of **SH-34** or **SH-3** helicopters.

The three U.S.M.C. Aircraft Wings differ appreciably in strength, the 1st Marine Aircraft Wing possessing two Air Groups equipped with combat types, the 2nd M.A.W. having four and the 3rd M.A.W. having two. The Marine Air Groups include 13* attack squadrons, one having the **A-6A Intruder** and the remainder having the **A-4 Skyhawk,** 15* fighter squadrons with the **F-8 Crusader** and **F-4B Phantom II,** and three reconnaissance squadrons with the **RF-4B Phantom II** and **RF-8A Crusader.** Both the U.S.N. and the U.S.M.C. are to receive the **Ling-Temco-Vought A-7A Corsair II** from 1967 to replace the **A-4 Skyhawks** not supplanted by **A-6 Intruders,** and the **Phantom II** will continue to be procured in substantial quantities into 1968, the **F-4B** giving place to the **F-4J.** Production of the **F-111B** for the U.S.N. is expected to commence in 1968, and the U.S.M.C. is to receive 100 **North American OV-10A** counter-insurgency aircraft for the combined utility and close-support role.

UPPER VOLTA

Force Aérienne de Haute-Volta: The Republic of Upper Volta has established the nucleus of an air arm with French aid. Largely staffed by seconded *Armée de l'Air* personnel, it is concerned solely with communications and light transport tasks, and possesses no plans for the establishment of a combat element.

URUGUAY

Fuerza Aérea Uruguaya: Uruguay's air arm possesses a small combat element comprising one fighter-bomber squadron operating the **F-80C Shooting Star** and one tactical bomber squadron equipped with the **B-25J Mitchell.** There has been no recent procurement of combat aircraft, and no increase in the number of operational units is currently envisaged.

Aviación Naval: The Uruguayan Navy's small air arm, the *Aviación Naval,* is concerned primarily with light transport, communications and training tasks, but a small combat element in the form of a fighter-bomber squadron existed until 1961 when it was operating a small number of **F6F-5 Hellcats.**

VENEZUELA

Fuerzas Aéreas Venezolanas: Possessing an operational element of seven combat squadrons, the F.A.V. purchased early in 1966 a batch of 47 ex-*Luftwaffe* **F-86K Sabres,** a proportion of which was completely unused, and it may be presumed that these will re-equip *Escuadrones de Caza-Bombardeo* Nos. 35 and 36 which have been operating **Vampire F.B.Mk.5s** since 1950, as well as the **Venom F.B.Mk.4s** of the *Escuadron de Caza-Bombardeo* No. 34 acquired in 1955–56. The two day fighter squadrons, *Escuadrones de Caza* Nos. 37 and 38 currently operate the **F-86F Sabre,** 22 examples of which were acquired in 1955–56, *Escuadron de Bombardeo* No. 39 has operated six **Canberra B.Mk.2s** and eight **Canberra B.(I).Mk.8s** for a number of years, the former being acquired in 1952 and the latter in 1957, and the purchase of a batch of reconditioned **Canberra B.Mk.2s** in 1965 has enabled the F.A.V.'s second bomber squadron, *Escuadron de Bombardeo* No. 40 to convert to this type from **B-25J Mitchells.**

VIETNAM (Republic of)

Vietnamese Air Force: Possessing five operational wings with over 400 fixed-wing aircraft and helicopters, the Vietnamese Air Force (V.N.A.F.) has expanded rapidly over the past three years with U.S. assistance, and operates alongside U.S. formations in strikes against the Viet Cong. The principal combat aircraft type currently employed by the V.N.A.F. is the single-seat **Skyraider,** both the **A-1G** and **A-1H** versions being in service, five squadrons and one group operating 26 A-1G and 106 A-1H attack bombers of this type. The 41st Wing at Da Nang, the 62nd Wing at Nha Trang, and the 74th Wing at Bihn Thuy, which serve the 1st, 2nd, and 4th Corps areas respectively, each possess one squadron of **A-1 Skyraiders,** together with one squadron of **O-1 Bird Dogs** and one squadron of **Sikorsky CH-34s.** The 23rd Wing in the 3rd Corps Area at Bien Hoa has two **A-1** squadrons, and the 33rd Wing at Tan Son Nhut includes the **A-1 Skyraider**-equipped 83rd Special Air Group. Four **Martin B-57Bs** have been assigned to the V.N.A.F. but currently remain attached to the U.S.A.F.

Phased out of R.A.F. service in 1962, *the de Havilland Venom remains in service with Switzerland and Venezuela, that illustrated above being a Venom F.B.Mk*.4 *of the* Escuadron de Caza-Bombardeo *No.* 34 *of the* Fuerzas Aéreas Venezolanas. *Powered by a* 5,150 *lb.s.t. de Havilland Ghost* 105, *the Venom F.B.Mk*.4 *attains* 597 *m.p.h. at sea level and* 576 *m.p.h. at* 20,000 *ft*.

B-57 squadron at Da Nang. The V.N.A.F. is in process of receiving the **Northrop F-5** to replace a number of **A-1 Skyraiders,** and in 1967 will begin to receive the **Cessna AT-37D** for both training and attack roles. All **T-28Ds** and **B-26 Invaders** have now been removed from the V.N.A.F. operational inventory.

VIETNAM (Democratic Republic of)

Vietnamese People's Air Force: Steadily expanded with Chinese and Russian assistance, the Vietnamese People's Air Force now possesses 60–70 **MiG-17s** and 20–30 **MiG-21s,** the latter being based on airfields in the vicinity of Hanoi. Most V.P.A.F. personnel have undergone training in China and a Chinese Mission acts in an advisory capacity, but a small number of pilots and ground personnel have received training on the **MiG-21** in the Soviet Union. The V.P.A.F. has also received a token force of 6–10 **Il-28** light-bombers.

YEMEN

Air Force of the Yemen: A small Yemeni air arm has

existed for some twenty years, this force having received spasmodic assistance from both the Soviet Union and Czechoslovakia. However, few Yemeni personnel received flying or technical training, all Yemeni aircraft being flown and maintained by Russian or Czech personnel until their withdrawal as a result of more extensive Egyptian participation in the fighting between Republican forces and royalist tribesmen. The air arm now possesses a small number of piston-engined trainers, transports and helicopters which are flown by Egyptian personnel seconded from the Air Force of the U.A.R., and there is no active combat element.

YUGOSLAVIA

Jugoslovensko Ratno Vazduhoplovstvo: Essentially a tactical air arm equipped primarily with obsolescent combat aircraft of U.S. origin, the J.R.V. received a number of **MiG-21** day interceptors from the Soviet Union during 1963–64, and the acquisition of these aircraft may be indicative of major purchases of combat equipment from this source in the future. Since 1953,

*Last operator of the Republic F-*84*G Thunderjet is Yugoslavia's air arm, the* Jugoslovensko Ratno Vazduhoplovstvo.

A few North American B-25J Mitchell bombers remain with Latin-American air arms, that illustrated belonging to the Fuerza Aérea Uruguaya.

combat equipment acquired by the J.R.V. has included 169 **F-84G Thunderjets** from the U.S.A., these later being supplemented by 50 similar aircraft purchased from Greece; 121 ex-R.A.F. **F-86E(M) Sabres** were received in 1958–59, and 130 **F-86D Sabres** were added to the inventory during the early 'sixties. The major formation of the J.R.V. is the Air Corps which is sub-divided into Air Divisions each with a statutory strength of 75 aircraft. At the present time there are believed to be three interceptor fighter divisions equipped with the **MiG-21,** the **F-86D Sabre** and the **F-86E(M) Sabre.** There are also two fighter-bomber divisions equipped with the obsolete **F-84G Thunderjet,** but it is unlikely that these are now at full statutory strength, and an indigenous replaeement is reportedly under development.

ZAMBIA

Zambia Air Force: Derived from the defence elements allocated to Northern Rhodesia after secession from the Central African Federation, the Zambia Air Force is currently engaged primarily with training, transport and communications tasks, and possesses no combat element. However, armed jet trainers are being sought for the combined training and close-support roles.

THE DEVELOPMENT OF FIGHTER AIRCRAFT

BY TRADITION fighters have been distinguished from other classes of aircraft by their small size, high speed, manoeuvrability, relatively low cost, and by being primarily concerned with interception. Taking an example from the days of the "Battle of Britain", the Hurricane I weighed only 6,600 lb. fully loaded, cost little more than £10,000, or about $40,000, to produce, and had been designed mainly to shoot down bombers, over which it had a worthwhile edge in most aspects of performance. In contrast, a typical present-day fighter might not only weigh seven times as much, but also differ fundamentally in being no faster than its best bomber contemporary, and in being designed with just as much emphasis on ground attack or nuclear strike as on interception. Nor is the fighter any longer cheap to develop and construct; very few projects are now produced in runs of thousands. Unit costs range from roughly £285,000 ($800,000) for the simple, lightweight Northrop F-5 through the £420,000 ($1,176,000) for the fairly sophisticated Saab 35F to around £800,000 ($2,235,000) for the very much larger and more complex F-4D Phantom II and £1,180,000 ($3,305,000) for the F-106A Delta Dart. The ceiling price agreed between the British government and the U.S. Defence Department for the R.A.F.'s General Dynamics F-111Ks is £2,100,000 ($5,880,000) per aircraft, although this price does not include provision for costs of replacing certain U.S. equipment with British equivalents. The expense of future operations may likewise be gauged from reports that the Lockheed YF-12A was consuming fuel to the value of £1,000 ($2,800) per hour during its Mach 3.1 record-breaking flight on May 1, 1965.

The blame for the tremendous growth in weight must be shared between the increased military loads, the insatiable appetites of powerful turbojets, and the ever-growing demands for range. Whereas the typical fighter of World War II was equipped simply with radio, primitive IFF, gyro gunsight, and guns, its present-day equivalent would have a much more comprehensive selection of navigation aids, far more sophisticated means of identification, computers for its air-to-air and air-to-surface weapons, and quite possibly forward-looking radar for interception and terrain avoidance. As for range demands, the Korean War showed the desirability of long strike radius with heavy loads, so that F-84 Thunderjets and F-86 Sabres could fly close support missions direct from bases in Japan. It also demonstrated the vast organisation required to ferry combat aircraft across an ocean by means of flight refuelling, and eventually gave rise to a U.S. requirement for a fighter-bomber which could respond to the urgent needs of a brush-fire war, ferrying out over a distance of 4,000 miles without refuelling. On the British side, range demands were likewise on the increase because of the gradual closing of overseas bases, and the growing number of countries not only prepared to close their airfields to the R.A.F. in times of emergency, but also equipped with Mach 2.0 interceptors and surface-to-air missiles potentially capable of denying the use of their airspace, and thus enforcing lengthy detours.

The overall effect on fighter weights may be seen from a comparison of leading types over the past twenty years. The Meteor I which combatted the V-1 flying bombs of 1944 weighed 13,800 lb.; i.e., rather more than twice as much as the Hurricane. Nine years later, at the end of the Korean War, the F-86F-30 Sabre was taking off at 20,350 lb. with drop tanks and two 1,000 lb. bombs. Although some designers then made serious efforts to halt the upward trend, the fighters ordered in quantity by the U.S.A.F. were the heavyweight F-100, F-101, F-102, F-105, F-106 and, more recently, the F-4C, which is reported to gross up to 59,000 lb. in maximum loaded condition. Future projects show no real change in the trend: the General Dynamics F-111A is already said to weigh 77,000 lb., and an interceptor version of the Lockheed SR-71 is on offer at over 136,000 lb. putting it in almost the same weight category as a British V-bomber!

However, it is undoubtedly in the matter of speed that the fighter has changed most remarkably in relation to other classes of aircraft. Most air forces are indeed still at least partly equipped with subsonic types such as the Sabre, Hunter, and MiG-17, which cruise at altitude at almost identical speeds to present-day transports such as the Boeing 707 and VC10. At full bore these fighters may increase their speed from the cruise region of Mach 0.83 to perhaps Mach 0.95, but they are only significantly faster than transports or subsonic bombers at low altitudes, where the latter are limited by inferior flutter speeds. The more advanced air forces obviously possess fighters which are capable of Mach 2.0 in level flight, and a small elite are reportedly cleared up to Mach 2.4, but this gives little edge over the Mach 2.1 B-58 Hustler or the Mach 2.2 Mirage IV. By the early 1970s, the fighter's loss of its former pre-eminent position in aviation development will be rubbed home by the introduction of the Concorde and Tu-144 SSTs into airline operations, with cruise speeds of Mach 2.2. Indeed, unless urgent steps are taken by the U.S.A.F. to initiate their IMI (Improved Manned Interceptor) programme, then by the mid-1970s ordinary commercial passengers will be flying considerably faster than any fighter pilot, since the U.S. SST may then be operating at speeds approaching Mach 3.0.

The facts behind the present levelling-off of fighter speeds are that their attainment is not only extremely difficult, but also of very dubious operational value. From consideration of the regular mass-produced aluminium alloy airframe, a sustained speed of Mach 2.2 is about the maximum that can be tolerated if adequate strength and lack of distortion are to be maintained, but a speed of Mach 2.5 may be tolerated for short periods. The low drag wing required for these high speeds is also difficult to make compatible with normal fighter bases: a fighter can usually be blasted off the runway by its high thrust/weight ratio, but landing performance is purely a matter of wing loading and maximum lift coefficient. In comparison with an airliner, the design problem is much worse because of the shorter field lengths available and the need to manoeuvre subsonically, which rules out the slender delta shape carefully optimised for the Concorde, and results in the fighter having a far lower lift/drag ratio at high supersonic speed. In addition, the necessarily shorter endurance of the smaller aircraft means that a proportionately longer time is spent in accelerating and decelerating, so that the practical significance of the few moments spent at Mach 3.0 or above appears slight.

While the fighter designer has thus suddenly encountered major obstacles to further speed increase, the need for this type of improvement has simultaneously waned due to the development of second-generation guided weapons for head-on attacks, coupled with a lessening demand for manned interceptors. The general demise of the land-based interceptor has been due to the widespread substitution of the ICBM for the strategic bomber, the use of long-range stand-off weapons by such bombers as remain, and the development of surface-to-air missiles to deal with either bombers or stand-off bombs.

This changeover from manned aircraft to guided missiles was heralded in Britain by the famous 1957 White Paper on Defence, but this failed to give adequate recognition to two important issues. Firstly, due to their speed and ability to change course at will, naval units will always present a very difficult target for attack by ballistic missiles, and therefore major fleet units will require defence against manned bombers into the foreseeable future. Furthermore, unlike land targets which can be defended by concentric rings of surface-to-air missile bases, a naval task force can only achieve defence in depth through the use of fighters, not only intercepting the enemy before he can launch a stand-off bomb, but also eliminating the threat of the force being shadowed at long range by reconnaissance aircraft. The second failing of the White Paper was to foresee a major change in the international situation, such that the fear of an all-out war with Russia should be replaced by the reality of continual brush-fire wars and border incidents in the Middle and Far East. Emergencies at Suez, Kuwait, the Aden Protectorate, Brunei, the Indo-Chinese border,

One of the few genuine air superiority fighters currently under development, the United Arab Republic's Messerschmitt-designed HA-300 is expected, in its definitive form (illustrated by the general arrangement drawing on the right) to achieve speeds of the order of Mach 2.0. The first prototype (below, right) was originally flown on March 7, 1964, with a 4,850 lb.s.t. Orpheus turbojet, but the second prototype is powered by the Brandner-designed E-300 turbojet rated at 7,055 lb.s.t. and 9,840 lb.s.t. with afterburning.

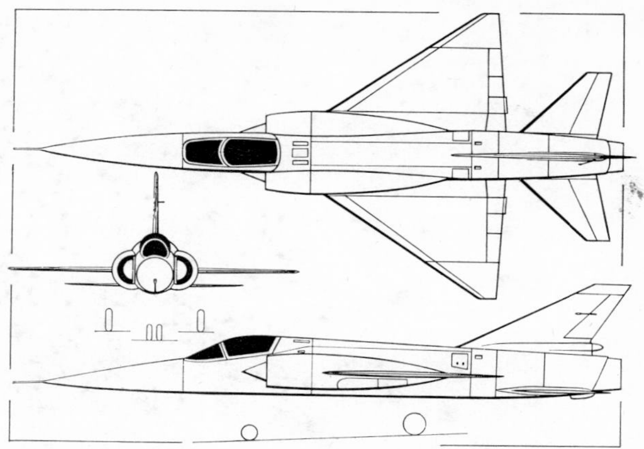

Vietnam, and Kashmir have proved the need—not for ICBMs—but for conventional fighter-bombers to provide mainly close support for ground forces, and occasionally air cover.

As a result of this tragically inept planning, the development of military aircraft was virtually abandoned in Britain, save for the Lightning interceptor which has little relevance to minor wars, plus the Royal Navy's Buccaneer strike aircraft, and the ill-fated and over-ambitious TSR-2 project. Hawker's private venture P.1121 fighter-bomber was suppressed lest it should interfere with the TSR-2 programme, and procurement of the V/STOL P.1154 was delayed for four years, so that it eventually became necessary to buy the F-4M Phantom II to replace the Hunter. However, Britain was not alone in miscalculating her future needs for fighters: the U.S.A.F. had prepared for an all-out war, calling for emphasis on nuclear weapons and sophisticated equipment, and found itself ill-equipped for the counter-insurgency war in Vietnam. In consequence, the U.S. has been obliged to undertake the development of simple low-cost turpoprop aircraft, which can operate from small airfields, and find and destroy targets in the jungle. As an interim measure, the U.S. even attempted to buy back (from France) piston-engined A-1 Skyraiders, previously discarded as obsolete.

The emphasis in fighter development has thus switched from interception to ground attack for small wars, with an eye on nuclear strike for such possibility as there remains of a major conflict. One effect of this change in role is that it is now far from easy to decide which aircraft should be classed as fighters. At one extreme stand

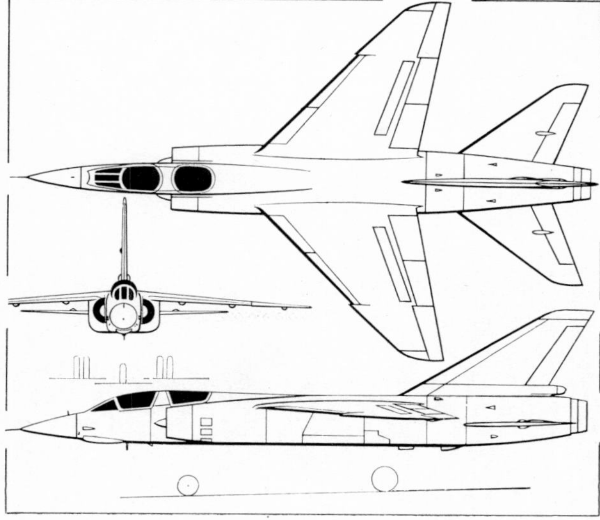

The Dassault Mirage F (left) two-seat tactical strike fighter is currently under test as part of an experimental programme. The first prototype (illustrated) flew on June 12, 1966 *with a Pratt & Whitney TF*30 *turbofan, and the second prototype will have a French derivative of this engine, the SNECMA TF*-306 *of* 11,685 *lb.s.t. and* 20,500 *lb.s.t. with afterburning. With this power plant speeds of the order of Mach* 2.2–2.3 *are anticipated. Empty weight is approximately* 22,100 *lb., loaded weight in clean condition being of the order of* 36,600 *lb. Internal fuel capacity totals some* 1,720 *Imp. gal.* (2,065 *U.S. gal.*)*, and dimensions include a span of* 34 *ft.* 5⅓ *in., a length of* 57 *ft.* 5 *in., a height of* 18 *ft.* 7 *in., and a wing area of* 387.5 *sq. ft.*

the specialised COIN projects and armed versions of light aircraft, which are intended primarily for close support, but could also be used to intercept enemy helicopters. At the opposite end of the scale, the Buccaneer was originally designed for nuclear strike duties, yet it could be used in exactly the same way as the Hunter F.G.A. Mk. 9, since it can carry conventional bombs and rockets, and is stressed for fighter-type manoeuvres. In the following discussion fighters are examined according to the type of mission which predominated in their design.

AIR SUPERIORITY

Of all the fighter categories, those designed for the air superiority role conform most closely to the established idea of an aircraft combining the maximum possible performance with an armament intended solely for aerial combat. The purpose of this type is to provide cover for the battle area, out-performing and out-gunning anything that the enemy can put up, and thus permitting friendly close-support aircraft to operate with impunity, pinning the enemy down and stopping his supplies from reaching the front. Most countries have taken the attitude that this function alone does not warrant the cost of developing a Mach 2.0 fighter, and therefore the pure air superiority fighter has become something of a *rara avis*, yet the need for the type has been repeatedly proven in emergencies such as Cuba and Borneo. The plain fact is that it is a losing game to put up expensive all-weather fighters such as the

Lightning or Phantom II against a MiG-21, which probably cost only one-quarter the price, yet has much the same performance.

Since its aim is to provide cover over a limited area, the air superiority fighter requires only a modest internal fuel capacity, and stress is placed instead on achieving the best possible speed, manoeuvrability, acceleration, ceiling, and rate of climb. As the ground forces' need for protection is mainly related to good weather conditions, the weight and complexity of search radar can be avoided, although simple radar ranging is normally employed to improve firing accuracy and to check whether a target is within the firing bracket of the fighter's air-to-air missiles. Aside from battlefront cover, this class of fighter may also be used for the defence of point targets such as cities or ports. To assist interception, a lightweight infra-red search device is sometimes used as a substitute for AI radar, giving the pilot final homing directions after he has been placed behind the bomber by ground control.

Because they are intended to bear the brunt of the fighting, losses of air superiority fighters are expected to be high, however good its design, and therefore it is important that it should be cheap to replace, and that it should present the smallest possible target to the enemy's guns. One of the major factors in keeping its size within reasonable limits has been the development of lightweight infra-red homing missiles, notably the U.S. Navy's diminutive Sidewinder. Thanks to the remarkable accuracy of such heat-seeking weapons, they can destroy a bomber by using a far smaller warhead than would be practicable in a radar-guided missile, and the size of both missile and fighter are scaled down in proportion.

Unfortunately, missiles cannot be used against all types of target, and there is the additional problem that fighter pilots have rooted objections to being left unarmed after the first few seconds of combat! On the subject of missile limitations, the difficulty is that a simple infra-red homing weapon will only see the target's heat emission from dead astern, and thus it is not the ideal armament for dogfights. In addition, it appears doubtful whether it would home on to piston-engined or turboprop aircraft, or helicopters, while a target flitting between clouds might prove unassailable. It has therefore become the practice to mount at least one cannon internally, and in all probability this is the armament that would score in a clash between two fighters, unless one could manage to sneak up unnoticed behind the other. Although no details have been published, it seems likely that this is in fact what happened in the two encounters over the Formosa Straits in September 1958, when Chinese Nationalist F-86F Sabres used Sidewinders to down a total of seven MiG-17s from the mainland.

On the Western side, the only genuine air superiority fighters are the F-104A and F-104C versions of the Starfighter, which are now available to the U.S.A.F. in embarrassingly small quantities in Air Defence Command and Tactical Air Command respectively. In addition some F-104As have been supplied to the Chinese Nationalists and the Pakistan Air Force, the former having now withdrawn theirs in favour of the F-104G, and the latter having used the type with allegedly some success against obsolescent fighters such as the Hunter and Gnat during the border conflict with India. The U.S.A.F. has relied on its Starfighters to counter the MiG-21 in crises such as Berlin, Formosa, and Cuba, while fifteen of TAC's F-104Cs were sent to Vietnam in the air superiority role, but were not used in earnest against fighters of their own calibre, and were withdrawn to the U.S. after nine months only to be returned to Vietnam in mid-1966 with the operational début of the MiG-21 in this area.

Combining a maximum speed of Mach 1.9 with an armament of two wingtip-mounted AIM-9B Sidewinder 1A missiles and a 20-mm. M-61 Vulcan rotary cannon, the F-104A is a very potent fighter, but its landing performance suffers from its thin, diminutive wing. In developing the F-104C (i.e., the TAC version) the aircraft was made considerably easier to handle at low speeds by the use of blown flaps, and at the same time a detachable flight refuelling probe was added, together with two wing pylons for additional Sidewinders, rocket batteries, or bombs. In addition a more powerful version of the General Electric J79 engine was

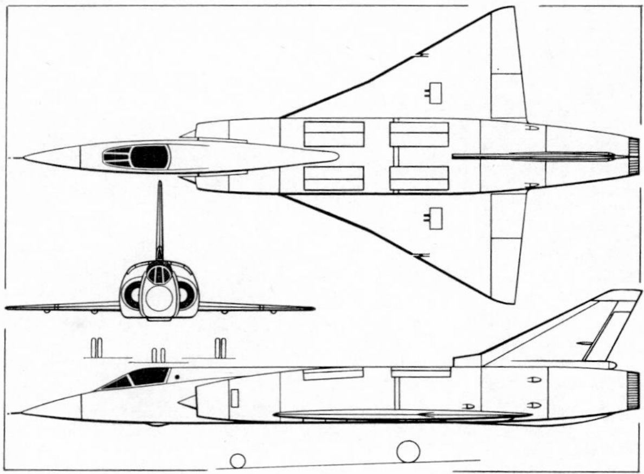

*Mirage IIIV development was initiated to provide a tactical strike aircraft with V/STOL capabilities. The Mirage IIIV-*01 *is currently powered by a SNECMA TF-*106*A*3 *turbofan rated at* 11,680 *lb.s.t. and* 16,755 *lb.s.t. with afterburning, plus eight* 3,640 *lb. Rolls-Royce RB.*162-1 *lift engines using a one-shot lubrication system permitting three minutes' running, and completed its first full transition on March* 24, 1966. *The Mirage IIIV-*02, *which joined the test programme on June* 22, 1966, *differs primarily in having a Pratt & Whitney TF*30 *propulsion engine of* 18,520 *lb.s.t. with afterburning, and paired lift engine doors (as illustrated by the general arrangement drawing) which replace the dorsal grills initially employed by the IIIV-*01 *(below, left). The Mirage IIIV has empty and loaded (VTOL) weights of* 22,050 *lb. and* 29,630 *lb. respectively, and overall dimensions include a span of* 28 *ft.* 7⅓ *in., a length of* 59 *ft.* 0⅔ *in., and a height of* 18 *ft.* 2½ *in. The proposed series prototype, the Mirage IIIV-*03 *for* 1969–70, *is to have TF-*306 *and RB.*162-81 *engines.*

fitted, producing a sustained level speed of Mach 2.0, and a service ceiling of 55,000 ft. with two missiles. In view of renewed U.S.A.F. interest in air superiority fighters, Lockheed has proposed various Starfighter improvements based on the later F-104G. The CL-901 project would employ a J79-J1F of 17,900 lb. (compared with the F-104A's 14,800 lb. and the F-104C's 15,800 lb.) to reach Mach 2.2, and leading- and trailing-edge flaps would be used to improve manoeuvrability. The CL-958 would use the same engine, but a larger wing would be fitted to enhance both manoeuvring and airfield performance.

The Russian equivalent of the Starfighter is the MiG-21, which is slightly lighter, and attains a level speed of Mach 2.0 in spite of its less powerful 13,200 lb. turbojet. It carries two Atoll missiles (apparently copies of the Sidewinder) on underwing pylons, and it has provision for two 30-mm. cannon in the belly, although most photographs show only one gun in place. However, unlike the F-104, its cannon is only a single-barrel design, and it is estimated that it can only fire at one-quarter the rate of the six-barreled Vulcan. At the time of the Indian Air Force evaluation of the MiG-21, a number of adverse comments were reported in the press, including criticism of its armament, avionics, poor engine response, lack of anti-surge device, low engine overhaul life, and short radius of action. The Russians offered to increase radius from 100 miles to almost 140 by deleting the cannon and using the space for fuel, but this offer was not taken up. A proposal to fit a new airborne fire control system was apparently rejected in favour of ground control based on U.S. radar. In spite of these Indian comments on its effectiveness, the MiG-21 is universally praised for its ease of handling and high performance: few aircraft are more popular with their pilots.

The sole remaining type in this class is the United Arab Republic's HA-300, which follows the tailed delta configuration of the MiG-21, but has lateral intakes which are possibly derived from those of the F-104G. Designed largely by Messerschmitt engineers, this is undoubtedly the smallest fighter with Mach 2.0 potential, grossing only 12,000 lb., but its development is at present held up by lack of a suitable engine. Plans call for the installation of two 30-mm. Hispano or four Russian Nudelmann-Suranov 23-mm. cannon, but it seems unlikely that a speed of over Mach 1.5 will be achieved due to the limited expectations of the indigenous Brandner engine.

ALL-WEATHER DEFENCE

Rather than accept the operational limitations of the air superiority fighter, many countries have developed interceptors with some degree of all-weather capability. This is possibly the most difficult type to design, since it should carry a heavy equipment load to enable it to operate in all conditions, day or night, and to find its target and destroy it without relying on help from other fighters. Target detection range depends upon the size of radar dish, and a worthwhile improvement can be effected by having a radar operator. The two-man crew and 32-in. dish of the Phantom give 25 per cent more acquisition range than the single-seat F-106A Delta Dart and its much smaller radar, but few designers were able to adopt such powerful engines as the Phantom's 17,000 lb. J79-

Essentially a variable-geometry version of the Mirage F, utilising basically similar fuselage, undercarriage and tail surfaces, the Mirage G is scheduled to commence its flight test programme during the early summer of 1967. *Powered by a SNECMA TF-*306 *turbofan of* 11,685 *lb.s.t. and* 20,500 *lb.s.t. with full afterburning, the Mirage G tandem two-seat strike fighter is intended to attain speeds of the order of Mach* 2.2–2.3. *Its wing employs similar principles to the VASCAAR wing of the General Dynamics F-*111 *(see pages* 87–91*), and at the time of closing for press it seemed likely that France would continue development of the Mirage G at the expense of the proposed Anglo-French V-8 project.*

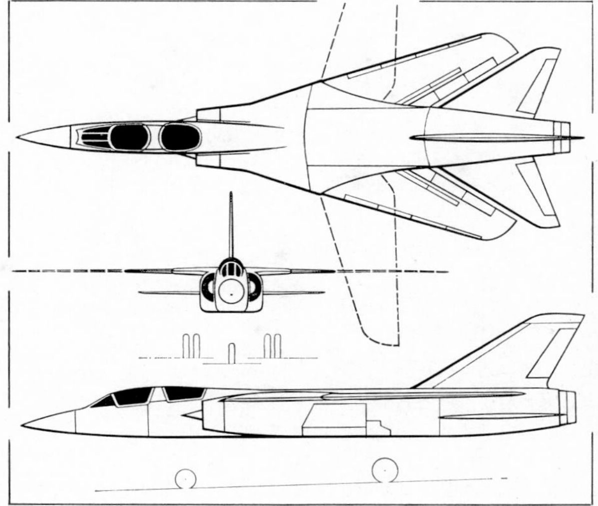

GE-15s. This problem of engine availability also militated against the provision of really effective mixed armaments on many European fighters. Ideally an all-weather interceptor should have a number of infra-red homers for their accuracy under clear day or night conditions, backed up with weapons that can strike through cloud; i.e., radar homers or possibly unguided rockets which can be fired on a collision course.

There is little doubt that the outstanding all-weather interceptor of the present day is the McDonnell F-4 Phantom II, which was originally developed for the U.S. Navy, later selected by the U.S.A.F. in preference to its own F-106A, and is now on order for the R.A.F. and Royal Navy. Basic armament consists of four semi-recessed Sparrow III semi-active radar homers, and with these in place it can still achieve a speed of Mach 2.2. Additional weapons in the form of four Sidewinders can be mounted on wing pylons, and its electronic fit is probably in advance of any other fighter, combining Westinghouse APQ-72 radar with CW target illumination for low altitude combat, and an infra-red detector although the indifferent results attained with the i-r sensor have led to its deletion from recent models.

In comparison with the Phantom all other interceptors pale into insignificance. The Federal German *Luftwaffe* has made it clear that the single-seat F-104G (armed with two Sidewinders) fails to meet its interceptor requirements in performance, radar, and weapons. The Swiss Air Force spent a long time looking for an effective interceptor that could operate from mountain airfields, finally chose the Mirage III, but insisted on the development of a completely new weapons system, combining Hughes TARAN radar with the HM-55 Falcon. The R.A.F. Lightning F.Mk.6 is one of the fastest-climbing fighters extant, but it only mounts two Red Top missiles, which may be replaced by an internal battery of forty-eight 2-in. rockets for attacks in cloud.

NUCLEAR STRIKE

Being designed for a short-lived, all-out war, the nuclear strike aircraft must be able to attack its targets irrespective of weather conditions, flying fast and low in order to have a reasonable chance of survival in the face of sophisticated defences. In Europe, the F-104G Starfighter has virtually become the standard NATO strike aircraft, following a multilateral production programme which supplied over 1,000 machines for the air forces of Federal Germany, Italy, Belgium and the Netherlands, adding to the CF-104s operated by the R.C.A.F. in Germany. The Starfighter is a good illustration of the type of airframe required for this role, the sleek fuselage and embryonic wing of only 3.26 per cent thickness/chord ratio giving the minimum possible wetted area and probably delaying the drag rise to beyond 0.9 Mach. In terms of equipment the aircraft has been a pace-setter, featuring the first airborne operational inertial navigation system (Litton LN-3) and the first radar suitable for both the strike mission and the counter-air mode (Autonetics NASARR F-15A). Aside from its complexity, the principal drawback to this aircraft is that it relies on blown flaps to achieve a reasonable airfield performance. This is not a desirable feature in single-engined fighters, since engine failure almost certainly results in the normal service pilot abandoning an aircraft that is too "hot" to land dead-stick, and this may account in part for the initially high write-off rate of this type.

The best of the U.S.A.F.'s strike fighters is probably the F-105D Thunderchief, which is almost twice as heavy as the F-104G, having been designed to provide the long range needed for global deployment. Its weapons system is of earlier conception, combining, APN-131 Doppler and NASARR R-14A, which can only be used in the air-to-surface mode, but the F-105D is more fully developed system-wise than the F-104G at the present moment, and would obviously give a good account of itself in the strike role if the need arose. Both of these fighters are armed with a Vulcan gun for secondary interceptor duties, and the F-105D benefits from its greater size in having a useful load-carrying capability for small wars. At the present moment it is proving to be one of the most battle-worthy aircraft of the Vietnam war, operating with an additional fuel tank in the nuclear weapon bay and a rack of six 750-lb. bombs mounted on the centre-line pylon. Using wing pylons, the military load can be increased to sixteen of these bombs or four Bullpups.

GROUND ATTACK

It is quite normal for a fighter to be used for both nuclear strike and ground attack duties, as we have seen above, but there are important differences in the design techniques adopted, according to which role is felt to have the greater importance. Ground attack is essentially a matter of providing close support for land forces from airfields which are often short and badly surfaced. It follows that instead of carrying (for instance) a single 2,000-lb. NATO nuclear weapon, this class of fighter must lift off a heavy load of high explosive, and that rather than delivering a bomb in a straight fly-over, it must be able to manoeuvre in narrow valleys, attacking targets of opportunity with great precision. In addition, front-line serviceability takes precedence over the equipment demands of all-weather capability or the ultimate in navigational accuracy, while the aircraft must have a sturdy undercarriage with low-pressure tyres, and a modest wing loading, although maximum speed suffers in consequence.

In providing a really useful load-carrying capability, there is no alternative but to design a relatively heavy fighter: the F-100D for instance grosses up to 34,832 lb. The advantages of this approach are obvious: the effect of a heavy load is acceptable from both airfield performance and level speed standpoints, and the sheer size of airframe makes it far easier to accommodate external stores. The F-100D has no fewer than six wing pylons, two of which are mounted ahead of the main undercarriage units, an arrangement that would be impractical for a smaller fighter. Store location is basically difficult on a conventional low-wing fighter because so much of the wing span is taken up in providing under-carriage stowage, and heavy outboard stores are unacceptable on a swept wing because of the pitching moments they produce when

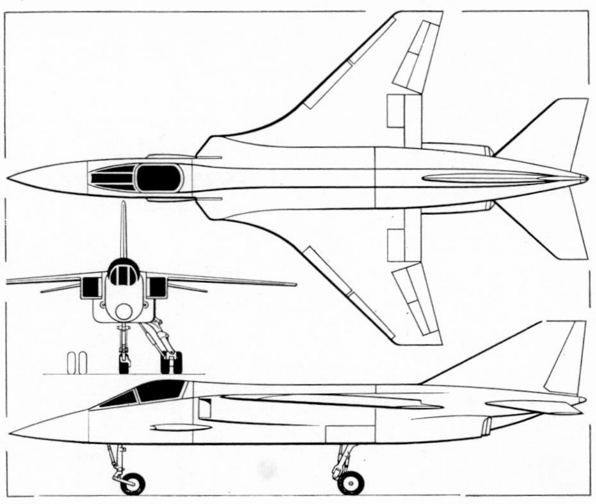

A collaborative effort between France and the U.K., the Jaguar is being developed by Breguet and BAC, a joint company, SEPECAT, having been formed to manage the programme. To be powered by two Rolls-Royce/Turboméca RB.172/T-260 Adour turbofans rated at 4,200 lb.s.t. and 6,835 lb. with afterburning, the Jaguar is to be produced in single-seat strike fighter and two-seat advanced trainer forms for both the R.A.F. and the Armée de l'Air, the former being illustrated above. The first of some seven prototypes will fly in April 1968 with production deliveries commencing in 1970. The Jaguar will have a gross weight of 21,165 lb. and is expected to attain Mach 1.8.

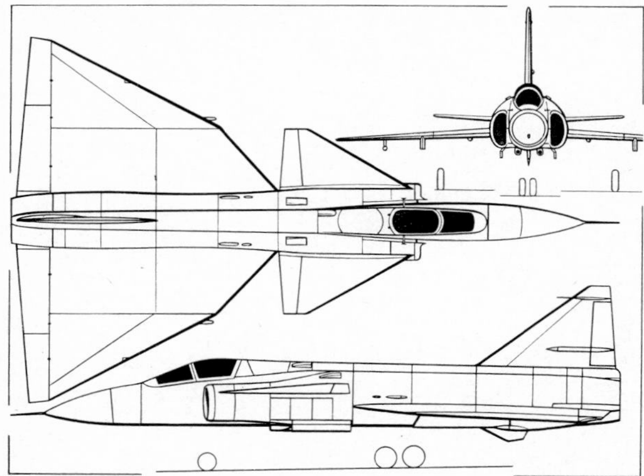

The Saab 37 Viggen single-seat multi-purpose fighter, the first of seven prototypes of which is scheduled to commence its flight test programme early in 1967, reflects the "standardized platform" philosophy, the same basic airframe being proposed for manufacture in several versions for widely differing roles. To be powered by a single Svenska Flygmotor RM 8 turbofan, evolved from the Pratt & Whitney JT8D-22 and offering approximately 26,450 lb.s.t. with full after-burning, versions currently proposed are the AJ 37 ground attack and strike fighter, the JA 37 interceptor with secondary attack capability, the S 37 tactical reconnaissance aircraft with both optical and non-optical systems, and the two-seat Sk 37 trainer.

released. On the other hand a high-wing layout rules out any possibility of a centre-line rack, although it is worthy of note that the A-7A Corsair II provides the commendable total of six pylons on its high-mounted wing, plus two on the sides of the fuselage.

Bomb locations are much easier to find on a straight wing, since external fuel can be moved out to tip tanks, and since none of the stores will produce embarrassing pitch effects when released, being all abreast of the aircraft's c.g. The use of an almost straight wing in the case of the Northrop F-5 enables this lightweight fighter to mount five pylons, in addition to which two Sidewinders or fuel tanks can be mounted on the wingtips. However, the addition of 6,200 lb. of external stores to this basically 13,000 lb. aircraft obviously has a serious effect on take-off performance, and this has led to the original 4,080 lb. engines being superseded by 4,300 lb. J85–GE-15s, and to proposals to use 5,250 lb. J85-J1As. On the side of the small fighter concept it is argued that there is no requirement to release more than two bombs during each run over the target, so why expose a large aircraft to enemy fire, when a small one can do the job?

The relative merits of the two approaches have been evaluated by the U.S.A.F. under operational conditions in Vietnam. For the R.A.F., the question was virtually decided several years ago, when a competition was held to choose a ground-attack fighter to replace the Venom in the Middle East. Although the official favourites were the lightweight Gnat and an armed version of the Jet Provost trainer, it was found in practice that both of these aircraft were short on range (partly due to their low-pressure engines), and that neither could combine a heavy military load with a reasonably short airfield performance. The decision therefore went to the much larger Hunter F.G.A. Mk.9, which has since had a distinguished service record in this role, and has demonstrated one of the best fatigue lives ever achieved in ground attack duties.

Two other fighters which have earned a reputation for longevity are the F-84F Thunderstreak and the Sukhoi Su-7, although the latter is far from being the ideal ground attack configuration. The principal fault in the Su-7 is its highly swept wing, which downgrades subsonic manoeuvrability and makes it impractical to carry stores on the outboard wing panels. This aircraft is, in fact, normally seen with two small rocket pods just outboard of the undercarriage, and two large stores under the fuselage where interference drag must be severe. The only way for a designer to provide satisfactory manoeuvrability, assuming that swept wings have to be accepted for a good combination of top speed and airfield performance, is to employ a planform of moderate sweep and taper, as on the Hunter or Etendard. The Indian HF-24 Marut was designed as a supersonic fighter-bomber to replace the Hunter F.Mk.56 and Mystère IVA, but its wing appears (aside from being surprisingly far forward) to be more highly tapered than desirable for the close support role.

FUTURE FIGHTERS

Quite aside from the many technological changes that have taken place in the fighter field, development costs have been rising steeply while the risk of an all-out war has steadily become more remote, so that governments are now far less inclined to embark on new designs unless some major improvement can be offered in cost-effectiveness. This problem is open to attack in three ways: by sharing costs with another government, through minimising development costs by the use of a simple design (or an adaptation of an existing machine), or by producing an aircraft that can replace more than one existing type. The principle of sharing development has already been successfully proved with larger aircraft such as the Breguet Atlantic and Transall C.160, and it will shortly be extended to the lightweight category with the SEPECAT Jaguar, which will be used by the *Armée de l'Air* primarily as an attack fighter, and by the R.A.F. for advanced training and strike.

This trend may be continued with the forthcoming FX project, which it is envisaged will be jointly developed by the U.S.A. and Canada for service with both air forces and navies, acting in the close support and air superiority roles. Companies selected for preliminary design studies are North American, Boeing (who are making a half-scale submission of their TFX design), and Lockheed, who have a project designated CL-981 based on the F-104. A speed of Mach 2.4 would be achieved by the CL-981, which would be powered by a reheated Spey or advanced J79 engine, and have a wing area increased from 196 to 250 sq. ft., and improved stability through the use of rear fuselage strakes and a canard surface behind the cockpit. In mid-1966, Lockheed was offering the U.S.A.F. production of the CL-981 within a year as an answer to the problems resulting from the attrition of strike aircraft employed in Vietnam, claiming that production tempo within 16 months would be sufficient to form one squadron per month. As currently envisaged, the FX will be a 30–35,000 lb. aircraft powered by two 24,500 lb.s.t. engines and possessing STOL capabilities, with distances of 1,500–2,000 ft. to and from an altitude of 50 ft. Rough field capability is a design prerequisite, and with about half fuel gross weight will be reduced to around 24,000 lb. for intercept missions, the resulting thrust/weight ratio of approximately 2:1 enabling the FX to achieve a truly spectacular climb rate. The FX promises to be one of the most important of future developments, the only other project in this category being the Mirage F1, a high-wing Mach 2.2 fighter with an afterburning SNECMA TF-306 of 20,500 lb. thrust, but considered solely as a research aircraft at the present time, a scaled-down interceptor variant being the Mirage F3, two prototypes of which have been ordered. With a Mach 2.5 performance, the Mirage F3 will attain an attitude of 40,000 ft. in five minutes with full intercept armament.

Provided that an aircraft is to be used purely in ground attack, then it has no real need for supersonic capability, and if it is further restricted to counter-insurgency work, then its performance can be very modest indeed. For example, the ground attack Hunters of the Iraqi Air Force will remain effective for many years, thanks to their top-cover of MiG-21s.

The concept of reducing development costs by working on the

*The VFW VAK-*191*B subsonic VTOL strike fighter, illustrated below in its side-by-side two-seat version, is being developed jointly by Germany and Italy, with initial flight trials scheduled to take place in* 1968. *Three two-seat prototypes are being built in Germany and three single-seat prototypes are being built in Italy for research and development and subsequent operational evaluation. The VAK-*191*B, which will have an* 8,000 *lb.s.t. vectored-thrust RB.*193 *lift/cruise turbofan and two* 6,000 *lb.s.t. RB.*162–81 *lift engines, is expected to have an empty weight of only* 9,900 *lb. and a gross weight of* 19,400 *lb., including* 3,850 *lb. of stores, overall dimensions including a span of* 18 *ft.* 0 *in. and a length of* 42 *ft.* 7¼ *in. The VAK* 191*B will feature an internal weapons bay and is not intended to use short take-off techniques. The requirement to which it has been designed called for high subsonic performance with a target approach speed of Mach* 0.92 *at low level.*

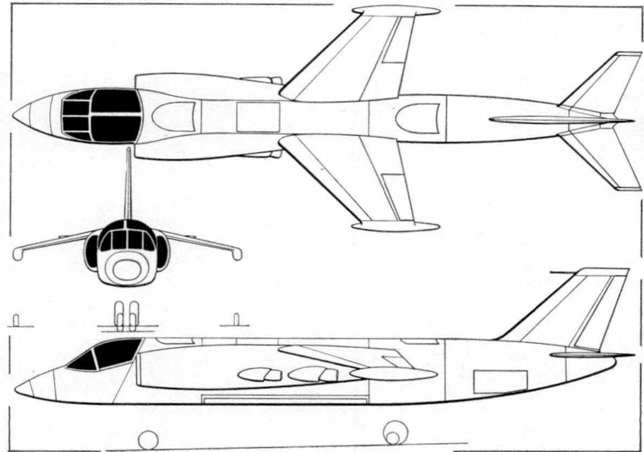

basis of proven airframes was extremely well illustrated during 1966 by the case of the F-4 Phantom II which is being transformed into a ground-attack aircraft from an all-weather interceptor. The F-4 normally lacks a fixed cannon armament, its wings are rather sharply tapered for subsonic manoeuvrability, and its structure may well need strengthening for arduous close-support work, but the final product should be an outstanding dual-purpose fighter, and the lack of built-in gun armament is rectified in the experimental Phantom TSF, an adaptation of the unarmed RF-4C, with a 20-mm. Vulcan cannon replacing the reconnaissance equipment. Other examples of the adaptation of existing designs to meet new or changed requirements are provided in the prolific Dassault Mirage family by the Mirage IIIE2 and Mirage M5. The former, flight testing of which was imminent at the time of closing for press, is being proposed as an interim low-level strike fighter, and results from the marriage of the fuselage of the existing IIIE with swept wing and tail surfaces which are preferable to the delta configuration for its intended role. Its Atar 9K turbojet offers substantially more thrust than the 9C of the standard IIIE, although low-level supersonic performance of the IIIE2 may be limited by the maximum turbine inlet temperature for this power plant of 950 C. Although as yet no more than a study, the Mirage M5 is essentially a simplified version of the IIIE with increased internal fuel capacity and greater potential variety in external ordnance loads. Capable of carrying a 4,410-lb. ordnance load over 310 miles at low altitude, the M5 has been offered as a competitor to the Northrop F-5 and A-7A Corsair in Europe, but fulfils no *Armée de l'Air* requirement. To fulfil the same close support fighter requirement for which the Mirage M5 has been offered, Lockheed has proposed the CL-984 which is an adaptation of the basic F-104G design with the General Electric J79-J1Q turbojet offering a maximum afterburning thrust of 17,900 lb. and lower specific fuel consumption, nine external stores stations capable of lifting 7,000 lb. of ordnance and fuel, and a Mach 2.4 performance.

Evolved from the G.91R (*see pages* 84–86), *the Fiat G.91Y tactical reconnaissance and strike fighter is intended to operate from grass or semi-prepared strips, and the first of two prototypes was expected to commence its flight test programme in December* 1966. *Unlike previous aircraft in the G.91 series, the G.91Y is twin-engined, being powered by two General Electric J85-GE-13A turbojets each rated at* 2,725 *lb.s.t. and* 4,080 *lb.s.t. with afterburning. Estimated performance includes maximum speeds of* 714 *m.p.h. at sea level* (*Mach* 0.94) *and* 690 *m.p.h. at* 32,810 *ft.* (*Mach* 0.975), *and empty and normal loaded weights are* 8,378 *lb. and* 17,196 *lb. respectively. Overall dimensions are as follows: span,* 29 *ft.* 6½ *in., length,* 38 *ft.* 7⅜ *in., height,* 14 *ft.* 6⅓ *in., wing area,* 195.149 *sq. ft. Built-in armament will comprise four* 0.5-*in. Colt-Browning machine guns, and typical external ordnance loads will include four* 500-*lb. bombs, twelve* 3-*in. or six* 5-*in. HVARs, or two Nord AS.*20 *or AS.*30*L ASMs.*

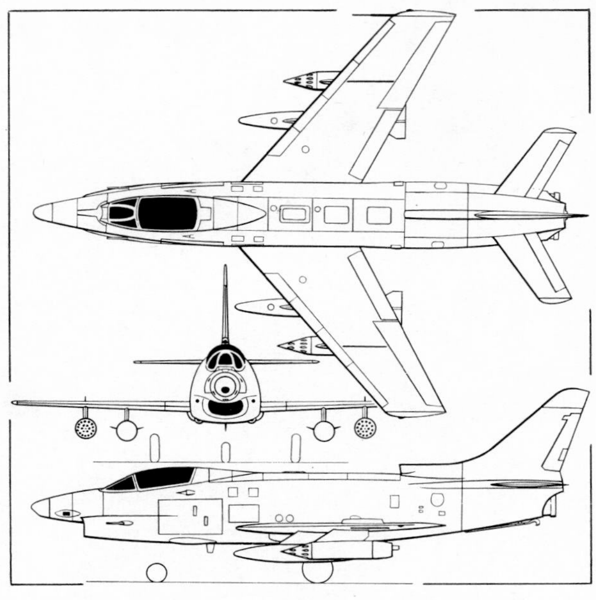

As stated earlier, new designs can be justified if they replace two or more existing types, and this need for flexibility has been the main driving force behind variable-sweep, which combines minimal airfield/carrier requirements with long patrol endurance, Mach 2.0 plus at altitude, and supersonic dash at low level with the smallest possible gust response. First service aircraft to use the swing-wing principle will be the GD/Grumman F-111, already slated to serve with the U.S.A.F., U.S. Navy, R.A.F., and R.A.A.F. The winner of one of the most bitterly fought design contests, the F-111 combines an unusual number of novel features, and it is likely that a number of changes will be required before its development is complete. The only other military variable-sweep project definitely under development is the Mirage G, of which one prototype has been ordered, this being scheduled to commence its flight test programme during the summer of 1967. Possessing a somewhat uncertain future is the variable-sweep fighter proposed for joint development by the U.K. and France. No firm agreement has been reached between the British and French air staffs concerning the exact tasks for which this type will be designed, although it is envisaged as a two-seat aircraft, powered by two SNECMA/Bristol Siddeley M45H turbofans of 12,125 lb.s.t. each with afterburning. Current cost studies combined with the imminence of flight testing of the purely French Mirage G could well result in the demise of this project.

Yet another variable-geometry fighter project is the U.S. Navy's

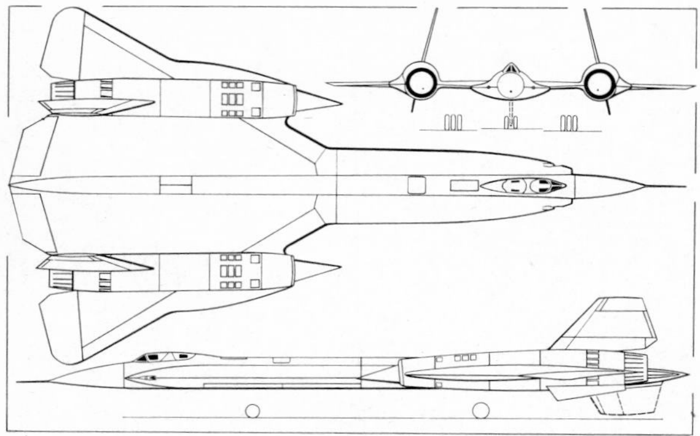

*Derived, like the SR-*71 (*Vol. II, pages* 85–87), *from the Lockheed A-*11, *the YF-*12*A experimental two-seat interceptor has been under test and evaluation since mid-*1964. *Possessing a similar wing to that of the SR-*71, *with a span of* 55 *ft.* 7¼ *in., the YF-*12*A has an overall length of some* 104 *ft., and is powered by two Pratt & Whitney J*58 *turbojets each rated at some* 34,000 *lb.s.t. with afterburning. Armament comprises four Hughes AIM-*47*A Falcon missiles which are explosively ejected downwards from individual bays, and equipment includes ASG-*18 *pulse Doppler fire control. Infra-red sensors are mounted in cut-outs in the forward ends of the wing extensions. The YF-*12*A weighs* 136,000 *lb. in loaded condition and has a short-period maximum speed of approximately* 2,300 *m.p.h.* (*Mach* 3.5), *maximum sustained cruise allegedly being* 1,980 *m.p.h.* (*Mach* 3.0). *Three YF-*12*As have been flown, but the production future of this remarkable interceptor is uncertain.*

VFAX, interpreted in some quarters as a substitute for the controversial F-111B. Intended for service in the early 'seventies, the VFAX, as currently envisaged, will be in the 50,000–60,000 lb. weight category, and will be capable of performing such widely differing roles as fleet defence, attack and reconnaissance without any modifications. To meet the VFAX requirement, McDonnell has submitted to the U.S. Navy a proposal for a variable-sweep version of the ubiquitous Phantom with J79-GE-10 engines and a substantially similar airframe to that of the current F-4J, the only major changes being those dictated by the new wing.

Failing an order for a fighter version of the Mach 3.0 Lockheed SR-71, the F-12B, or initiation of the IMI project, it appears likely that the main performance improvement over the next decade will be in take-off and landing distances, and the ability to operate from rough surfaces. Semi-prepared fields have hitherto received more thought in the Communist Bloc than in the West; Russian fighters have rugged undercarriages as a matter of course, and a special twin-wheel version of the MiG-17 was produced in some quantity in Poland.

In France and the U.K. work has begun on seven prototypes of the previously-mentioned Jaguar fighter which is intended to fulfil several roles. The design team leader, Breguet, is building five of the prototypes, the first of which will fly in 1968, and these will comprise two single-seat Jaguar-A attack fighters, two two-seat Jaguar-E trainers, and one Jaguar-M single-seat shipboard fighter. Simultaneously, BAC is building two single-seat prototype Jaguar-S strike fighters. To be powered by a pair of Rolls-Royce/Turboméca RB.172/T-260 Adour turbofans, the Jaguar had been evolved from the Breguet Br. 121 design which was a slightly less ambitious winning contender in an *Armée de l'Air* light strike fighter contest. It is anticipated that both the *Armée de l'Air* and the R.A.F. will have some 150 machines, those for the former service being primarily single-seat Jaguar-As with a small number of two-seat Jaguar-Es, whereas the latter service will initially acquire the two-seat Jaguar-B trainer followed by the Jaguar-S strike fighter which will free some of the R.A.F.'s F-4M Phantoms for the intercept role as successors to the Lightning. France's *Aéronavale* currently envisages the Jaguar-M as a successor to the Etendard. In Italy, Fiat is now building the G.91Y which, with two reheated J85 engines augmented by JATO units, will operate from grass airfields. One important advance in this context is the U.S. Marine Corps' SATS (Short Airfield Tactical System), which includes aluminium plank runways, arrester gear, and catapults powered by turbine engines. A rather more spectacular alternative (although it requires conventional runways for landing) is the zero-length launch technique, by which fighters can be literally rocketed into the air from dispersed trailers. It has been suggested that this may be adopted for some of the F-104S Starfighters, of which 165 are currently planned for the Italian Air Force, using 30,000 lb. rocket boosters. These aircraft are to be a follow-on to the F-104G, with a strengthened structure, new avionics, Sparrow missiles, and the improved J79-J1Q engine.

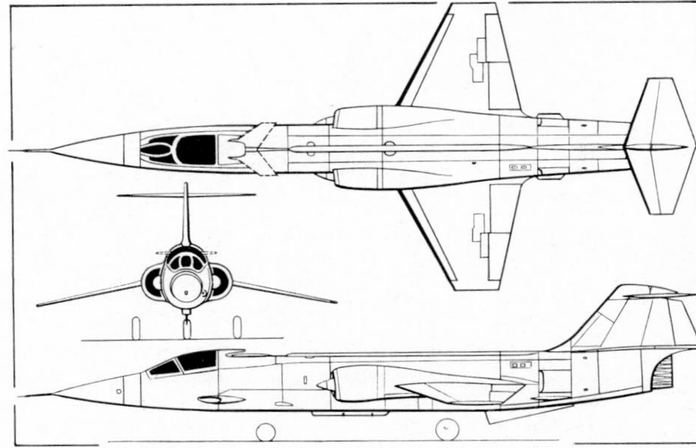

*Lockheed has undertaken a number of company-funded studies based on the F-*104 *Starfighter design to meet possible future fighter requirements, these varying appreciably in the amount of redesign involved. One such study is the CL-*981 (*right*) *which is a Lockheed proposal to meet the current requirement for a fighter combining close support and air superiority capabilities. The CL-*981 *embodies an increase in wing area to* 250 *sq. ft. from the* 196.1 *sq. ft. of the standard Starfighter wing, aspect ratio being raised from* 2.5 *to* 3.0, *the larger wing being intended to improve subsonic manoeuvrability, subsonic cruise and supersonic ceiling. Small retractable foreplanes would be extended at speeds in excess of Mach* 1.0 *to boost acceleration, climb and manoeuvrability, longitudinal strakes on each side of the lower aft fuselage improving the aircraft's stability above Mach* 2.0 *and permitting an extension of the placard speed to Mach* 2.4. *Power plants considered for the CL-*981 *have included the General Electric J*79-*J*1*Q and the Rolls-Royce RB.* 168 *Spey turbofan. Although the increased power and enlarged wing of the CL-*981 *would offer substantial improvements over the take-off and landing performance of the standard F-*104, *it is unlikely that the latest short-field requirements for the FX could be met.*

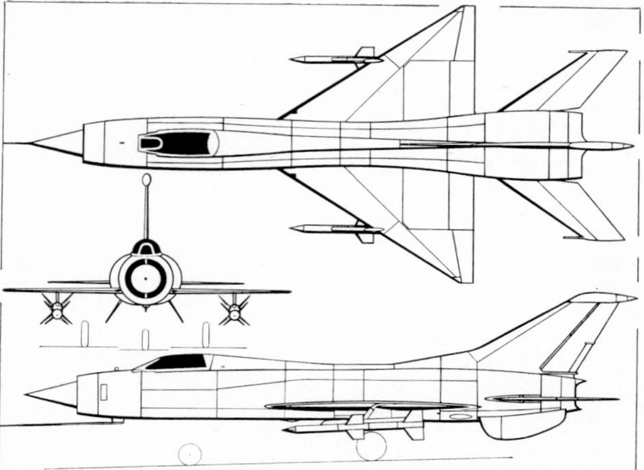

Although the single-seat experimental all-weather interceptor illustrated above was displayed publicly in 1961, *it is still the latest example of Russian interceptor fighter design to have been revealed. Evolved by the design bureau headed by Artem Mikoyan, and dubbed 'Flipper' in the West, this experimental machine was a fairly straightforward development of the MiG-*21 *series (see pages* 136–140) *with twice the weight and thrust of its predecessor. As the Ye-*266, *an example of this Mikoyan design established a new* 1,000-*km. closed-circuit record of* 1,441.5 *m.p.h. (Mach* 2.18) *at* 69,000–72,200 *ft. with a* 4,410-*lb. payload in April* 1965. *Retaining the basic wing of the MiG-*21 *series coupled with an entirely relatively new fuselage with side-by-side mounted turbojets, this short-endurance point-defence fighter does not seem to have attained service status with the V.-V.S.*

Aside from relying on external aids, airfield performance can be improved by conventional high-lift devices. The British versions of the Phantom II, for instance, will have larger blown flaps, drooped ailerons, and a slotted tailplane! The TSR-2 had blown flaps with a drooped tab at the trailing edge, but this concept appears to have been out-dated by the Saab Viggen, which uses a canard layout so that both horizontal surfaces are lifting, and has a blown flap on the foreplane.

The practical application of V/STOL techniques through the use of lift engines or deflected thrust has been much slower in reaching fulfilment than was originally expected. This has been partly due to the heavy development costs and the performance penalties involved, and the difficulties now forseen in supplying, maintaining and controlling a dispersed force. In addition, it is feared in some quarters that V/STOL operations are not as flexible as once hoped: the idea was first justified by the fear of nuclear war in Europe, and later advocated for the ability to fight wars where airfields do not exist, but few can imagine V/STOL in the context of Vietnam or Brunei, where dispersal would merely invite sabotage by infiltrators.

In spite of these reservations, initial V/STOL trials have been held by the U.K., the U.S.A., and Federal Germany, using the Kestrel F.G.A. Mk.1. On this basis an advanced development of the aircraft is being produced for the R.A.F., while the other two partners from the trials are collaborating in studies of a far heavier fighter-bomber, combining lift engines, deflected thrust, and variable-sweep. Referred to as the AVS (Advanced V/STOL Study), this project is to have Mach 2.0 capability, a maximum load of 13,200 lb., a radius of 350–500 miles (depending on the take-off distance), and a gross weight in the region of 45,000 lb. Evaluation of the various AVS project studies submitted by U.S. and German companies was continuing at the time of closing for press when it was expected that one U.S. and one German contractor would be selected before the end of 1966 to produce a definitive design. The programme calls for 12 prototypes of the selected AVS design to be completed by early 1970, with production deliveries from 1974. In addition, West Germany is continuing with the development of the VAK 191B, which is in the same weight category as the P.1127, but is intended for pure VTOL operation from hardened sites, rather than catering for overload sorties and semi-prepared surfaces.

The most advanced V/STOL fighter currently under active development is the Mirage IIIV which, it was envisaged, would offer Mach 2.0 performance at altitude, combined with a combat radius of 290 miles with a 2,000-lb. nuclear store in the low-level Mach 0.92 attack mode, this radius being stretched to 460 miles with a 1,200-lb. store and using a high-level approach coupled with a final low-level penetration attack. The first prototype, the Mirage IIIV-01, made its initial hovering flight on February 12, 1965 on the thrust of eight vertically-mounted Rolls-Royce RB.162–1 lift engines each offering 3,640 lb. thrust. The SNECMA TF-104 propulsion engine, a modified Pratt & Whitney JTF10 subsonic turbofan, proved unsuitable for the full transition which was not effected until March 24, 1966, by which time a SNECMA TF-106A3 turbofan had been installed. The second prototype, the Mirage IIIV-02, joined the test programme on June 22, 1966, this differing from its predecessor primarily in having a Pratt & Whitney TF30 turbofan, but the proposed Mirage IIIV-03, considered as a potential production prototype for trials in 1969–70, will have a SNECMA TF-306 turbofan for forward propulsion and 6,000 lb.s.t. RB.162-81 lift engines. Following the cancellation of Hawker Siddeley's P.1154 and the EWR VJ 101D, this aircraft is the sole remaining contender from the NBMR-3 competition for a heavy strike fighter, but various technical difficulties, such as protracted life engine development, and the inordinate costs involved, have led to some disenchantment with the V/STOL concept, restricting this to an experimental programme, and may well lead to the abandonment of the Mirage IIIV in favour of a more conventional aircraft, such as the Mirage F, or the variable-geometry Mirage G.

*The production version of the Hawker Siddeley P.*1127 *(illustrated below) will differ in a number of respects from the tri-partite evaluation model (see pages* 101–3*), but overall dimensions are only marginally increased. It will embody an all-weather navigation and attack system, and weapons capability for STOL operation will be raised to* 4,000 *lb. Power will be provided by a Pegasus B.Pg.*6 *vectored-thrust turbofan of some* 19,000 *lb.s.t., and the P.*1127 *will be compatible with most tactical ASMs currently envisaged for use by the R.A.F. until the mid 'seventies. The first of six P.*1127 *(R.A.F.) prototypes flew on August* 31, 1966.

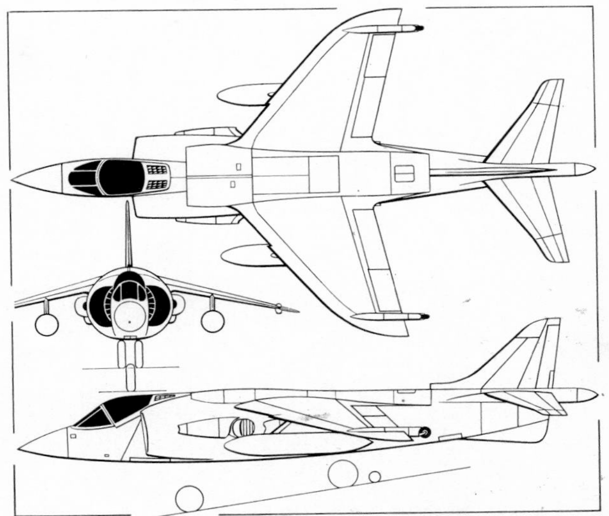

BAC LIGHTNING

Generally accepted to be the fastest-climbing service interceptor fighter extant, and progressively refined during the 10 years in which it has been in continuous production, the Lightning, in its current F.Mk.6 form, bears little more resemblance to the F.Mk.1 variant ordered into production in November 1956 than a general external similarity. Conceived as a pursuit-type weapons system, using classic stern-chase tactics to position itself for an attack with cannon, unguided rockets or AAMs, the Lightning F.Mk.1 followed three prototypes, the first of which flew as the P.1B on April 4, 1957, and 20 pre-production aircraft, the first production example flying on October 29, 1959. Powered by two Avon 201s of 11,250 lb.s.t., which were boosted by afterburners with four nozzle setting for fixed-thrust outputs to 14,430 lb.s.t., the Lightning F.Mk.1 carried a built-in armament of two 30-mm. Aden Mk.4 cannon flanking the cockpit, this being supplemented by an interchangeable weapons pack housing the equipment for two externally-mounted Firestreak infra-red homing AAMs, two retractable boxes each containing 24 2-in. rockets, or two additional Aden cannon and their ammunition. The fixed intake cone housed the Ferranti Airpass (Airborne Interception Radar and Pilot's Attack Sight System), and a 250 Imp. gal. (300 U.S. gal.) ventral tank was normally carried. Possessing an initial climb rate exceeding 50,000 ft./min., the F.Mk.1 could attain its operational ceiling in about two minutes, accelerate from Mach 0.9 to Mach 2.0 in 3.1 minutes, and fly supersonically at half power. After the completion of 20 production aircraft, UHF was added and a flight refuelling probe introduced beneath the port wing to result in the F.Mk.1A, some 40 examples of which had been delivered when production gave place to the F.Mk.2.

(Below) A Lightning F.Mk.3 of No. 56 Squadron, R.A.F. Currently equipping five R.A.F. squadrons, the F.Mk.3 will eventually be brought up to the latest F.Mk.6 standards.

F.Mk.2: Essentially an interim model pending the introduction of the more sophisticated F.Mk.3, the F.Mk.2 is currently the oldest version of the Lightning single-seat all-weather interceptor remaining in first-line operational service, equipping Nos. 19 and 92 Squadrons assigned to the R.A.F.'s 2nd Tactical Air Force in Germany. Possessing the same armament as the F.Mk.1, the F.Mk.2 differs from its predecessor primarily in having fully variable afterburning for its Avon 210 engines which are of similar rating to the Avon 201. Some changes were introduced in the electrical systems, liquid replaces gaseous oxygen, and an integrated instrument panel is provided. Between 40 and 50 Lightning F.Mk.2s were manufactured, the first of these flying on July 11, 1961. Four F.Mk.2s have been supplied to the Royal Saudi Air Force from R.A.F. stocks, under the designation F.Mk.52.

F.Mk.3: Representing a major advance over the F.Mk.2 in that it is capable of employing far more sophisticated interception techniques, cannon armament being deleted and provision made for carrying either the Red Top or Firestreak AAM, the F.Mk.3 appeared in 1963, the first example being delivered to the R.A.F.

GENERAL ARRANGEMENT DRAWING: *A Lightning F.Mk.6 XR763 of No. 5 Squadron, R.A.F. Fighter Command, based at Binbrook.*

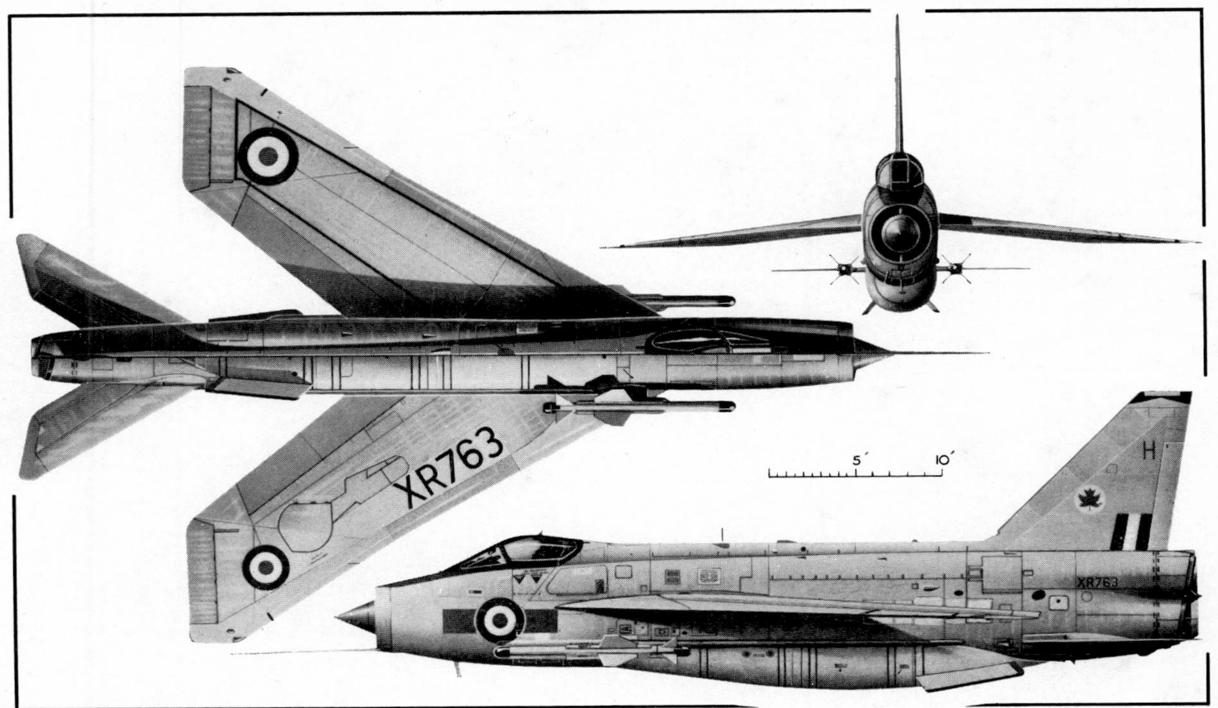
XR763
5′
10′
H
XR763

(Above) The fifth production Lightning F.Mk.3 modified to F.Mk.6 standards and carrying overwing ferry tanks and refuelling probe. This aircraft (XP697) is a trials machine for the F.Mk.6.

on January 1, 1964. Powered by two Avon 301 turbojets each rated at 12,690 lb.s.t. and 16,360 lb.s.t. with full afterburning, the F.Mk.3 may be distinguished from the F.Mk.2 by its more angular vertical tail surfaces of 15 per cent greater area which were adopted to offset the effect of the larger Red Top missiles. The Lightning F.Mk.3 currently equips five of R.A.F. Fighter Command's six home-based all-weather interceptor squadrons, these being Nos. 23, 56, 64, 74 and 111.

T.Mk.4: A two-seat dual-control operational weapons system trainer variant of the Lightning equivalent to the F.Mk.1A, the T.Mk.4 was first flown on May 6, 1959. The forward fuselage was widened by almost one foot to permit the installation of side-by-side Martin-Baker Mk.4BST ejection seats, plus duplicated pilot attack sights and radar scopes. The revised cabin profile results in only a marginal effect on performance, enabling the two-seater to undertake fully operational sorties. Two have been supplied to the Royal Saudi Air Force from R.A.F. stocks as T Mk.54s.

T.Mk.5: A two-seat dual-control equivalent to the F.Mk.3 with similar power plants and revised tail surfaces, the T.Mk.5 flew in aerodynamic prototype form on March 29, 1962, and has since been built in small numbers for Lightning operational conversion units plus one or two for each Fighter Command squadron, the first two-seater of this type being delivered on March 30, 1965.

F.Mk.6: The current production version of the single-seat Lightning interceptor for the R.A.F., and considered to be the definitive model to which standards all F.Mk.3s will be progressively converted, the F.Mk.6 (initially known both as the Mk.3A and Mk.3★) was flown for the first time on June 16, 1965, entering service with No. 5 Squadron in March 1966. By comparison with the F.Mk.3, the F.Mk.6 has a modified wing configuration incorporating camber and an outboard leading-edge extension at approximately one-third span. The F.Mk.6 overcomes the principal shortcoming of earlier versions of the Lightning, relatively short range, in having 600 Imp. gal. (720 U.S. gal.) ventral fuel pack which incurs virtually no performance penalty and increases range by some 20 per cent, resulting in greater afterburning acceleration capacity, longer supersonic endurance and extended patrol time. The flight refuelling probe on the port side of the fuselage may be carried supersonically, and for ferrying purposes twin over-wing tanks may be carried. The fuel in the ferry tanks may be dumped and the tanks jettisoned in the event of a 'hot' situation developing.

F.Mk.53: Featuring the cambered and extended wing of the F.Mk.6, the F.Mk.53 is an export version of the Lightning with extended mission capabilities, and 34 aircraft of this type were ordered for the Royal Saudi Air Force early in 1966. The F.Mk.53, unlike earlier single-seat Lightnings which were wholly specialist interceptors, adds strike and reconnaissance capabilities to Mach 2.0 interception, two underwing pylons being provided, each with 1,000 lb. bearing capacity and suitable for bombs or 68-mm. rocket pods. Two 30-mm. Aden cannon and their ammunition are housed in the forward third of the ventral tank fairing, and minor modifications to the radar sighting system suits the aircraft for launching air-to-ground weapons.

(*Above*) *A Lightning T.Mk.*4 *side-by-side two-seat trainer from the Operational Conversion Unit at Coltishall.*

T.Mk.55: A side-by-side, two-seat training equivalent of the F.Mk.53, the T.Mk.55 is also to be delivered to the Royal Saudi Air Force which has six aircraft of this type on order.

Power Plants: *Two Rolls-Royce RB.*146 *Avon* 301 *turbojets of* 12,690 *lb.s.t. and* 16,360 *lb.s.t. with afterburning.*
Performance: *Max. speed*, 1,500* *m.p.h. at* 40,000 *ft.* (*Mach* 2.27); *range cruise*, 595* *m.p.h. at* 36,000–40,000 *ft.; range* (*at normal cruise with* 600 *Imp. gal.*/720 *U.S. gal. ventral fuel pack*), 700–800* *mls.; initial climb*, 50,000 *ft./min.; time to* 40,000 *ft.*, 2.5* *min.; service ceiling*, 55,000–60,000 *ft.*
Weights: *Loaded*, 40,000–42,000* *lb.; max. loaded*, 48,000–50,000* *lb.*
Dimensions: *Span*, 34 *ft.* 10 *in.; length* (*including probe*), 55 *ft.* 3 *in.; height*, 19 *ft.* 7 *in.; wing area*, 460* *sq. ft.*
*APPROXIMATE
Note: *Specification is applicable to F.Mk.*6.

COMMONWEALTH CA-27 SABRE

Serving with the three day fighter-bomber squadrons of No. 78 Wing of the R.A.A.F., comprising Nos. 3, 77 and 79 operating from Butterworth, Malaysia, Ubon, Thailand, and Darwin, the CA-27 is generally conceded to have been the best of the numerous variants of the Sabre, and current plans call for the phasing out of the last of these aircraft by the R.A.A.F. during 1969–70. The CA-27 Sabre stemmed from an Australian decision to acquire a manufacturing licence for the North American fighter in October 1951, and its subsequent adaptation to meet R.A.A.F. requirements. These requirements included more power and larger calibre armament, and accordingly the General Electric J47 was supplanted by the Rolls-Royce Avon, and the sextet of 0.5-in. guns gave place to a pair of 30-mm. Aden cannon. These changes dictated some radical modifications to the Sabre's fuselage, for the Avon demanded a larger air intake and weighed some 400 lb. less than the American engine that it replaced. In order to avoid major changes to the cockpit arrangement, the extra intake area was obtained by slicing the forward fuselage horizontally and inserting a 3½-in. splice, and the Avon engine was moved further aft to maintain the c.g., the forward fuselage being lengthened to support the power plant, and the aft fuselage, which was redesigned to support the jet pipe, was shortened accordingly. Thus, only some 40 per cent of the original fuselage structure remained when the Australian prototype, designated CA-26, was flown on August 3, 1953.

Some cockpit revision, the introduction of propylnitrate starting, and an increase in fuel capacity resulted in the production model being redesignated CA-27, and the first example, subsequently designated Sabre Mk.30, was flown on July 13, 1954. Twenty-two Sabre Mk.30s were manufactured, these having imported Avon R.A.7 engines and featuring wing slats, and the first fighter of this type was delivered to No. 3 Squadron on March 1, 1956. The 23rd production aircraft introduced the C.A.C.-built Avon 20

(Left) CA-27 Sabre Mk.32 fighter-bombers of No. 3 Squadron, No. 78 (Fighter) Wing, at Butterworth, Malaysia. Current plans call for the phasing out of first-line operational service the last CA-27 Sabres in 1969–70.

engine, had the wing slats supplanted by extended leading edges, and the 352 Imp. gal. (423 U.S. gal.) internal fuel capacity could be supplemented by two 100 or 166.5 Imp. gal. (120 or 200 U.S. gal.) drop tanks, alternative underwing loads including 16 5-in. HVARs or two 500-lb. bombs. The modified CA-27 was designated Sabre Mk.31, 21 aircraft of this type being completed of which the 17th and 21st introduced a further modification in the form of wing leading-edge tanks raising internal capacity by 70 Imp. gal. (84 U.S. gal.) to 422 Imp. gal. (507 U.S. gal.).

The definitive model, the Sabre Mk.32, employed the C.A.C.-built Avon 26 engine and embodied two additional wing strong-points, these reducing wing leading-edge fuel capacity to 60 Imp. gal. (72 U.S. gal.), but permitting underwing launching shoes for a pair of AIM-9 Sidewinder infra-red homing AAMs to be introduced inboard of the main "wet" stations, these missiles augmenting the 30-mm. Aden cannon for the intercept role. Alternative ordnance loads on the inboard pylons included two 500-lb. bombs or clusters of four 5-in. or six 3-in. rockets, these being carried with 100 Imp. gal. (120 U.S. gal.) drop tanks outboard.

Sixty-eight Sabre Mk.32 fighter-bombers were manufactured, most Mk.31s being retrospectively brought up to similar standards, and these are now being modified to counter some metal fatigue discovered in the wings of some early production machines, and to extend their useful life for at least a further two years.

Power Plant: *One C.A.C.-built (Rolls-Royce) Avon 26 turbo-jet rated at 7,500 lb.s.t.*
Performance: *Max speed, 700 m.p.h. at sea level* (Mach 0.92), 672 *m.p.h. at* 10,000 *ft.*, 607 *m.p.h. at* 38,000 *ft.; normal cruise*, 550 *m.p.h. at* 35,000 *ft.; tactical radius (clean)*, 290 *mls. at* 36,000 *ft.*, (*with two* 100 *Imp. gal.*/120 *U.S. gal, drop tanks*) 400 *mls.; max. range* (*with two* 166.5 *Imp. gal.*/200 *U.S. gal. drop tanks*), 1,150 *mls.; initial climb*, 12,000 *ft./min.; service ceiling*, 53,000 *ft.*
Weights: *Empty*, 12,120 *lb.; loaded (clean)*, 15,990 *lb.; max.*, 18,650 *lb.*
Dimensions: *Span*, 37 *ft.* 1¼ *in.; length*, 37 *ft.* 6 *in.; height*, 14 *ft.* 4¾ *in.; wing area*, 302.26 *sq. ft.*

GENERAL ARRANGEMENT DRAWING: *A CA-27 Sabre Mk.32 (A94-957) of No. 3 Squadron, No. 78 (Fighter) Wing, at Butterworth, Malaysia.*

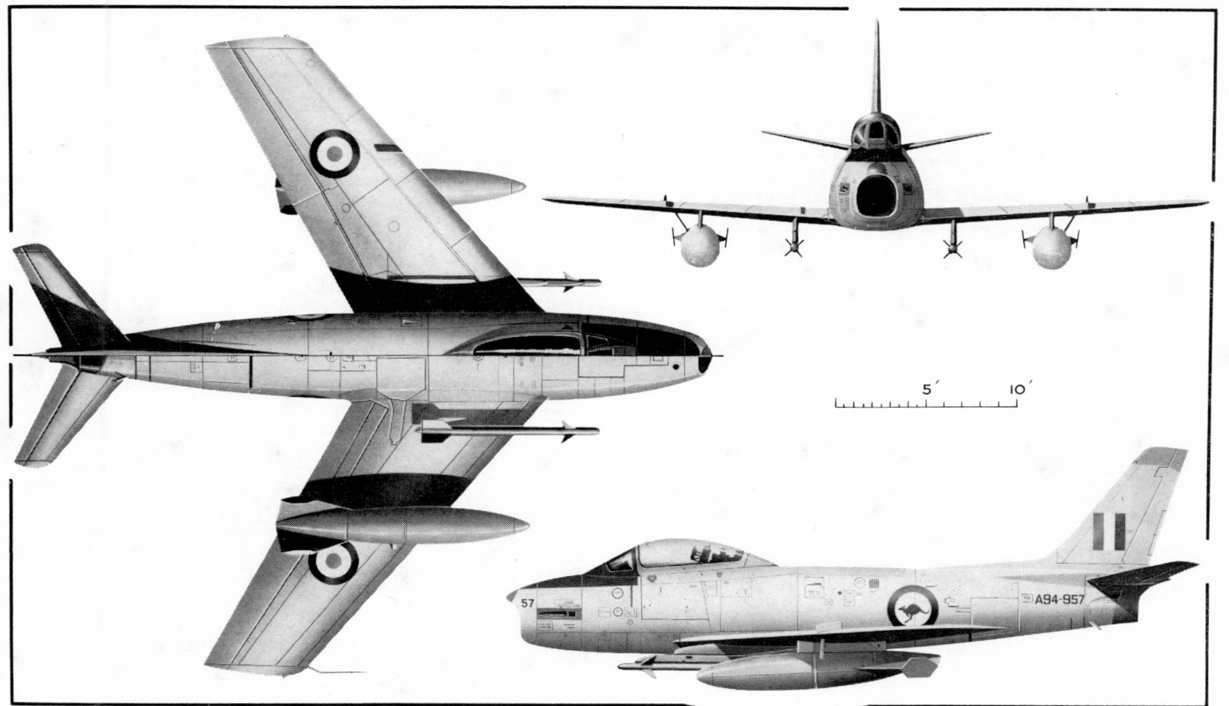
5´
10´
57
A94-957

(Left) A Convair F-102A Delta Dagger (56-1220) serving with the U.S.A.F.'s Pac.A.F. This F-102A has the new camouflage finish adopted as standard for U.S.A.F. operational aircraft in S.E. Asia.

CONVAIR F-102A DELTA DAGGER

Currently being retrofitted for in-flight refuelling, the F-102A single-seat all-weather interceptor has now been supplanted in the U.S.A.F. Fighter-Interceptor Squadrons of the Air Defence Command deployed at bases in the continental U.S.A., but it serves with units assigned to the U.S.A.F.E. and the Pac.A.F., and equips 16 of the Air National Guard Fighter-Interceptor Squadrons. The first manned interceptor to be designed from the outset as part of a weapons system, the F-102 underwent as extensive a metamorphosis between October 24, 1953, when the first YF-102 made its initial flight, and mid-1956, when the 327th Fighter-Interceptor Squadron became the first unit to convert to the F-102A, as any post-war combat aircraft, and since its service introduction it has been subjected to a series of modernisation programmes. Production terminated in April 1958 with the 873rd F-102A, and at the peak of its operational deployment it equipped 25 A.D.C. squadrons.

In its current form, the F-102A possesses full infra-red capability for target acquisition, lock-on and completion of run, and has data link equipment enabling it to be flown by remote control from the ground, course and height directions being fed via the data link directly into the autopilot. No gun armament is carried, and normal armament comprises three AIM-4A or -4E beam-riding and three AIM-4C or -4F infra-red homing Falcon missiles used in conjunction with the MG-10 fire control system, an alternative armament being a single AIM-26B Nuclear Falcon plus a trio of AIM-4C Falcons. Internal fuel capacity is 1,070 U.S. gal. (891 Imp. gal.), and this may be supplemented by a pair of 230 U.S. gal. (191.5 Imp. gal.) underwing tanks which have to be jettisoned in a 'hot' situation as they limit the F-102A to subsonic speeds. The F-102A has undertaken close-support missions in Vietnam, and the Convair-developed in-flight refuelling system now being retrospectively fitted to the F-102A is intended to ease deployment overseas, the probe, mounted above the cockpit, permitting fuel to be drawn from the tank for the fighter's engine at the same time as the tank is being filled. Flight refuelling was

GENERAL ARRANGEMENT DRAWING: *An F-102A Delta Dagger (56-1266) of the 526th Fighter-Interceptor Squadron, 86th Air Division, with the U.S.A.F.E. at Ramstein, Germany, as a component of the 4th Allied Tactical Air Force.*

USAF
5′ 10′
61266
U.S. AIR FORCE FC-266

(*Above*) *F-102A Delta Daggers* (57-0779 *and* -0783) *carrying* 230 *U.S. gal* (191.5 *Imp. gal.*) *drop tanks. New pylons and supporting structure introduced in* 1966 *permits retention of the pylons after jettisoning the tanks.*

employed by an F-102A unit, the 82nd Fighter-Interceptor Squadron, for the first time in April 1966 during deployment to Okinawa.

Power Plant: *One Pratt & Whitney J57-P-23 turbojet rated at* 11,200 *lb.s.t. and* 17,200 *lb.s.t. with afterburning.*
Performance: *Max. speed* (*without drop tanks and refuelling probe*), 825 *m.p.h. at* 40,000 *ft.* (*Mach* 1.25), (*with two* 230 *U.S. gal.*/191.5 *Imp. gal. drop tanks*), 630 *m.p.h. at* 36,000 *ft.* (*Mach* 0.95)*; range cruise*, 540 *m.p.h. at* 35,000 *ft.* (*Mach* 0.8)*; tactical radius* (*with two* 230 *U.S. gal.*/191.5 *Imp. gal. drop tanks*), 500 *mls.; ferry range*, 1,350 *mls.; time to* 32,800 *ft.*, 2.7 *min.; service ceiling*, 54,000 *ft.*
Weights: *Normal loaded*, 27,700 *lb.; max. loaded*, 31,500 *lb.*
Dimensions: *Span*, 38 *ft.* 1½ *in.; length* (*including probe*), 68 *ft.* 4⅔ *in.; height*, 21 *ft.* 2½ *in.; wing area*, 695 *sq. ft.*

TF-102A: Retaining the weapons capability of the F-102A, the side-by-side, two-seat TF-102A lacks the MG-10 fire control and is subsonic, attaining 646 m.p.h. at 38,000 ft. (Mach 0.97) at its normal loaded weight of 27,778 lb. Essentially a combat proficiency trainer, the TF-102A flew on November 8, 1955, and 63 were delivered to the U.S.A.F., each F-102A squadron normally having two TF-102As on strength.

CONVAIR F-106A DELTA DART

Employed exclusively by the U.S.A.F.'s Air Defence Command in which it equips some 13 Fighter-Interceptor Squadrons, the F-106A is a progressive development of the F-102A and is probably the most sophisticated all-weather interceptor extant. The first of 17 test and development F-106As was flown on December 26, 1956, and the interceptor attained operational status in June 1959 with the 539th Fighter-Interceptor Squadron, a total of 257 single-seat examples having been manufactured when the last was delivered to the A.D.C. on July 20, 1961.

F-106A: Progressively up-dated in successive modernisation programmes, the first of which brought all aircraft up to the definitive production standard and the latest, completed mid-1966, providing zero-zero pilot escape capability and the installation of a ballistically-deployed braking chute, the F-106A is equipped with the Hughes MA-1 electronic guidance and fire control system operating with the SAGE (Semi-Automatic Ground Environment) defence system. The MA-1, the basis of which is a compact digital com-

GENERAL ARRANGEMENT DRAWING: *An F-106A Delta Dart* (58-0779) *of the 94th Fighter-Interceptor Squadron at Selfridge A.F.B. Michigan.*

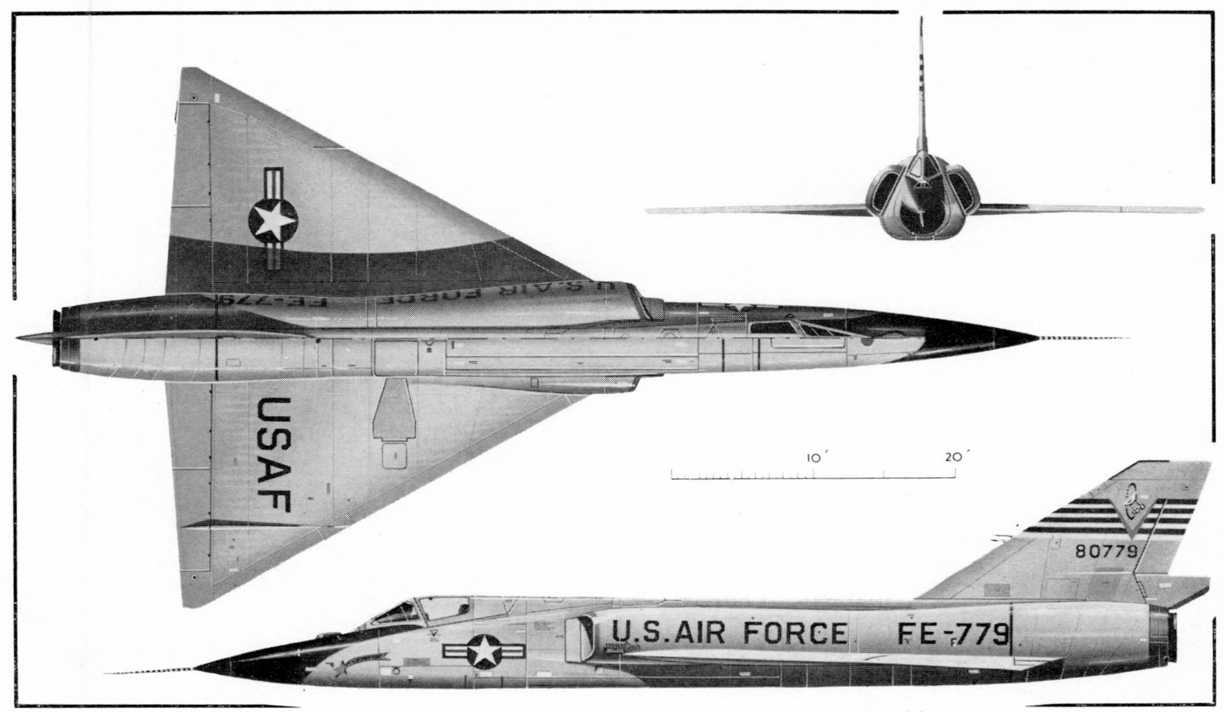
USAF
U.S.AIR FORCE
FE-779
80779
10′
20′

puter, takes control of the aircraft soon after take-off, guides it through climb and cruise to attack position, detects the target and launches the missiles at optimum range, the pilot acting principally as a monitor with the ability to override the MA-1. The F-106A also possesses an infra-red search and tracking system, and several armament combinations may be accommodated by the internal weapons bay, such as four AIM-4E semi-active radar homing or AIM-4F infra-red homing Super Falcon AAMs and one AIR-2A Genie or AIR-2B Super Genie nuclear AAM. Approximately 1,450 U.S. gal. (1,200 Imp. gal.) of fuel is housed by four integral wing tanks and a tank in the fuselage aft of the weapons bay, and for ferry purposes the internal fuel may be supplemented by a pair of 230 U.S. gal. (191.5 Imp. gal.) drop tanks. During 1967, F-106As will begin to receive external fuel tanks that can be carried at supersonic speed, refuelled in flight or jettisoned, as well as new TACAN equipment.

F-106B: In addition to the single-seat F-106A, A.D.C. units received a tandem two-seat dual-purpose version combining the combat proficiency training task with the operational role. With the second seat inserted immediately aft of the standard seat at some expense to fuselage fuel capacity, the F-106B retains the MA-1 system and missile armament of the F-106A, and each Delta Dart squadron has several two-seaters on strength. The F-106B has a J75-P-9 turbojet with similar thrust ratings to the J75-P-17 of the single-seater, and flew initially on April 9, 1958, a total of 63 being manufactured.

Power Plant: *One Pratt & Whitney J75-P-*17 *turbojet rated at* 17,200 *lb.s.t. and* 24,500 *lb.s.t. with afterburning.*
Performance: *Max. speed,* 1,525 *m.p.h. at* 40,000 *ft.* (*Mach* 2.31)*; max. stabilised speed,* 1,255 *m.p.h.* (*Mach* 1.9)*; range cruise,* 610 *m.p.h. at* 41,000 *ft.* (*Mach* 0.92)*; combat radius* (*internal fuel at range cruise*), 575 *mls.; ferry range* (*with two* 230 *U.S. gal./*191.5 *Imp. gal. drop tanks*), 1,450* *mls.; service ceiling,* 57,000 *ft.*
Weights: *Empty,* 23,646 *lb.; loaded* (*clean*), 35,500 *lb.; max. loaded,* 38,250 *lb.*
Dimensions: *Span,* 38 *ft.* 3½ *in.; length* (*including probe*), 70 *ft.* 8¾ *in.; height,* 20 *ft.* 3⅓ *in.; wing area,* 697.83 *sq. ft.*
*APPROXIMATE

DASSAULT ETENDARD IVM

Operated by *Aéronavale Flottilles* 11F, 15F and 17F in the shipboard strike fighter role, and with *Flottille* 16F for the tactical reconnaissance task, the marginally supersonic Etendard is the only European shipboard aircraft capable of attaining Mach 1.0 in level flight. Operated from the carriers *Clémenceau* and *Foch*, the Etendard IVM was derived from the private venture Etendard IV evolved in parallel with the Etendard II and VI which were respectively intended to fulfil the requirements of an *Armée de l'Air* tactical strike fighter specification and the NATO BMR-1 specification. The Etendard IV-01 flew on July 24, 1956, and the *Aéronavale* interest in the type resulted in an order for a semi-navalised prototype and six fully-navalised pre-production aircraft, the suffix letter "M" being applied to the designation to indicate *Marine*. The semi-navalised prototype, the Etendard IVM-01, flew on May 21, 1958, the pre-production aircraft following during 1959–60. The final pre-production aircraft, the Etendard IVP-07, served as a prototype for the tactical reconnaissance model.

Etendard IVM: The first production Etendard IVM flew in July 1961, entering service during the following January with *Flottille* 15F, and 69 examples of this model were manufactured, in addition to the pre-production aircraft. The Etendard IVM enjoys exceptional manoeuvrability, and with the hydraulically-operated nose flaps drooped 15° it can commence a loop at less than 290 m.p.h. The nose flaps have a maximum droop angle of 30°, this deflection normally being used only for catapult take-offs with the plain trailing-edge flaps deflected 60° and the electrically-operated compensating flaps on the all-flying tail deflected 20°. Lateral control is boosted by spoilers with which a roll can be effected in three seconds at 690 m.p.h. The Aïda 7 fire control radar can be used in the intercept mode with limited search and automatic tracking and ranging, and for the intercept mission the built-in armament of one 30-mm. DEFA cannon is usually accompanied

Marginally supersonic, the Etendard IVM (above) has no direct counterpart in any naval air arm. Seen here in clean condition, the Etendard IVM enjoys exceptional manoeuvrability.

by four AIM-9 Sidewinder AAMs on the underwing pylons. A fin-type antenna is mounted beneath the nose for Nord AS.30 visual radio command (line of sight) ASMs, the Etendard IVM carrying two of these formidable missiles on the inboard pylons for the attack mission, the outboard pylons carrying two 496-lb. bombs or two MATRA 150 rocket pods. A pair of 882-lb. bombs or 132 Imp. gal. drop tanks provide alternative loads for the

(Left) The Etendard IVM equips three strike fighter squadrons of France's Aéronavale, 11F, 15F and 17F, this type having entered service in January 1962. Production of the Etendard was completed in 1965.

inboard pylons. Provision is made for the installation of twin 30-mm. DEFA cannon with 125 r.p.g., but one cannon and its ammunition tanks are normally removed to provide space for TACAN. Fuselage tanks house 590 Imp. gal. (708.5 U.S. gal.) of fuel, a further 140 Imp. gal. (168 U.S. gal.) being housed by the integral wing tanks. Two 132 Imp. gal. (158 U.S. gal.) drop tanks may be carried on the inboard pylons, and a retractable flight refuelling probe is mounted immediately ahead of the cockpit.

Etendard IVP: Basically an unarmed tactical reconnaissance version of the Etendard IVM, the IVP, the prototype of which flew on November 19, 1960, carries five OMERA cameras, three of these being mounted in a modified nose from which the Aïda 7 fire control radar has been deleted, and a twin vertical installation being inserted in the bay originally intended for the twin 30-mm. cannon. A fixed refuelling probe is mounted immediately above the nose and provision is made for a "buddy" flight refuelling pack to be carried beneath the fuselage. The first production Etendard IVP was completed in June 1962, and the manufacture of this type terminated in 1965 with the delivery of the 21st aircraft. The *Aéronavale* anticipates operating the Etendard until the early 'seventies, its proposed successor being a navalised version of the Anglo-French Jaguar.

Power Plant: *One SNECMA Atar 8B turbojet rated at* 9,700 *lb.s.t.*
Performance: *Max. speed*, 673 *m.p.h. at* 36,000 *ft.* (*Mach* 1.02), 683 *m.p.h. at sea level* (*Mach* 0.9)*; tactical radius* (*internal fuel*), 186 *mls. at sea level*, 435 *mls. at* 42,000 *ft.; ferry range* (*with two* 132 *Imp. gal./*158 *U.S. gal. drop tanks*), 1,750 *mls. at* 510 *m.p.h. at* 36,000–40,000 *ft.; initial climb*, 19,685 *ft./min.; time to* 42,000 *ft.*, 6 *min.; service ceiling*, 50,850 *ft.*
Weights: *Empty*, 12,786 *lb.; loaded*, 19,400 *lb.; max.*, 22,486 *lb.*
Dimensions: *Span*, 31 *ft.* 6 *in.; length*, 47 *ft.* 3 *in.; height*, 12 *ft.* 7½ *in.; wing area*, 306 *sq. ft.*

GENERAL ARRANGEMENT DRAWING: *An Etendard IVM of Flottille 15F of France's Aéronavale.*

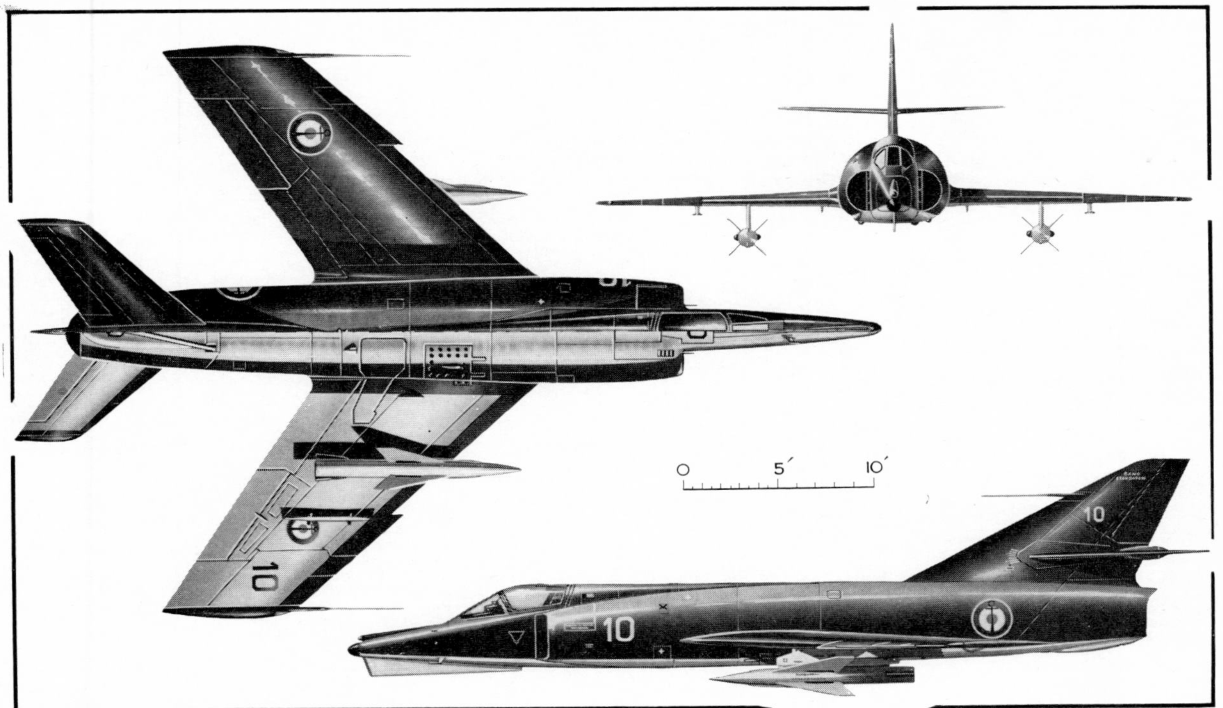
0
5´
10´
10
10
10

DASSAULT MIRAGE III

One of the most successful European military aircraft of its generation, the Mirage III has been adopted by the air arms of Australia, Israel, the Lebanon, South Africa, and Switzerland, as well as by the *Armée de l'Air*. From the first flight of the prototype,the Mirage III-001, on November 17, 1956, the basic design has been continuously developed, and all current production models are derived from the Mirage IIIE which offers greater mission versatility than its predecessor, the Mirage IIIC. The latter, which equips the three *escadrons* of the *Armée de l'Air*'s 2e *Escadre de Chasse*, is primarily an all-weather interceptor with secondary day ground attack capability, and the first of 95 fighters of this type for the *Armée de l'Air* flew on October 9, 1960, following 10 Mirage IIIA 'pre-series' aircraft. A tandem two-seat training equivalent, the Mirage IIIB evolved in parallel with the IIIC, serves with the *Armée de l'Air*, the first of 36 examples for this service having flown on July 19, 1962. Ten similar aircraft have been delivered to the R.A.A.F. under the designation Mirage IIID, two have been supplied to Switzerland (as the IIIBS), and three to South Africa (as the IIIBZ).

Mirage IIIC: Carrying Cyrano I*bis* fire control which has search, lock-on and ranging modes, the Mirage IIIC can carry a variety of ordnance loads on pylons beneath the fuselage and wings, normal intercept armament comprising a semi-active radar-homing MATRA R.511 or R.530 AAM beneath the fuselage and an infra-red homing AIM-9 Sidewinder AAM on each of the two outboard underwing pylons. This armament is usually accompanied by two 137 Imp. gal. (164 U.S. gal.) drop tanks on the inboard wing pylons, these limiting performance to Mach 1.3 and being jettisoned before an interception. Alternatively, two JL-50 pods each with 36 rockets of 37-mm. calibre, or two JL-100 pods each with 16 rockets and 132 Imp. gal. (158 U.S. gal.) of fuel may be carried by the inboard pylons. Take-off and climb performance may be enhanced by a SEPR 844 rocket motor offering 3,372 lb. thrust at sea level and 3,703 lb. at 52,500 ft. A tank for the TX2 secondary rocket fuel is then introduced in the forward fuselage bay, the nitric acid being housed in the rocket pack itself. When the rocket is not fitted, the forward bay can house a twin 30-mm. DEFA 5-52 cannon pack or an 83.6 Imp. gal. (100 U.S. gal.) auxiliary fuel tank. Normal internal fuel capacity is 484 Imp. gal. (581 U.S. gal.), and for ferrying purposes two 286 or 374 Imp. gal. (343 or 449 U.S. gal.) underwing tanks may be carried. The Mirage IIICJ is an essentially similar export model for Israel with rocket motor facilities deleted and the twin 30-mm. cannon installed as standard. A total of 72 Mirage IIICJ interceptors has been supplied to the Israeli Defence Force/Air Force, and 16 aircraft supplied to South Africa as the Mirage IIICZ are intended primarily for the low-level strike role with Nord AS 20 command-guidance ASMs.

Mirage IIIE: Originally developed for the *Armée de l'Air* for the tactical nuclear strike role, and operated by the 3e and 13e *Escadres de Chasse*, the Mirage IIIE has an 11.8-in. increase in the length of the forward fuselage, bringing the cockpit further forward of the engine air intakes, some minor structural changes, and forward-raked main undercarriage members providing sufficient clearance when retracted for a large central store or fuel tank. A fairing beneath the nose houses Marconi Doppler navigation radar, TACAN is installed, Cyrano IIA fire control supplants the I*bis* of the Mirage IIIC, and the more advanced Atar 9C3 with steel compressor and improved afterburner is employed. The forward fuselage bay, the capacity of which has been increased to permit a 121 Imp. gal (145 U.S. gal.) auxiliary tank to be mounted, can accommodate the TX2 rocket fuel tank or the twin 30-mm. DEFA 5-52 cannon and ammunition pack as alternatives to fuel, bombing manoeuvres such as LABS (Low Altitude Bombing System) can be performed, and a wide variety of external ordnance loads may be carried, including a 2,000-lb. store on the centreline pylon and two 1,000-lb. stores beneath the wings.

(Right) Mirage IIIC interceptors of Escadron 1/2 of the 2ᵉ Escadre de Chasse at Dijon. The aircraft are seen carrying the MATRA R.511 AAM, and in the lower photograph the SEPR 844 rocket motor is lit.

One hundred and twenty Mirage IIIE strike fighters have been ordered for the *Armée de l'Air*, but total contracts for the service are expected to reach 200 aircraft, later contracts possibly covering the currently experimental Mirage IIIE2 which has the more powerful Atar 9K engine. The Mirage IIIE2, while retaining the avionics and the fuselage structure of the basic model, embodies swept wings and tail similar to the Mirage F (which see page 48) as a hybrid interim strike aircraft for the late 'sixties. The first of three prototypes of the Mirage IIIE flew on April 5, 1961, the first production example following on January 14, 1964, and in the following year this type supplanted the Mirage IIIC equipping the 13ᵉ *Escadre*.

Derivatives of the basic Mirage IIIE are being manufactured under licence in Australia and Switzerland. In the former country, where the Commonwealth Aircraft Corporation and Department of Supply factories are producing two aircraft per month to meet R.A.A.F. orders for 100 Mirages, two variants are being manufactured. The first 52 aircraft are intended primarily for the attack role under the designation Mirage IIIOA, and the remaining 48 are to be primarily all-weather interceptors with two MATRA R.530 AAMs supplemented by twin 30-mm. DEFA cannon, and will be designated Mirage IIIOF. All 100 aircraft will have been delivered by late 1968. The Swiss version, the Mirage IIIS, was originally to have been based on the Mirage IIIC, but a succession of changes has resulted in an airframe essentially similar to that of the Mirage IIIE but embodying a hinging nose to facilitate storage in underground hangars, more powerful brakes and a stronger undercarriage, some local structural strengthening, and

(*Above and below*) *The Mirage IIIE may be distinguished from the IIIC by the lengthened forward fuselage and Doppler housing.*

a Hughes TARAN-1S fire control and navigation system. Primary armament for the intercept role will consist of a pair of Hughes HM-55S Falcon AAMs. Thirty-three Mirage IIIS interceptors are being manufactured in Switzerland, the first of these having flown on October 27, 1965, and all are scheduled to have been delivered to the *Flugwaffe* by the beginning of 1968.

Mirage IIIEZ is the designation applied to a number of standard production Mirage IIIEs for the South African Air Force, an initial batch of eight having been delivered in 1965, and an essentially similar aircraft is to be supplied to the Lebanese Air Force.

Power Plant: *One SNECMA Atar 9B* (*9C*) *turbojet of* 9,370 (9,436) *lb.s.t. and* 13,225 (13,624) *lb.s.t. with afterburning plus* (*optional*) *one SEPR* 844 *rocket motor of* 3,372 *lb.s.t. at sea level and* 3,703 *lb. at* 52,500 *ft. for* 80 *sec.*
Performance: *Max. speed,* 1,386 *m.p.h. at* 40,000 *ft.* (*Mach* 2.1)*; max. stabilized speed,* 1,188 *m.p.h.* (*Mach* 1.8)*; range cruise,* 594 *m.p.h. at* 36,000 *ft.* (*Mach* 0.9)*; tactical radius,* (*supersonic intercept mission—internal fuel*) 180 *mls.,* (*patrol mission with two* 137 *Imp. gal./*165 *U.S. gal. drop tanks*) 480 *mls. at Mach* 0.9 *at* 36,000 *ft.; ferry range* (*with two* 286 *Imp. gal./*343 *U.S. gal. drop tanks and* 83.6 *Imp. gal./*100 *U.S. gal. auxiliary tank in fuselage*), 1,430 *mls.; time to* 36,000 *ft.* (*with two Sidewinder AAMs*), 6 *min.* 30 *sec., to* 60,000 *ft.* (*with rocket motor*), 7 *min.* 20 *sec.; service ceiling* (*intercept mission with two Sidewinder AAMs*), 54,100 *ft.*
Weights: *Empty,* 13,040 (14,375) *lb.; loaded* (*clean*), 18,620 (21,165) *lb.; max.,* 26,015 (29,760) *lb.*
Dimensions: *Span,* 26 *ft.* 11$\frac{1}{2}$ *in.; length,* 45 *ft.* 5$\frac{1}{4}$ *in.* (46 *ft.* 2$\frac{1}{3}$ *in.*)*; height,* 13 *ft.* 9$\frac{1}{3}$ *in.* (14 *ft.* 9 *in.*)*; wing area,* 365.97 *sq. ft.*
Note: *Specification applies specifically to Mirage IIIC but is generally applicable to IIIE engine data, weights and dimensions quoted in parentheses relating to the latter.*

GENERAL ARRANGEMENT DRAWING: *A Mirage IIIC of Escadron* 1/2 '*Cicogne*' *of the* 2e *Escadre de Chasse, Armée de l'Air, based at Dijon.*

0 5´ 10´
2-EG
2-EG

DASSAULT MYSTÈRE IVA

The Mystère IVA, used extensively by the Indian Air Force in the close-support role during the fighting between India and Pakistan in September 1965, remains in first-line *Armée de l'Air* service despite its obsolescence, being operated by the 7e and 8e *Escadres* each with two *escadrons*, although it is expected to be phased out of French service in 1967. A robust single-seat fighter-bomber, the Mystère IVA was blooded in action during the Israeli invasion of the Sinai of October 1956, and remains in service with two fighter-bomber squadrons of the Israeli Defence Force/Air Force. Resembling its predecessor, the Mystère IIC in little more than general configuration, the Mystère IVA flew as a prototype for the first time on September 28, 1952, off-shore procurement orders subsequently being placed for 325 production aircraft, a proportion of these eventually being exported, 110 being delivered to India and 60 being supplied to Israel, and production terminated late in 1958 with the 421st aircraft.

The first 50 Mystère IVA fighters received the 6,280 lb.s.t. Hispano-Suiza Tay 250A turbojet, these aircraft entering service in 1955 with the 12e *Escadre*, but all subsequent aircraft of this type received the more powerful Verdon 350. The Mystère IVA houses it ranging radar antenna in a small cone mounted on the bifurcating wall in the intake duct, and fuselage and integral wing tanks accommodating 572 Imp. gal. (687 U.S. gal.) of fuel may be supplemented by two or four 106 Imp. gal. (127 U.S. gal.) drop tanks. Armament comprises two 30-mm. DEFA cannon, and wing attachment points provide for external ordnance loads, including four 500-lb. or two 1,000-lb. bombs, four MATRA pods each with 19 37-mm. rockets, or two clusters of six and two clusters of three HVARs.

(*Above and below*) *Mystère IVAs of the Indian Air Force.*

Power Plant: *One Hispano-Suiza Verdon* 350 *turbojet rated at* 7,710 *lb.s.t.*
Performance: *Max. speed*, 696 *m.p.h. at sea level* (*Mach* 0.913), 615 *m.p.h. at* 39,370 *ft.* (*Mach* 0.94)*; range cruise*, 510 *m.p.h. at* 36,000 *ft.; range* (*clean*), 570 *mls.*, (*with two* 106 *Imp. gal./*127 *U.S. gal. drop tanks*), 820 *mls.; ferry range* (*with four* 106 *Imp. gal./*127 *U.S. gal drop tanks*), 1,050 *mls.; initial climb*, 8,860 *ft./min.; service ceiling*, 45,000 *ft.*
Weights: *Empty*, 12,950 *lb.; loaded* (*clean*), 16,530 *lb.; max.*, 20,050 *lb.*
Dimensions: *Span*, 36 *ft.* 5¾ *in.; length*, 42 *ft.* 1¾ *in.; height*, 15 *ft.* 1 *in.; wing area*, 344.5 *sq. ft.*

GENERAL ARRANGEMENT DRAWING: *A Mystère IVA* (*IA*936) *of the Indian Air Force*

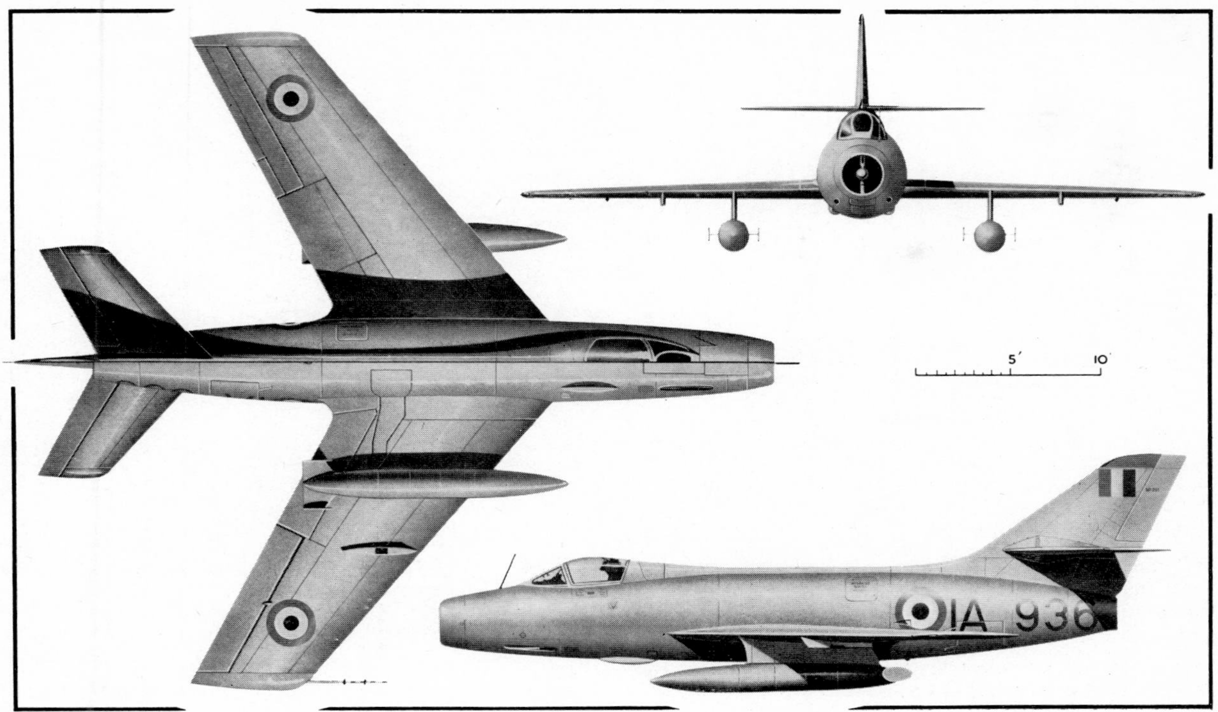
5′
10′
IA 936

(Left) Super-Mystère B2 (No.172) of the 5e Escadre de Chasse.

DASSAULT SUPER-MYSTÈRE B2

Possessing the distinction of having been the first aircraft capable of attaining supersonic speeds in level flight to attain production status in Western Europe, the Super-Mystère B2 was evolved primarily as an interceptor with secondary fighter-bomber capabilities. An aerial in the upper lip of the air intake feeds the radar gunsight, and built-in armament comprises two 30-mm. DEFA cannon backed by a fuselage pack housing 35 SNEB 68-mm. Type 22 folding-fin aircraft rockets. Two underwing pylons can be fitted to carry two 180 Imp. gal. (216 U.S. gal.) drop tanks or, for the close support role, two 1,100-lb. bombs, two MATRA M.116E launchers each with 19 SNEB 68-mm. rockets, or two clusters of six 5-in. HVARs.

Design development of the Super-Mystère was initiated in October 1953 as the "Mystère XX", the first prototype, the Super-Mystère B1 powered by a Rolls-Royce Avon RA.7R, flying on March 2, 1955. Five Atar-powered Super-Mystère B2 pre-production aircraft followed, the first of these flying on May 15, 1956, and production contracts were subsequently awarded for 200 aircraft which, in the event, were cut back to 180 owing to the appreciably higher performance offered by the Mirage III which flew as a prototype three months before the début of the first production Super-Mystère B2 on February 26, 1957. The Super-Mystère B2 was subsequently issued to the 5e, 10e and 12e *Escadres de Chasse* of the *Commandement "Air" des Forces de Défense Aérienne* during 1958–59, and still equipped these units in 1966. Twenty-four were supplied to Israel and currently equip one interceptor squadron of the Israeli Defence Force/Air Force.

Power Plant: *One SNECMA Atar* 101*G rated at* 7,495 *lb.s.t. and* 9,920 *lb.s.t. with afterburning.*
Performance: *Max. speed*, 743 *m.p.h. at* 38,000–41,000 *ft.* (*Mach* 1.125), 686 *m.p.h. at sea level* (*Mach* 0.9)*; max. cruise*, 620 *m.p.h. at* 40,000 *ft.* (*Mach* 0.94)*; range cruise*, 560 *m.p.h. at* 36,000 *ft.; tactical radius* (*clean*), 270 *mls. at* 36,000 *ft.; range* (*with two* 180 *Imp. gal.*/216 *U.S. gal. drop tanks*), 730 *mls.; initial climb*, 17,500 *ft./min.; ceiling*, 55,750 *ft.*
Weights: *Empty*, 15,400 *lb.; normal loaded*, 19,840 *lb.; max.*, 22,046 *lb.*
Dimensions: *Span*, 34 *ft.* $5\frac{3}{4}$ *in.; length*, 46 *ft.* $1\frac{1}{4}$ *in.; height*, 14 *ft.* $10\frac{3}{4}$ *in.; wing area*, 377 *sq. ft.*

GENERAL ARRANGEMENT DRAWING: *A Super-Mystère B2 of the Heil Avir Le Israel.*

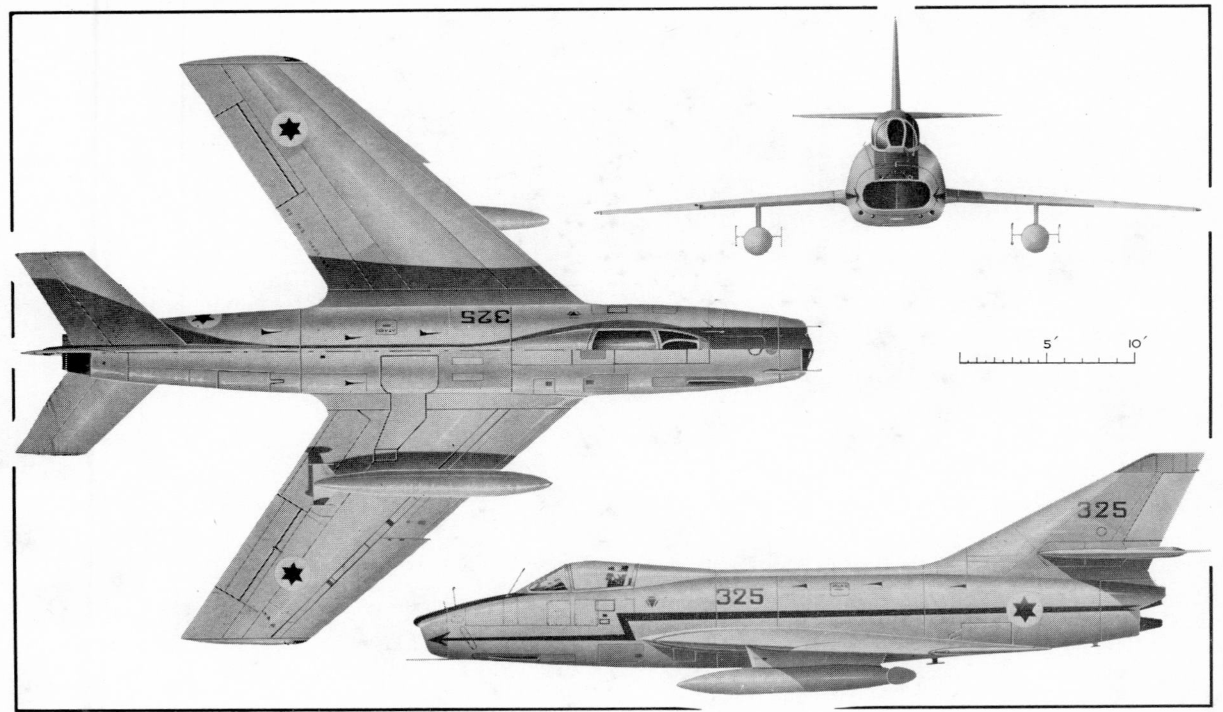
325
5´
10´
325
325

(*Left*) *Fiat G.91R.3 light reconnaissance and strike fighters of the Luftwaffe. This service currently possesses four operational Geschwader equipped with the G.91R.3, 270 examples having been manufactured under licence in Germany.*

FIAT G.91

The successful contender in the NATO contest for a lightweight strike and reconnaissance fighter announced in December 1953, the G.91 has not enjoyed the widespread acceptance within NATO originally envisaged, and has been adopted by only two air arms, the *Aeronautica Militare Italiano* and the *Luftwaffe*. In the former service it equips only the two *Gruppi* of the 2° *Stormo*, and in the latter service, which has become somewhat disenchanted with the G.91's capabilities and has progressively reduced the number of units scheduled to operate the type, only four *geschwader* have received the Fiat fighter.

The first of three prototypes of the G.91 flew on August 9, 1956, and 27 pre-production aircraft were produced for test and evaluation, the first of these flying on February 20, 1958. Sixteen of the pre-production aircraft were converted to G.91 PAN configuration six years later for Italy's national aerobatic team, the *Pattuglia Acrobatica Nazionali*, armament being removed and replaced by ballast, pitch dampers being fitted, and smoke canisters being mounted beneath the wings. The production G.91R differed from the pre-production model in having a redesigned fuselage nose housing three Vinten cameras for forward and lateral oblique photography, and three single-seat versions were ordered.

G.91R.1: The initial production model, the G.91R.1 for the *Aeronautica Militare*, carries an armament of four 0.5-in. Colt-Browning machine guns and has two underwing pylons for two 250-lb. bombs, napalm tanks, or various combinations of 2.75-in., 3-in. or 5-in. HVARs. All fuel is housed in the fuselage, seven split tanks having a total capacity of 352 Imp. gal. (423 U.S. gal.), and no provision is made for external drop tanks. With the delivery of 25 aircraft of this type, a further 25 were manufactured for the *Aeronautica Militare* under the designation G.91R.1A, the second series introducing Doppler radar, and a third series of 50 aircraft ordered under the designation G.91R.1B introduced two additional underwing pylons; an increase in internal fuel capacity to 372 Imp. gal. (447 U.S. gal.) and provision for two 57 or 114 Imp. gal. (68 or 136 U.S. gal.) drop tanks; a more advanced IFF transponder; a Position and Homing Indicator; provision for JATO

GENERAL ARRANGEMENT DRAWING: *A Fiat G.91R.1A of the Aeronautica Militare's 2° Stormo CTRL at Istrana, Treviso.*

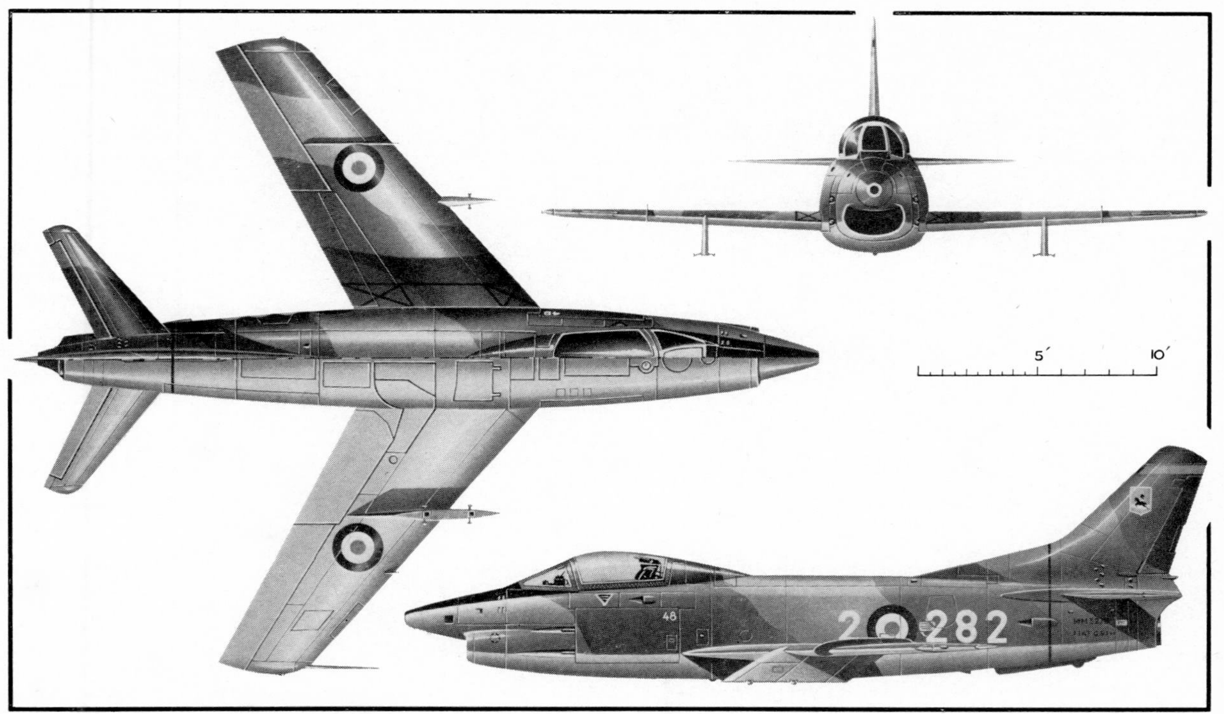
5´
10´
2 282
48

units; enlarged air brakes; boosted electric and air conditioning systems; a pitch damper (the 1A having only a yaw damper) and a reinforced undercarriage. The G.91R.1B retains the four 0.5-in. guns with 300 r.p.g., and external loads can include two AS.20 or AS.30L ASMs or two 500-lb. bombs on the inboard pylons and two pods containing 19 2-in. or 12 2.75-in. rockets or two clusters of six 3-in. rockets on the outboard supplementary wing attachments. All *Aeronautica Militare* G.91Rs are gathered within the 2° *Stormo CTRL* comprising the 13° and 14° *Gruppi* at Istrana, Treviso, for the tactical fighter and light reconnaissance roles.

G.91R.3: The variant ordered for the *Luftwaffe*, the G.91R.3, possesses essentially similar equipment to the G.91R.1B, including Doppler and PHI, and provision for four underwing pylons, but armament differs in that the four 0.5-in. weapons are replaced by two 30-mm. DEFA cannon with 125 r.p.g. Seventy-four G.91R.3s were manufactured by the parent company for the *Luftwaffe*, 12 of these being delivered in the form of major components for assembly by Dornier at Oberpfaffenhofen. Subsequently, a consortium of Dornier, Messerschmitt and Heinkel manufactured 270 G.91R.3s under licence, but a number of these are now surplus to the *Luftwaffe's* requirements owing to a substantial reduction in the number of units that were to have received this light strike and reconnaissance fighter, and these are being disposed of abroad. *Luftwaffe* units operating the G.91R.3 are LeKG 41 at Husum, LeKG 44 at Leipheim, Jabo G 42 at Pferdsfeld and Jabo G.43 at Oldenburg.

G.91R.4: Essentially similar to the G.91R.3 but possessing the same armament as the G.91R.1, the G.91R.4 was purchased under the MAP for supply to Greece and Turkey, 50 examples of this type being manufactured. In the event, both countries declined to accept the G.91R.4, and the 50 aircraft passed into the *Luftwaffe's* inventory, 40 of these being disposed of to the *Força Aérea Portuguesa* in 1965–66, currently equipping Nos. 20 and 21 Squadrons of that service.

G.91T: A tandem two-seat training development of the G.91R, the G.91T may also be used as a tactical fighter, and the first of two prototypes flew on May 31, 1960. Two versions have since been manufactured, the first of those being the G.91T.1 for the *Aeronautica Militare* which has acquired 76 aircraft of this type for the *Scuola Volo Basico Avanzato Aviogetti* at Amendola, and the G.91T.3 for the *Luftwaffe* which has received 44 aircraft for operation from the school at Fürstenfeldbruck. The G.91T.1 and T.3 differ in equipment, the latter being some 200 lb. heavier, but both have a built-in armament of two 0.5-in. machine guns, and can lift two 500-lb. bombs, 62 2-in. rockets, 38 2.75-in. rockets, or two Nord AS.20 or AS.30L ASMs on their two underwing pylons. According to equipment empty weight ranges from 7,240 to 7,405 lb. and loaded weight from 11,800 to 11,995 lb.

Power Plant: *One Bristol Siddeley Orpheus* 80302 *turbojet rated at* 5,000 *lb.s.t.*
Performance: *Max. speed* (*at* 11,880 *lb.*), 650 *m.p.h. at* 5,000 *ft.* (*Mach* 0.87), 637 *m.p.h. at* 20,000 *ft.* (*Mach* 0.91)*; econ. cruise*, 403 *m.p.h. at* 5,000 *ft.; tactical radius at econ. cruise* (*on internal fuel and including* 10 *min. loiter*), 200 *mls.; ferry range* (*with two* 114 *Imp. gal.*/137 *U.S. gal. drop tanks*), 1,150 *mls. at* 253 *m.p.h. at* 35,000 *ft.; initial climb*, 6,000 *ft./min.; service ceiling*, 40,000 *ft.*
Weights: *Empty*, 8,130 *lb.; normal loaded*, 11,180 *lb.; max.*, 12,125 *lb.*
Dimensions: *Span*, 28 *ft.* 1 *in.; length*, 33 *ft.* 9¼ *in.; height*, 13 *ft.* 1½ *in.; wing area*, 176.74 *sq. ft.*
Note: *Specification applies specifically to G.91R.1B but is generally applicable to other single-seat versions.*

GENERAL DYNAMICS F-111

The first combat aircraft featuring a variable-geometry wing to attain production, and the first tactical fighter to be designed from the outset for use by both the U.S.A.F. and the U.S. Navy. the F-111 was selected as the winner of the 1960 contest resulting from formulation of the TFX (Tactical Fighter Experimental) requirement in February of that year. The selection of the General Dynamics design was announced on November 24, 1962, and 23 research, development, test and evaluation aircraft were ordered under an initial contract, 18 of these being of the F-111A version for the U.S.A.F., and the remaining five being F-111Bs for the U.S. Navy. The original TFX requirement demanded a Mach 2.5 high-altitude dash and Mach 1.2 interdiction at zero altitude; the ability to take-off and clear a 50-ft. obstacle within 3,000 ft., landing from this altitude within a similar distance; suitability for operation from short, rough strips in forward areas for the support of ground forces, and a range exceeding 4,000 miles to enable the aircraft to fly between any two airfields in the world in one day. In addition, the U.S. Navy demanded a five-six hour loiter capability, and take-off and landing speeds not exceeding 115 and 90 knots respectively. Furthermore, a high degree of 'commonality' was called for between versions for the two services. From the outset it was appreciated that such an aircraft could be produced only if a practical variable-geometry wing could be evolved, and such a wing—known by General Dynamics as a VASCAAR wing (variable area, sweep, camber and aspect ratio)—was successfully developed to represent one of the major advances in the field of airframe design over the past decade.

F-111A: Possessing the primary role of supersonic low-altitude penetration for interdiction or tactical reconnaissance, secondary tasks being the provision of air superiority over ground forces and high-altitude reconnaissance, the F-111A is expected to attain operational status in 1968, initial U.S.A.F. deliveries commencing early in 1967. The first research and development F-111A was flown on December 21, 1964 with YTF30-P-1 turbofans, and most of the 18 had joined the development programme by mid-1966, the eleventh serving as the prototype RF-111A and the twelfth, flown on May 28, 1966, embodying all significant changes so far contemplated for the initial production model, including a 16.5-in.

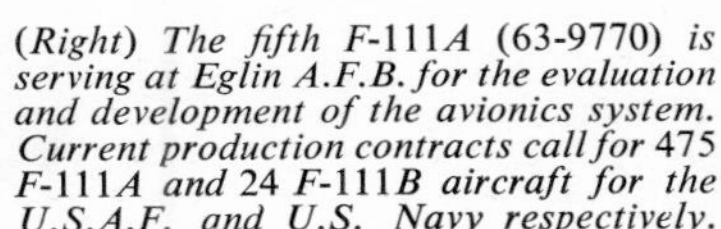

(*Right*) *The fifth F-*111*A* (63-9770) *is serving at Eglin A.F.B. for the evaluation and development of the avionics system. Current production contracts call for* 475 *F-*111*A and* 24 *F-*111*B aircraft for the U.S.A.F. and U.S. Navy respectively.*

increase in fuselage length, a 14 sq. in. increase in air intake area, full-span flaps, rotating-nose leading-edge slots, and some re-design of key structural areas reducing weight by some 4,000 lb., all subsequent trials aircraft being to the same standard.

Possessing an 85 per cent numerical component part commonality with the U.S. Navy's F-111B, the F-111A, intended primarily for the low-altitude role, has a 7.33 *g* strength factor, and its two crew members—pilot and co-pilot—are seated side-by-side in a McDonnell-designed rocket-powered escape module which, eventually to be installed in the twelfth trials aircraft, comprises the entire cockpit section, and can be used in zero-zero (sea-level static) conditions or even 50 ft. below water. The VASCAAR wing's movable portions pivot on points well out from the centre line and sweep through 16° to 72.5°, the wing-sweep mechanism being powered by both hydraulic systems of the aircraft, mechanically-interconnected individual irreversible actuators safeguarding against asymmetrical wing sweep. In the event of a failure with the wings fully swept a landing can be accomplished at a touch-down speed of the order of 230 m.p.h. The sweep angles are 16° (at which the limiting Mach number is near the best subsonic cruising speed), 26° (at which the Mach number is close to unity and which is the optimum sweep angle for long-range cruise), 50° (which will take the F-111A up to its limiting Mach number), and 72.5° (dictated by skin-friction heating considerations). Although the U.S.A.F. role demands more and heavier underwing stores than does the U.S. Navy role, the same strong points are fitted to both the F-111A and B—four under each wing. The two outboard pylons on each wing are fixed and can only be used between 16° and 26° wing sweep, the two inboard pylons pivoting to remain parallel to the centreline throughout the entire sweep range. There is a small internal weapons bay, and the F-111A could carry 50 750-lb. conventional bombs, two of these being accommodated internally, or 26 1,000-lb. bombs, but these could only be carried with the wing swept at 26°, and such loads are unlikely to be carried in practice. At a sweep angle of 54° bomb load is limited to 26 750-lb. weapons, and in standard U.S.A.F. form, the F-111As payload varies from 8,000 lb. to 20,000 lb. according to range. For example, for a mission radius of 1,725 miles in adverse temperature and runway conditions payload is of the order of 16,000 lb. A wide variety of alternative offensive loads may be carried by the F-111A, both internally and externally, the weapons bay being capable of housing a pair of tactical nuclear weapons or such missiles as the AGM-53A Condor, and the pylons carrying AGM-12 Bullpup ASMs or, in the case of the R.A.F. version, the Hawker Siddeley/MATRA Martel. Consideration is being given to the installation of a 20-mm. M-61 Vulcan rotary cannon on the starboard side of the weapons bay.

The initial production version of the F-111A has what is known as the Mk.1 avionic system. This includes a Litton AJQ-20 inertial navigation and attack system, the General Electric APQ-113 navigation and attack radar, Honeywell APN-167 pulsed-type radar, the Texas Instruments APQ-110 terrain-following radar, and Collins ARC-109 UHF and ARC-112 HF transceivers. Later F-111As, including those to be delivered to the R.A.F., will incorporate the more advanced Mk.2 avionic system which will include a new attack radar providing a narrow, continuous-wave beam for the guidance of the advanced semi-active radar homing AAMs with which it is planned to augment the infra-red homing AAMs and Shrike AGMs that are to be carried by early F-111As. It will also have tactical strike ground mapping and air-to-air modes. A newer, more accurate inertial navigator will be employed, together with more extensive penetration aids and several optical target acquisition aids, including a laser range-finder, an infra-red search and detection sub-system, and a low-light-level television camera.

Contracts for 383 F-111As for the U.S.A.F. and 24 for the

GENERAL ARRANGEMENT DRAWING: *The fifth R. & D. General Dynamics* F-111*A* (63-9770) *which has been used at Eglin A.F.B. for electronic and environmental systems testing.*

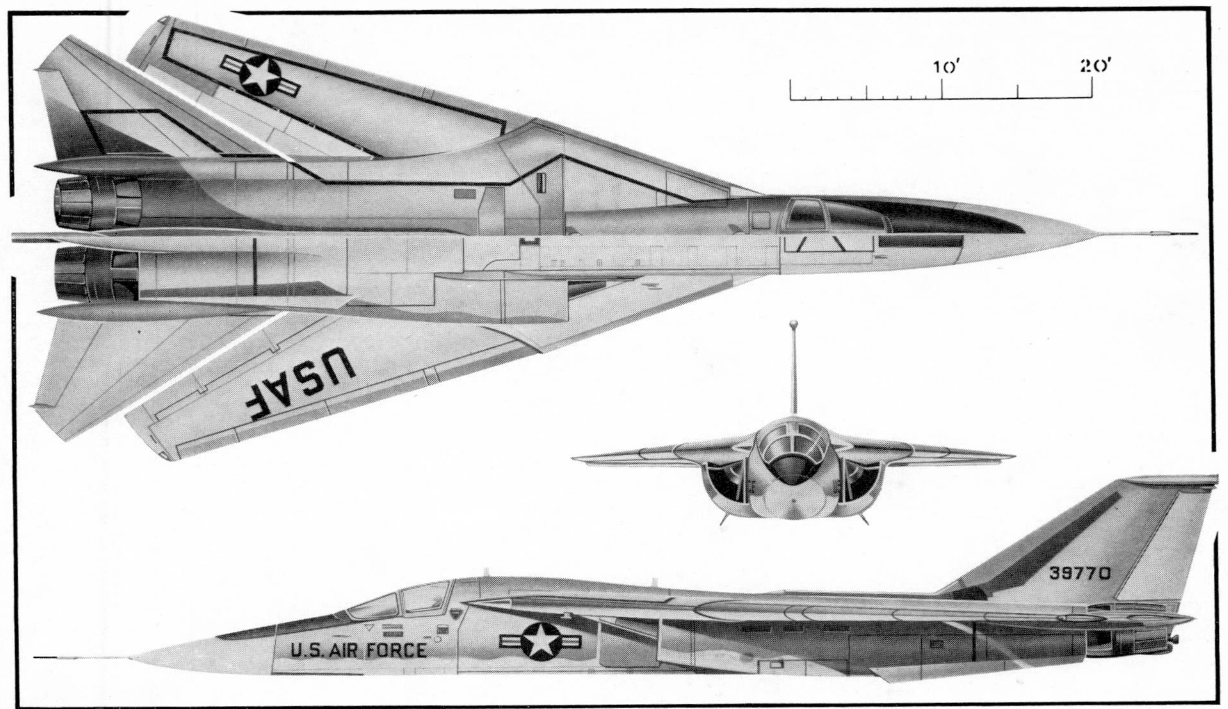
10'
20'
USAF
39770
U.S. AIR FORCE

(*Above*) *The third F-*111*A* (63-9768) *flying in slow speed configuration with wing at minimum sweep angle and full-span leading-edge slats and trailing-edge flaps extended. The minimum sweep angle of* 16° *offers a limiting Mach number close to the best subsonic cruising speed. The aircraft illustrated, which flew for the first time on April* 30, 1965, *has been employed on systems-testing at Edwards Air Force Base.*

R.A.A.F. were placed in April 1965, deliveries to the former service being scheduled to commence in January 1967 and to the latter from 1968, the last six for the R.A.A.F. later being converted to RF-111As for long-range low- or high-altitude reconnaissance. To these were added early in 1966 an order for 10 F-111Ks for the R.A.F., together with an option on a further 40 to be ordered by April 1967, all for delivery by January 1970. Whereas the R.A.A.F. F-111As will be virtually standard production-line aircraft with few differences from the U.S.A.F. model, the R.A.F. version, which will be required for the long-range strike and reconnaissance tasks and will be crewed by a pilot and navigator, will embody features of the FB-111 with a similar strengthened undercarriage for higher gross weights and advanced ballistic computer, British communications equipment, and facilities for installing a sensor pod and equipment for reconnaissance missions.

RF-111A: A reconnaissance version of the F-111A, designated RF-111A and incorporating the minimum number of changes compatible with fitting all-weather and night sensor systems, is being developed in parallel with the tactical fighter model, authorisation for this version being announced by the U.S. Department of Defense in December 1965. The U.S.A.F. has a requirement for about 100 RF-111As, and the eleventh trials aircraft is serving as a prototype for the reconnaissance model which will carry a pod housing electronic gear or cameras in the weapons bay, equipment including Westinghouse APD-7 high-resolution side-looking radar. Six of the R.A.A.F.'s F-111As will be converted to RF-111A standard two years after delivery to Australia.

F-111B: Although scheduled to enter production in 1968, the U.S. Navy had not, at the time of closing for press, committed itself to large-scale procurement beyond five trials and twenty-four production examples of the F-111B owing to weight and drag problems, and also difficulties with the AIM-54A AAM which is intended to serve as primary armament. Whereas the primary role of the F-111A is that of low-altitude penetration, that of the F-111B is air superiority, the crew comprising pilot and missile control officer. By comparison with the F-111A, the F-111B has 3 ft. 6 in. outer wing panel extensions to improve cruise efficiency at altitude, and reduce take-off and landing speeds, the extensions reducing the strength factor to 6.5 *g*. The fuselage nose is some 5 ft. 8 in. shorter than that of the F-111A, this being dictated primarily by existing carrier elevator sizes, and whereas the F-111A houses its APQ-113 attack radar, APQ-99 terrain-following radar and virtually all its other avionics in the nose, the F-111B has only sufficient space in this portion of the fuselage for its AWG-9 air intercept radar, its MAU-48A missile launcher and other avionics being accommodated in a bay immediately aft of the cockpit and resulting in a substantial reduction in fuselage fuel capacity, tota internal fuel capacity being of the order of 3,600 U.S. gal. (3,000 Imp. gal.) as compared with 4,800 U.S. gal. (4,000 Imp. gal.) for the F-111A.

The primary armament of the F-111B comprises six AIM-54A Phoenix AAMs, two of these being housed by the weapons bay and four being mounted on the inboard pivoting pylons, and an additional fixed pylon may be fitted outboard beneath each wing. The first trials F-111B was flown on May 18, 1965, and the fourth aircraft embodying all changes contemplated for the production version, joined the test programme in May 1966, these being powered by the TF30-P-1 turbofan with a military rating of about 11,000 lb.s.t. and 19,000 lb. with full afterburning, but production examples will have the improved TF30-P-8. The F-111B is appreciably heavier than desired by the U.S. Navy, the original target loaded weight of 55,000 lb. having grown to 75,300 lb. in the trials aircraft by early 1966 when it was hoped to reduce the loaded weight of the production F-111B to slightly less than 70,000 lb. The fourth F-111B has an empty weight of 43,505 lb. as compared with 46,000–47,000 lb. for its predecessors. The original target empty weight was 38,800 lb. In an attempt to achieve the originally specified carrier performance at the new operating weights, a programme aimed at improving the maximum lift characteristics of the wing was initiated in 1965.

FB-111: Currently scheduled to attain operational status with the Strategic Air Command in 1969, the FB-111 strategic bomber retains the structure of the F-111A virtually unchanged, but embodies the wing extensions of the F-111B, new avionics, and a strengthened undercarriage to accommodate higher gross weights. The FB-111 is intended to carry the SRAM (Short-Range Attack Missile), a 50–100-mile range low-yield nuclear stand-off weapon, up to five such missiles being carried. For extreme-range missions one SRAM will be housed internally and two will be carried on the inboard pivoting pylons, four drop tanks being carried by the outboard pylons to provide a tactical radius of the order of 3,000 miles. On such missions the fuel contained by the drop tanks will be consumed during the subsonic portion of the journey to the target, the tanks then being jettisoned and increased wing sweep-back selected for the supersonic run-in and escape. For subsonic missions demanding conventional bombs, the FB-111 will lift 48 750-lb. bombs on its wing pylons plus 2 750-lb. bombs in the weapons bay, and is stressed to withstand up to 4 *g* during manoeuvres thus loaded, total weight exceeding 100,000 lb. The FB-111 will have essentially similar avionics to those of the F-111A with the addition of an astrotracker, a Doppler radar, a second ARC-109 UHF transceiver, and a special radar transponder compatible with Strategic Air Command tanker rendezvous systems. Initial funding for a total of 210 FB-111s was authorised by the U.S. Department of Defense in December 1965, and all are scheduled for operational deployment by 1971.

Power Plants: *Two Pratt & Whitney TF*30-*P*-3 *turbofans each rated at* 12,500* *lb.s.t. and* 21,000* *lb.s.t. with afterburning.*
Performance: *Design max. speed*, 1,650 *m.p.h. at* 40,000 *ft.* (*Mach* 2.5), 865 *m.p.h. at sea level* (*Mach* 1.2)*; mission radius* (*F*-111*A*), 1,700* *mls. for hi-lo-hi profile with* 16,000* *lb. payload; ferry range* (*F*-111*A*), 3,800 *mls. on internal fuel*, (*F*-111*B*), 2,900* *mls.; range cruise*, 575 *m.p.h. at* 40,000 *ft.* (*Mach* 0.87)*; operational ceiling*, 60,000–62,000 *ft.*
Weights: (*F*-111*A*) *Empty*, 43,500 *lb.; loaded*, 79,500 *lb.; max. overload*, 95,000* *lb.* (*F*-111*B*) *Empty*, 43,500* *lb.; loaded*, 69,500 *lb.*
Dimensions: (*F*-111*A*) *Span*, 63 *ft.* 0 *in.*, (*with* 72.5° *L/E sweep*), 31 *ft.* 11 *in.; length*, 73 *ft.* 6 *in.; height*, 17 *ft.* 1½ *in.* (*F*-111*B*) *Span*, 70 *ft.* 0 *in.*, (*with* 72.5° *L/E sweep*), 33 *ft.* 11 *in.; length*, 66 *ft.* 8 *in.*, (*with nose folded*), 61 *ft.* 8 *in.; height*, 16 *ft.* 8 *in.*
*APPROXIMATE

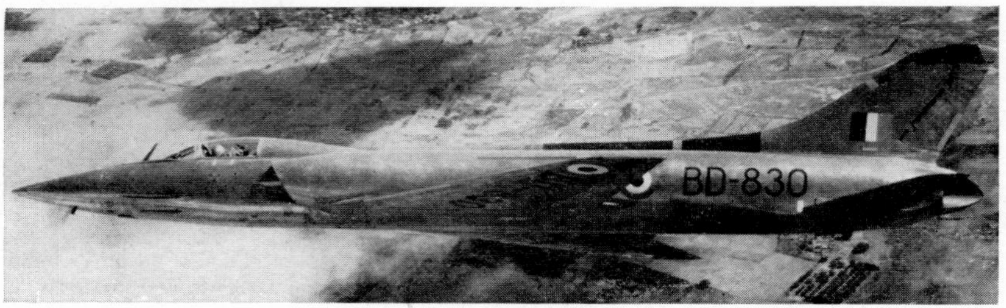

(*Left*) *The third pre-production HF-24 Mk.1 (BD-830). The entire development programme of this multi-purpose fighter is now more than two years behind schedule.*

HAL HF-24 MARUT

The HF-24 Marut (Wind Spirit), the first Indian jet combat aircraft of indigenous design, has suffered a number of setbacks during the decade in which it has been under development, and its evolution in production form has been unusually protracted. In consequence, this multi-mission fighter is not now expected to attain preliminary service status with the Indian Air Force before mid-1967. Design of the HF-24 was begun in 1956 by a team headed by Professor Kurt Tank, and from the outset it was envisaged that power would be provided by a pair of Orpheus B.Or.12 turbojets each offering 6,740 lb.s.t. and 8,170 lb. with afterburning. In the event, development of the afterburning Orpheus was abandoned by the parent company, necessitating production of an interim version of the HF-24 pending availability of turbojets of sufficient thrust to enable the fighter to attain its intended Mach 2.0 performance.

The prototype HF-24 was flown for the first time on June 17, 1961, and a second prototype and 16 pre-production aircraft for research and development purposes were produced over the next five years, the preparation of production tooling being retarded by shortages of skilled labour and priorities allocated to existing production programmes. Several of the pre-production aircraft have been tested with Indian-developed afterburners which, initially boosting the thrust of the Orpheus 703 by 16 per cent, offer a 36 per cent boost in their definitive form, raising thrust to 6,600 lb. for take-off.

Three interim versions of the HF-24 are to be manufactured pending introduction of the definitive Mk.2, these being the single-seat Mk.1A with non-afterburning engines, the similarly-powered tandem two-seat Mk.1B, and the single-seat Mk.1R with afterburning engines. With non-afterburning engines the Marut attains speeds marginally below Mach 1.0 in level flight, and with afterburning engines attains level speeds of the order of Mach 1.2. Fulfilling the intercept, strike and reconnaissance roles, the HF-24 Mks.1A and 1R carry four 30-mm. Aden cannon with 125 r.p.g., and up to 4,000 lb. of ordnance on four underwing stations, typical interdiction loads comprising four 1,000-lb. bombs, four MATRA pods each containing 19 3-in. rockets, or clusters of 60-lb. HVARs. The Aden cannon may be supplemented in the intercept

GENERAL ARRANGEMENT DRAWING: *The third pre-production HF-24 Marut Mk.1 (BD-830)*

BD-830
5′
10′
BD-830

role by a missile launcher immediately aft of the cockpit comprising four vertical rows of 12 spin-stabilised rockets. Alternatively, this bay can accommodate a camera pack or additional fuel. Equipment includes the Ferranti Airpass (Airborne Interception Radar and Pilot's Attack Sight System), and provision is to be made for two or four infra-red homing AAMs mounted on underwing launching shoes.

The HF-24 Mk.1B is essentially similar to the Mk.1A but a second cockpit with full dual controls is inserted immediately aft of the standard cockpit in the space occupied in the single-seater by the internal rocket or camera pack. Various power plants have been considered for the definitive Mk.2 version of the Marut, and a prototype has been fitted with two Brandner-designed E-300 turbojets each rated at 7,055 lb.s.t. and 9,480 lb. with afterburning. Financial and technical negotiations have taken place between the governments of India and the United Arab Republic for the cross-supply of HF-24 airframes and E-300 turbojets, and current plans call for deliveries of the HF-24 Mk.2 to the Indian Air Force from 1969 for the all-weather intercept role with collision-course missiles, and as a successor to the Hunter in the strike fighter role.

Power Plants: *Two HAL-built (Bristol Siddeley) Orpheus* 703 *turbojets each rated at* 4,850 *lb.s.t.*
Performance: *Max. speed*, 630* *m.p.h. at* 40,000 *ft.* (*Mach* 0.95), 705 *m.p.h. at sea level; range cruise*, 560* *m.p.h. at* 36,000 *ft.* (*Mach* 0.85)*; combat radius* (*internal fuel*), 380–420* *mls.; time to* 40,000 *ft.*, 7 *min.; service ceiling*, 46,000 *ft.*
Weights: *Empty*, 13,520 *lb.; loaded*, 19,450 *lb.; max.*, 24,250 *lb.*
Dimensions: *Span*, 29 *ft.* 6⅓ *in.; length*, 51 *ft.* 7⅓ *in.; height*, 13 *ft.* 1½ *in.; wing area*, 295* *sq. ft.*
*APPROXIMATE

HAWKER HUNTER

Possibly the most successful of post-war British combat aircraft, the Hunter has remained in the R.A.F.'s active inventory for more than 12 years, serves in various forms with the air arms of Denmark, India, Iraq, Jordan, Kuwait, Lebanon, Netherlands, Peru, Rhodesia, Saudi Arabia, Sweden and Switzerland, and is still being exported abroad in refurbished form. A total of 1,525 Hunters, excluding prototypes, was manufactured in the U.K., and a further 381 were produced in the Netherlands and Belgium to give a grand total of 1,906 aircraft. Of those manufactured in the U.K., 480 were exported as new aircraft, and more than 200 refurbished aircraft (both ex-R.A.F. and ex-*Force Aérienne Belge*) had been exported by mid-1966.

The first Hunter prototype was flown on June 20, 1951, and 139 F. Mk.1 and 45 F. Mk.2 Hunters were produced, these being essentially short-range day fighters differing from each other in having the 7,550 lb.s.t. Avon 113 and the 8,000 lb.s.t. Sapphire 101 respectively; carrying four 30-mm. Aden cannon with 150 r.p.g., and lacking any provision for external stores. These models were succeeded in production by the F.Mks.4 and 5 in which internal fuel capacity was increased from 334 Imp. gal. (401 U.S. gal.) to 414 Imp. gal. (497 U.S. gal.), and hard points were provided for two 100 Imp. gal. (120 U.S. gal.) drop tanks. The first 159 F Mk.4s retained the Avon 113 but subsequent aircraft had the Avon 115 which embodied modifications intended to overcome surging when the cannon were fired. Whereas only 105 Sapphire-powered Mk.5s were built, production of the Mk.4 reached 365 in the U.K., and licence manufacture was undertaken in the Netherlands by Fokker and Aviolanda with some assembly of Dutch-manufactured components being undertaken in Belgium by Avions Fairey and SABCA.

GENERAL ARRANGEMENT DRAWING: *Fokker-built Hunter F.Mk.*6 (*N*-289) *of No.* 325 *Squadron of the Koninklijke Nederlandse Luchtmacht*

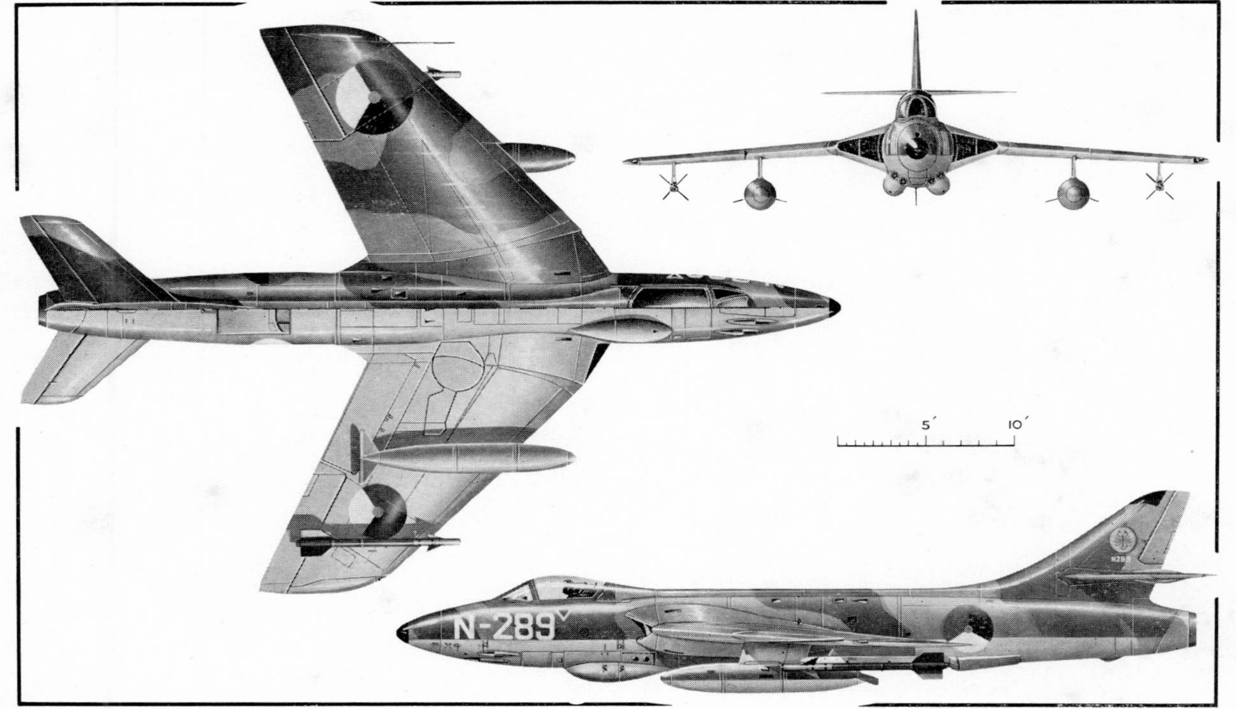
5´
10´
N-289

Initially, 396 Hunters were ordered but this total was later reduced to 381 aircraft, the larger proportion of which was completed to the later F.Mk.6 standards. Fokker produced 96 F.Mk.4s and 93 F.Mk.6s for the *Nederlandse Luchtmacht*, and 12 F.Mk.4s and 52 F.Mk.6s for the *Force Aérienne Belge*, and also supplied 128 sets of components for final assembly in Belgium, 92 of which were completed as or later converted to F.Mk.6s.

No Hunter F.Mk.4s now remain in service, but three export versions of this model continued in service in mid-1966, the F. Mks.50, 51 and 52. The designation F.Mk.50 was applied to 120 Hunter F.Mk.4s supplied in 1955–56 to the *Svenska Flygvapnet* and surviving in service with F 9 at Säve, Göteborg. F 9's Hunter F.Mk.50s, which serve under the designation J 34, have been adapted to carry two *Robot* 24 (Sidewinder) infra-red homing AAMs, and are expected to be phased out in favour of the J 35 Draken during 1967. The F.Mk.51 was the equivalent of the F. Mk.4 as supplied to the *Danske Flyvevåben*, 30 examples having been delivered to Denmark in 1956, and 16 of these remaining in service with No. 724 *Eskadrille* at the present time for the low-level intercept role. The designation F.Mk.52 was not applied to new production aircraft but to 16 ex-R.A.F. Hunter F.Mk.4s delivered to the *Fuerza Aérea del Peru* in 1956 and equipping *Escuadron* 14 of that service.

F.Mk.6: The final basic single-seat production version of the Hunter, the F.Mk.6, received the 10,050 lb.s.t. Avon 203 which substantially improved the fighter's load-carrying capability. Progressive modifications introduced during the production of this model included leading-edge wing extensions to counter high altitude pitch-up, gun blast deflectors to counter a tendency to pitch-down during high altitude firing, and a "flying tail". The prototype of the F.Mk.6, the P.1099, flew on January 22, 1954, the first production example following on March 25, 1955, and in addition to those built under licence in the Netherlands and Belgium, 415 were built in the U.K. Of these, 15 were supplied to Iraq, 12 to Jordan and five to the Lebanon, the survivors still serving the respective air arms to which they were delivered. The only other F.Mk.6s still in first-line service are those operated in the low-level intercept role by No. 325 Squadron of the *Nederlandse Luchtmacht*, and which is expected to retain its present equipment until at least 1968. No. 325 Squadron's Hunter F.Mk.6s have each been modified to carry two Sidewinder infra-red homing AAMs.

F.G.A.Mk.9: The principal current operational version of the Hunter in R.A.F. service is the F.G.A.Mk.9, a ground attack fighter conversion of the F.Mk.6 which serves with Nos. 1 and 54 Squadrons in No. 38 Group, Nos. 8, 43, and 208 Squadrons with Air Forces Middle East, and Nos. 20 and 28 Squadrons with the Far East Air Force. With an Avon 207 engine of 10,150 lb.s.t. in place of the Avon 203, a 10 ft. 6 in.-diameter ring-slot landing parachute in the tail, increased oxygen reserves for the pilot, and cutaway landing flaps to permit the attachment of 230 Imp. gal. (276 U.S. gal.) drop tanks, the Hunter F.G.A.Mk.9 carries two 500-lb. or 1,000-lb. bombs, four 100 Imp. gal. (120 U.S. gal.) napalm tanks, four packs of 37 2-in. rockets, or 48 3-in. rockets, in addition to four 30-mm. Aden cannon with 150 r.p.g. Twelve Hunter F.G.A.Mk.9s were supplied to Rhodesia in 1962–63, currently equipping No. 1 (Fighter) Squadron; five have been supplied to the Lebanon, and substantial numbers of equivalent conversions have been exported to other countries.

Essentially similar to the F.G.A.Mk.9 but retaining the Avon 203 engine, the Hunter F.Mk.56 equips three wings of the Indian Air Force. One hundred and sixty Hunters of this type were delivered to India between October 1957 and February 1961, and attrition has since been made up by the delivery of some additional refurbished Hunters brought up to F.Mk.56 standards. The F. Mk.57 is an equivalent conversion of ex-Belgian F.Mk.6 airframes, four examples having been supplied to Kuwait in 1964; the F. Mk.58 is the version for the *Schweizerische Flugwaffe* manufactured

(Right) A Hunter F.G.A.Mk.9 of No. 20 *Squadron, R.A.F., with* 230 *Imp. gal.* (276 *U.S. gal.) drop tanks and* 12 *HVARs, and (below, right) a Hunter F.R.Mk.*10 *of No.* 2 *Squadron, R.A.F., with* 100 *and* 230 *Imp. gal.* (120 *and* 276 *U.S. gal.) drop tanks.*

to an equivalent standard to the F.G.A. Mk.9 and currently equipping five *Flieger-Staffeln*, 100 aircraft having been purchased during 1958–60, and these being scheduled to remain in Swiss service well into the 'seventies, and the F.Mk.59 is the version for the Iraqi Air Force, 44 aircraft of this type having been delivered during 1964–66. Like the F.Mk.57s, the F.Mk.59s are conversions of ex-Belgian F.Mk.6 airframes.

F.R.Mk.10: The F.R.Mk.10 reconnaissance fighter, which serves with Nos. 2 and 4 Squadrons of the R.A.F.'s 2nd Tactical Air Force, has all the features of the F.G.A.Mk.9, including the Avon 207 and tail parachute, and is a further conversion of the F.Mk.6. The first F.R.Mk.10 flew on November 7, 1958, and while retaining normal cannon armament, this version has one forward-facing and two oblique cameras in the nose. Four similar conversions have been supplied to the Iraqi Air Force.

Trainers: Numerous training variants of the Hunter have been evolved, most of these being side-by-side two-seaters. An exception is, however, the G.A.Mk.11 single-seat advanced ground attack trainer converted from the F.Mk.4 for the Royal Navy, with guns and gunsight removed, comprehensive wing store wiring for a variety of weapons loads, an airfield arrester hook, and TACAN equipment. The first two-seat Hunter, the P.1101, flew on July 8, 1955, this being basically an F.Mk.4 with a new front fuselage. This was subsequently produced as the T.Mk.7 for the R.A.F.

and T.Mk.8 for the Royal Navy. The T.Mk.8B and 8C were two-seat conversions of F.Mk.4 airframes with different equipment, and export versions of the T.Mk.7 were the T.Mk.53, two examples of which were supplied to the *Danske Flyvevåben*, and the T.Mk.62, one example of which was delivered to the *Fuerza Aérea del Peru.*

Trainer Hunters using the more powerful Avon 203 or 207 were the T.Mk.66, 22 examples of which have been delivered to the Indian Air Force and two to the Royal Saudi Air Force; the T.Mk.66B, the two examples of which supplied to Jordan differing from the basic T.Mk.66 only in having the Avon 203 replaced by the Avon 207; the T.Mk.67, of which two have been delivered to Kuwait, and the T.Mk.69 for the Lebanon and Iraq, which countries have received two and six examples respectively.

Power Plant: *One Rolls-Royce RA.*28 *Avon Mk.*207 *turbojet rated at* 10,150 *lb.s.t.*
Performance: *Max. speed,* 715 *m.p.h. at sea level* (Mach 0.938), 627 *m.p.h. at* 36,000 *ft.* (*Mach* 0.95)*; range cruise,* 515 *m.p.h. at* 30,000 *ft.; tactical radius* (clean), 245 *mls. at* 30,000 *ft.,* (*with two* 1,000-*lb. bombs and two* 100 *Imp gal./*120 *U.S. gal. drop tanks*) 219 *mls. at* 1,000 *ft.,* 350 *mls. at* 39,000 *ft.; max. range* (*with two* 100 *Imp. gal./*120 *U.S. gal. and two* 230 *Imp. gal./*276 *U.S. gal. drop tanks*), 1,854 *mls.; initial climb* (*clean*), 17,200 *ft./min.; time to* 10,000 *ft.,* 2.25 *min., to* 20,000 *ft.,* 3 *min., to* 40,000 *ft.,* 5.25 *min.; absolute ceiling,* 53,400 *ft.*
Weights: *Empty,* 14,400 *lb.; loaded* (*clean*), 17,750 *lb.; max.,* 24,600 *lb.*
Dimensions: *Span,* 33 *ft.* 8 *in.; length,* 45 *ft.* 10½ *in.; height,* 13 *ft.* 1¾ *in.; wing area,* 349 *sq. ft.*
Note: *Specification relates to F.G.A.Mk.*9.

HAWKER SIDDELEY GNAT

One of the major surprises of the aerial fighting which formed part of the 23-day conflict between India and Pakistan in September 1965 was the operational success claimed by the Indian authorities for the Gnat single-seat lightweight fighter which has been manufactured under licence by Hindustan Aeronautics (HAL) since 1960. Indeed, such was the success of this diminutive warplane in combat that the production phase-out that had begun in the summer of 1965, and had been scheduled for completion by early 1966, was stopped, production fully reinstated, and preparations initiated for the establishment of addition Gnat squadrons. Air Chief Marshal Arjan Singh, the Indian Chief of Air Staff, subsequently stated that the Gnat proved capable of out-fighting both the F-86F Sabre and the F-104A Starfighter by which it was opposed during the conflict, and was particularly effective in air-to-air fighting at lower altitudes. The manoeuvrability of the Gnat enabled it to evade Sidewinder AAMs launched against it, and because of its small size, Pakistani pilots found the Gnat difficult to see and even more difficult to hit.

The Gnat fighter, designed by Folland Aircraft before the company's absorption by Hawker Siddeley, was flown as a prototype on July 18, 1955 with a 3,285 lb.s.t. Orpheus B.Or.1 turbojet. In the following month a contract was placed by the British Ministry of Supply for six trials aircraft, and the first of these flew on May 26, 1956. Three months later, the Indian government acquired a manufacturing licence for the Gnat, the agreement including the supply of 25 complete aircraft and 15 sets of components for Indian assembly. The Gnat was cleared for I.A.F. squadron service in mid-1959, and the first HAL-built aircraft of an initial order for 100 machines was delivered in 1962, manufacture of a second series commencing in 1965.

GENERAL ARRANGEMENT DRAWING: *A Gnat* (*GN*-101) *of the Finnish Havittäjälaivue* 21 *at Luonetjärvi*

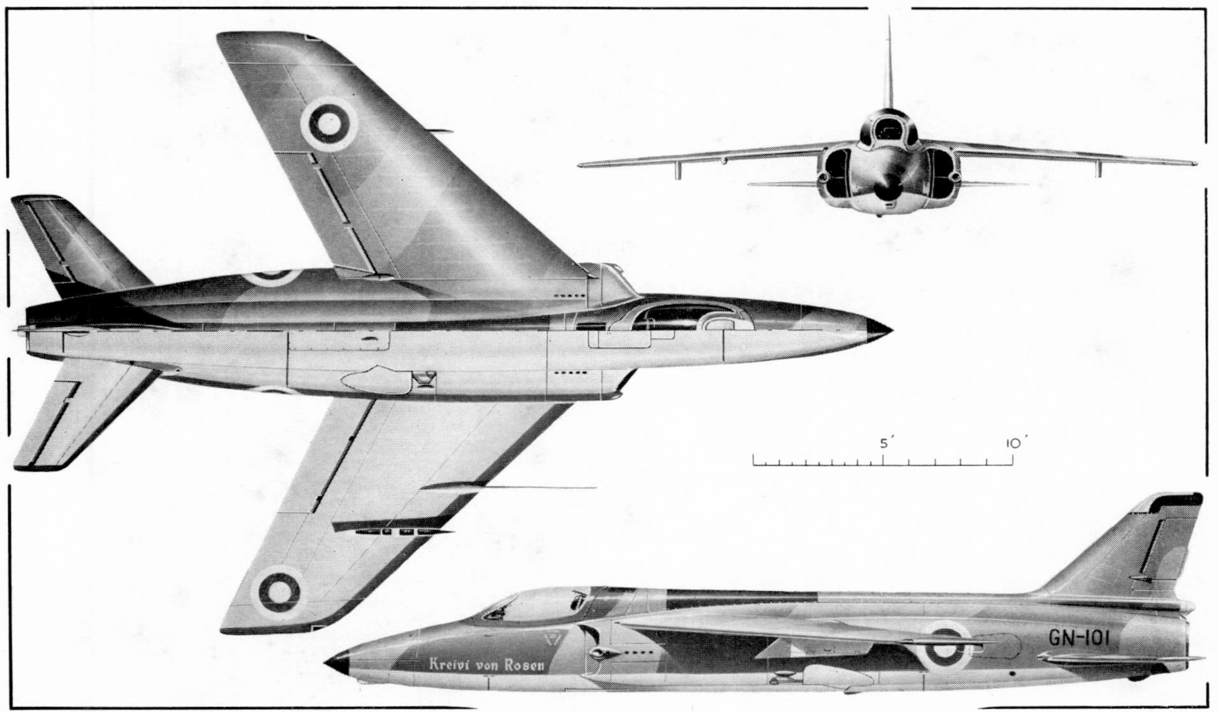
5´
10´
GN-101
Kreivi von Rosen

(Left) An Indian-built Gnat (IE1246) with undercarriage members partly extended to serve as air brakes. Production of the Gnat, which was being phased out by HAL in 1965, has been fully reinstated, partly as a result of its successful operation during the Indian-Pakistan conflict, and partly as a result of delays in the HF-24 production programme.

The second foreign purchaser of the Gnat was Finland which country placed an order for 12 aircraft for the *Ilmavoimat* in November 1956, two of these being equipped as reconnaissance fighters with a trio of 70-mm. Vinten cameras in a modified nose. The first two Gnats were delivered to the *Ilmavoimat* on July 30, 1958, but one was destroyed shortly afterwards as the result of an hydraulic failure, and one additional aircraft was supplied as a replacement. The Gnat currently equips HävLv 21 at Luonetjärvi. Two other Gnats were acquired for evaluation by the Yugoslav Air Force.

The Gnat fighter has a built-in armament of two 30-mm. Aden cannon with 115 r.p.g., and two underwing pylons can each carry a 500-lb. bomb or six 3-in. rockets. The fuel system comprises nine interconnected fuselage tanks with a total capacity of 200 Imp. gal. (240 U.S. gal.), and this may be supplemented by two 66 Imp. gal. (79 U.S. gal.) drop tanks. Avionic equipment is simple, and comprises 44-channel VHF and single-channel standby, a radio compass, IFF, radar ranging which feeds appropriate information into the gyro gunsight, and a combat camera. All systems are simple and primarily mechanical, the hydraulically-operated undercarriage may be partly extended to serve as air brakes, and the aircraft is stressed to withstand 12 *g*.

Power Plant: *One Bristol Siddeley Orpheus* 701 *turbojet rated at* 4,700 *lb.s.t.*
Performance: *Max. speed (clean)*, 695 *m.p.h. at* 20,000 *ft.*, 647 *m.p.h. at* 36,000 *ft. (Mach* 0.98*); range cruise*, 400 *m.p.h.; tactical radius (with two* 66 *Imp. gal./*79 *U.S. gal. drop tanks)*, 500 *mls.; max. climb rate*, 20,000 *ft./min.; time to* 45,000 *ft.*, 5.25 *min.; service ceiling*, 50,000 *ft.*
Weights: *Loaded (clean)*, 6,650 *lb.; max. loaded*, 8,885 *lb.*
Dimensions: *Span*, 22 *ft.* 2 *in.; length*, 29 *ft.* 9 *in.; height*, 8 *ft.* 10 *in.; wing area*, 136.6 *sq. ft.*

HAWKER SIDDELEY P.1127 (KESTREL)

The world's first strike and reconnaissance fighter capable of vertical take-off and landing, the P.1127 is expected to enter R.A.F. service in 1969 as a successor to the Hunter F.G.A.Mk.9. Project design of the P.1127 was initiated as a private venture in 1957, and contracts were subsequently placed for six prototypes, the first of these, powered by an early Pegasus vectored-thrust engine developing 11,300 lb.s.t., rising vertically for the first time on October 21, 1960 and effecting its first horizontal take-off and conventional flight on March 13, 1961. The prototypes embodied progressively uprated versions of the Pegasus engine and various aerodynamic changes, and these were followed by nine aircraft to equip a British-U.S.-German evaluation squadron, the first of these flying on March 7, 1964.

The version of the P.1127 for the tripartite trials squadron, which existed from October 15, 1964 until November 30, 1965, was known as the Kestrel F.(G.A.)Mk. 1, and at the conclusion of the trials six of the aircraft were shipped to the U.S.A. where they are now undergoing service evaluation by the U.S. services, four at Edwards AFB and two at Langley as the XV-6A. The tripartite evaluation P.1127 is powered by the BS.53 Pegasus B.Pg.5 vectored-thrust turbofan rated at 15,200 lb.s.t., providing for vertical take-off at an aircraft gross weight of 12,400 lb., and a maximum short take-off gross weight of 15,500 lb. Cruising at Mach 0.85 (645 m.p.h. at sea level) with a dash speed of Mach 0.87, it has a limited flight duration of approximately 30 minutes at sea level with VTOL operation. The wing contains two hard

*(Below) The sixth tripartite trials P.*1127 *(XS*693*), first flown on November* 25, 1964, *seen operating from an unprepared grass surface at Bircham Newton during operation by the Tripartite Evaluation Squadron. During a three-and-a-half-month test programme undertaken in the U.S.A. in* 1966 *with six P.*1127*s a total of* 374 *sorties was flown.*

*(Above) Four P.*1127 *Kestrel F.(G.A.)Mk.*1 *V/STOL strike fighters during service with the tripartite trials squadron at West Raynham. The production version of the P.*1127 *for the R.A.F. will differ from the tripartite evaluation Kestrel in a number of respects as may be seen from the drawing on page* 59.

points each capable of mounting stores of up to 1,000 lb., a typical offensive load comprising two 500-lb. or 1,000-lb. bombs for STOL operation.

The initial R.A.F. version of the P.1127 will embody considerable redesign, and a contract for four additional aircraft was placed on February 17, 1965, these incorporating features of the production model. The R.A.F.'s P.1127 will feature an all-weather navigation and attack system, the Pegasus B.Pg.6 of 19,000 lb.s.t., and improved weapons capability of up to 4,000 lb. for STOL operation. The installation of the more powerful engine will be accompanied by an increase in internal fuel capacity, and two of the four wing hard points will be "wet" to permit a pair of 100 Imp. gal. (120 U.S. gal.) drop tanks to be carried. Overall dimensions will be marginally increased, and the wings will extend beyond the outrigger wheel fairings. It will be compatible with most ASMs, such as the Bullpup and Martel, and will possess a radius of action exceeding 200 miles at low altitude, but maximum level speed is not expected to be increased much above Mach 0.9 in level flight. The first P.1127 (R.A.F.) development aircraft was flown on August 31, 1966, with a Pegasus B.Pg.5. At least the last two of the six development aircraft will be completed to full production standard with the B.Pg.6 engine. The initial R.A.F. order calls for 60 P.1127s with the Pegasus B.Pg.6 engine, and this batch is expected to include a number of side-by-side two-seaters, and follow-up procurement of a second batch of 50 single-seaters is anticipated, although the version of the P.1127 to be covered by the follow-up order had not been finalised at the time of closing for press. However, it is possible that the second production batch will incorporate Pegasus engines with PCB (Plenum Chamber Burning) to provide a maximum thrust of the order of 23,000 lb.

Power Plant: *One Bristol Siddeley BS.*53 *Pegasus B.Pg.*5 *vectored-thrust turbofan rated at* 15,200 *lb.s.t.*
Performance: *Max. speed,* 660 *m.p.h. at sea level (Mach* 0.87*); max. cruise,* 645–630 *m.p.h. at* 1,000–5,000 *ft. (Mach* 0.85*); tactical radius (VTOL operation);* 150 *mls. at sea level, (STOL operation),* 220 *mls. at* 1,000 *ft.,* 350 *mls. at* 40,000 *ft.; initial climb,* 35,000* *ft./time to* 50,000 *ft.,* 4* *min.*
Weights: *Loaded (VTOL),* 12,400 *lb., (STOL),* 15,500 *lb.*
Dimensions: *Span,* 22 *ft.* 10 *in.; length,* 42 *ft.* 0 *in.; height,* 10 *ft.* 9 *in.; wing area,* 186 *sq. ft.*
*APPROXIMATE
Note: *Specification applies to tripartite evaluation model.*

GENERAL ARRANGEMENT DRAWING: *A P.*1127 *Kestrel F.(G.A.)Mk.*1 *(XS689) in the markings applied during its service with the Tripartite Trials Squadron at West Raynham.*

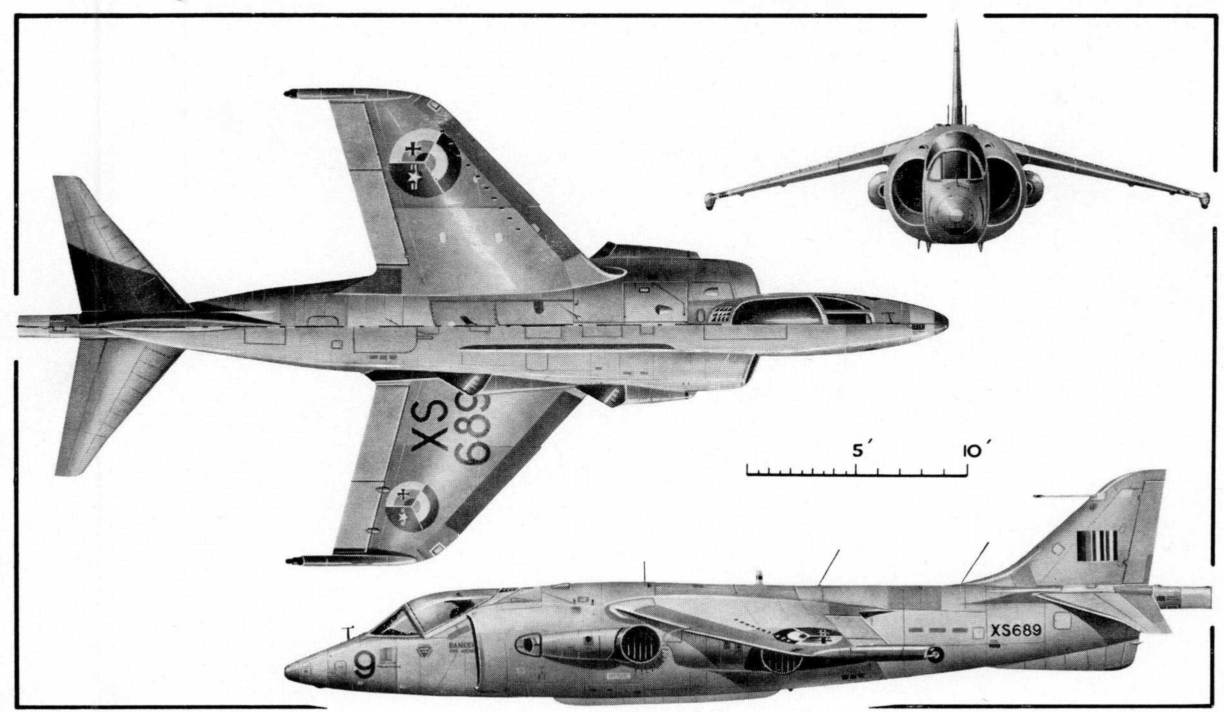
XS
689
5´
10´
XS689
9

(Above) The Sea Vixen F.A.W.Mk.2 is the definitive service version of this two-seat all-weather interceptor and strike fighter, offering a substantial increase in fuel capacity and improved intercept capability over the F.A.W.Mk.1.

HAWKER SIDDELEY SEA VIXEN

Operated by Nos. 890, 892, 893 and 899 Squadrons, the last-mentioned unit being the Headquarters Squadron at Yeovilton, and the others serving aboard the carriers *Ark Royal*, *Hermes* and *Centaur*, the Sea Vixen is currently the Royal Navy's standard shipboard two-seat all-weather fighter but will be progressively phased out of service in favour of the F-4K Phantom II from 1968. The first British aircraft designed from the outset as an integrated weapon system; the first British fighter to relinquish gun armament, and the first to attain operational status with AAMs, the Sea Vixen is the end product of a somewhat complex and protracted development which began with the issue of specification N.40/46 for an advanced shipboard all-weather fighter in 1946. Under its original designation of D.H.110, a non-navalised prototype flew on September 26, 1951, this being intended to meet the requirements of the later F.4/48 specification which called for a generally similar land-based aircraft, and the first fully-navalised machine, and, incidentally, the first production aircraft did not fly until five-and-a-half years later, on March 20, 1957.

The initial model received the designation Sea Vixen F.A.W. Mk.1, and the first squadron to equip with this type, No. 892, was commissioned on July 2, 1959, approximately 100 aircraft having been built when manufacture of the initial service version

GENERAL ARRANGEMENT DRAWING: *A Sea Vixen F.A.W.Mk.2 (XS582) of No. 766 Squadron, the Naval Air Fighter School at R.N.A.S. Yeovilton.*

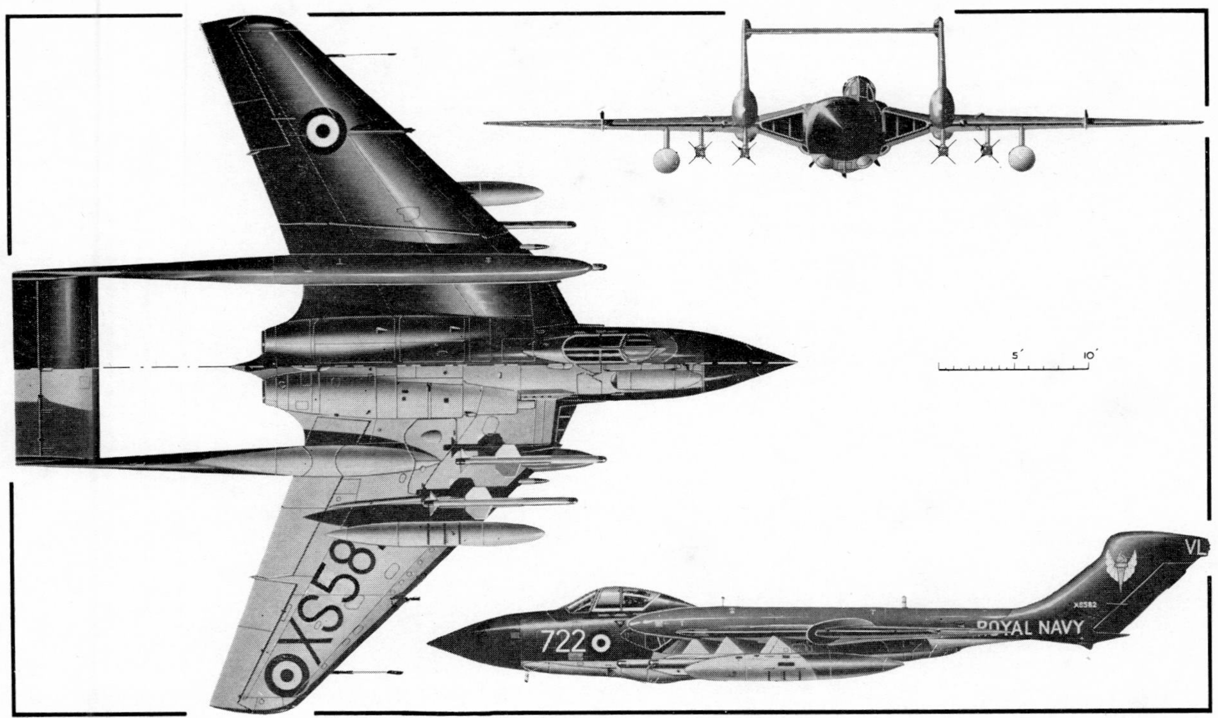
5´
10´
XS58
722
ROYAL NAVY
XS582
VL

(*Left*) *A Sea Vixen F.A.W.Mk.*2 (*XS-*582) *of No.* 766 *Squadron, the Naval Air Fighter School at Yeovilton.*

terminated in 1963. The F.A.W.Mk.1 had two retractable fuselage packs each housing 14 2-in. unguided rockets, and six underwing stores pylons, the four inboard pylons carrying a variety of weapons ranging from Firestreak infra-red homing AAMs or Bullpup-A ASMs to 500-lb. bombs, packs of 24 2-in. rockets or clusters of six 3-in. rockets, the two outboard pylons normally carrying two 150 Imp. gal. (180 U.S. gal.) fuel tanks. Considerable internal fuel tankage was provided in the wings and between the intake ducts, and provision for flight refuelling was standard, a probe being mounted in the port wing. The two crew members were seated side-by-side in Martin-Baker 4DS seats, that of the navigator being situated on a lower level than that of the pilot, and equipment included a Ferranti pilot attack sight, TACAN and LABS.

The 92nd Sea Vixen F.A.W.Mk.1 was modified on the production line late in 1962 as a prototype for the definitive F.A.W.Mk.2 which is now the standard service model. Retaining the 11,250 lb.st. Avon 208 engines of the F.A.W.Mk.1 version, the Sea Vixen F.A.W.Mk.2 differs externally from its predecessor primarily in having tail booms of deeper section which are carried over and project well forward of the wing leading edges, their capacity being employed primarily to boost internal fuel tankage. Up-dated avionics provide for collision-course intercept tactics with Red Top (Firestreak Mk.4) AAMs, and the same variety of external stores as carried by the F.A.W.Mk.1 may be carried by the later model as alternatives to the quartet of Red Top AAMs. The first production Sea Vixen F.A.W.Mk.2 was delivered in 1963, and this model first entered service with No. 899 Squadron early in 1964, late production F.A.W.Mk.1s being progressively up-dated to F.A.W.Mk.2 standard to supplement the limited new production of this fighter.

Power Plants: *Two Rolls-Royce RA.*24 *Avon Mk.*208 *turbojets each rated at* 11,250 *lb.s.t.*
Performance: *Max. speed,* 645* *m.p.h. at* 10,000 *ft.* (*Mach* 0.92), 610* *m.p.h. at* 40,000 *ft.; range cruise,* 495–530* *m.p.h. at* 36,000–40,000 *ft.* (*Mach* 0.75–0.8)*; range* (*with two* 150 *Imp. gal./*180 *U.S. gal. drop tanks*), 800* *mls.; time to* 40,000 *ft.,* 6–7* *min.; service ceiling,* 48,000* *ft.*
Weights: *Loaded,* 38,000–40,000* *lb.*
Dimensions: *Span,* 50 *ft.* 0 *in.; length,* 55 *ft.* 7 *in.; height,* 10 *ft.* 9 *in.; wing area,* 648 *sq. ft.*
*APPROXIMATE

LING-TEMCO-VOUGHT F-8 CRUSADER

Now serving primarily with U.S. Navy Fighter Squadrons operating from the five *Essex* class vessels rated as attack carriers, having been largely supplanted in U.S. Marine Corps first-line squadrons by the F-4B Phantom II, the F-8 Crusader single-seat shipboard limited all-weather interceptor, which, at the peak of its deployment, equipped 36 squadrons, is currently the subject of a major remanufacturing programme designed to modernise and extend the service life of its two final production variants, the F-8D and F-8E. The first shipboard combat aircraft capable of attaining speeds in excess of Mach 1.0 in level flight, the Crusader was first projected in 1952, and the prototype, originally designated XF8U-1, flew on March 25, 1955. The most unusual feature of the Crusader was its variable-incidence wing which, mounted on top of a slab-sided fuselage, was arranged to hinge upwards around the rear spar by 7°, providing the pilot with good forward visibility for deck landing despite a high angle of attack. The ailerons, a section of the flaps, and the wing leading edges were all drooped simultaneously with the increase in wing incidence, thus further increasing effective camber.

The initial production model, the F-8A, made its début on March 21, 1957, power being provided by a J57-P-12 in the first few dozen aircraft, and by the J57-P-4A in subsequent machines. Internal fuel capacity was 1,400 U.S. gal. (1,165 Imp. gal.), the built-in armament of four 20-mm MK-12 cannon with 144 r.p.g. was backed by a fuselage rocket pack containing 32 2.75-in. rockets and later supplemented by a pair of AIM-9A Sidewinder AAMs, and at a normal loaded weight of 27,000 lb., maximum speed was Mach 1.67. A total of 318 F-8As had been manufactured by September 3, 1958 when production switched to the F-8B which differed from its predecessor only in having a limited all-weather intercept capability, and 130 examples had been delivered before, in 1959, production began of the F-8C. The prototype of the new model flew in December 1957, and the first production F-8C flew on August 20, 1958. Differing from the F-8B in having a J57-P-16 turbojet offering an increase in maximum afterburning thrust from 16,200 to 16,900 lb., the F-8C introduced twin ventral strakes beneath the rear fuselage and intakes above the tail cone for afterburner cooling. Limited to Mach 1.7 by stability characteristics, the F-8C nevertheless offered an improved climb rate, and the 187th and last example of this model was delivered on September 20, 1960. All three initial production versions of the Crusader interceptor have now been withdrawn from first-line service, the last F-8C unit re-equipping during 1966, remaining U.S. Navy Crusader-equipped squadrons operating the F-8D and -8E, and at mid-1966 there were 10 squadrons operating the former and 15 squadrons operating the latter.

F-8D: Embodying further improvements in the electronic equipment, plus installation of a "push-button" autopilot for a higher degree of automaticity in defensive sorties, the F-8D introduced the J57-P-20 engine developing 10,700 lb. s.t. dry and 18,000 lb. with afterburning, this permitting the gross weight to be raised from the normal clean figure of 27,550 lb. to a maximum of 32,000 lb. for shipboard operation, or 34,000 lb. for shore-based operation. The basic cannon armament was retained, but the ventral missile pack was deleted and provision for AIM-9 Sidewinder stowage on the fuselage sides was doubled to four AAMs. The F-8D first flew on February 16, 1960, and the last of 152 Crusaders of this type was completed in January 1962.

F-8E: The final production variant of the Crusader for the U.S. Navy and the first to introduce underwing hard points for external loads, the F-8E received APQ-94 search and fire control radar to provide improved all-weather intercept capability, the enlarged and slightly extended nose radome being surmounted by a separate infra-red seeker. At an early stage in F-8E production two under-

(*Above*) *An F-*8*E Crusader of VF-*51. *In mid-*1966, *when a re-manufacture programme for the F-*8*D and -*8*E was initiated,* 25 *squadrons were operating Crusader interceptors.*

wing attachment points were standardised, this change being accompanied by a hump on the wing centre section enclosing the electronic equipment demanded by AGM-12 Bullpup ASMs. The first production F-8E was flown in September 1961, production being terminated with the 286th aircraft in the summer of 1964.

In March 1966, initial funding was provided for multi-step plan for the remanufacture of more than 200 F-8D and F-8E Crusaders over a period of four years. The remanufacturing process involves the complete modernisation of the aircraft, including the introduction of a direct lift control system providing rapid and precise changes in aircraft altitude during carrier landing approaches by permitting the pilot to raise or lower the flap-ailerons as flaps without altering longitudinal trim. In addition, main undercarriage members similar to those of the A-7A Corsair II are being fitted, and new, strengthened wings will be introduced, all remanufactured F-8D and -8E models being completed to a similar standard and all having wing pylon hard points. The wing pylons can carry the full range of attack weapons up to a maximum of 5,000 lb., loads including 12 250-lb. bombs, eight 500-lb. bombs or four 1,000-lb. bombs plus eight Zuni rockets, or two AGM-12A or -12B Bullpup ASMs.

F-8E (FN): Successor to the Aquilon as standard shipboard interceptor with France's *Aéronavale*, the F-8E (FN) is a derivative of the basic F-8E embodying modifications to render it more suitable for operations from the carriers *Clémenceau* and *Foch*. Currently

GENERAL ARRANGEMENT DRAWING: *An F-*8*E* (*FN*) *Crusader of Flottille* 12*F of France's Aéronavale.*

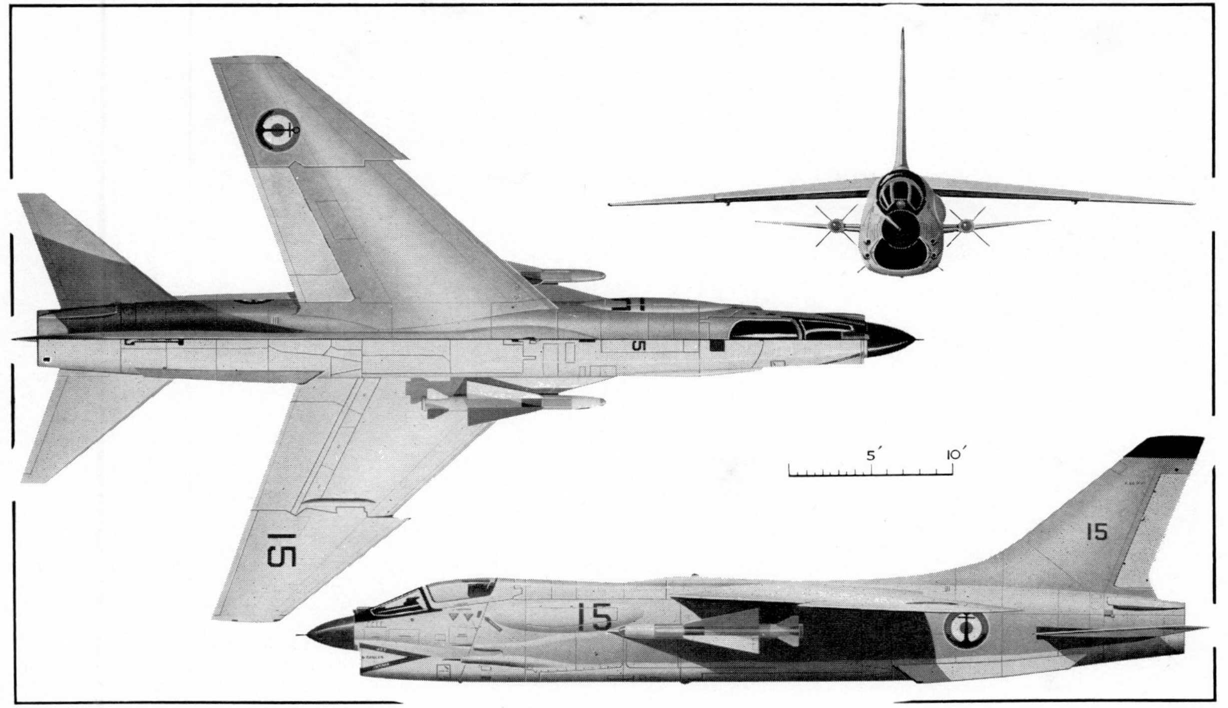
15
15
15
5´
10´

operated by *Flottille* 12F, which reformed at Lann-Bihoué to operate this type on October 15, 1964, and Flottille 14F which followed on March 1, 1965, the F-8E (FN) differs from the U.S. Navy F-8E in a number of respects. The principal changes are the chordwise separation of the drooping wing leading edges into two sections to increase camber; the introduction of flap blowing; double the aileron and flap deflection; a 2° reduction in wing incidence travel, and enlarged horizontal tail surfaces (the area being increased from 93.44 sq. ft. to 115.5 sq. ft.). The APQ-94 fire control radar has been replaced by APQ-104 for compatability with MATRA R-530 AAMs, a pair of which form the primary intercept armament on the French model. The built-in armament of four 20-mm. cannon is retained, and for the attack role up to 5,000 lb. of bombs or rockets may be carried externally. Overall performance is essentially similar to that of the basic F-8E, but the landing approach speed is some 17 m.p.h. lower. The first production F-8E (FN) was flown on June 26, 1964, and the last of 42 for the *Aéronavale* was delivered in January 1965.

Power Plant: *One Pratt & Whitney J57-P-20A turbojet rated at* 10,700 *lb.s.t. and* 18,000 *lb.s.t. with afterburning.*
Performance: *Max. speed* (*clean*), 1,120 *m.p.h. at* 40,000 *ft.* (*Mach* 1.7)*; range cruise* (*with four AIM-9A AAMs*), 560 *m.p.h. at* 36,000–40,000 *ft.; tactical radius* (*patrol mission*), 600* *mls.; max. unrefuelled range*, 1,300–1,400 *mls.; time to* 57,000 *ft.*, 6.5 *min.; max. ceiling*, 58,000 *ft.*
Weights: *Loaded* (*with four AAMs*), 28,000* *lb.; max. loaded* (*shipboard operation*), 32,000 *lb.*, (*shore-based operation*), 34,000 *lb.*
Dimensions: *Span*, 35 *ft.* 2 *in.; length*, 54 *ft.* 5¾ *in.; height*, 15 *ft.* 9 *in.; wing area*, 350* *sq. ft.*
*APPROXIMATE

LOCKHEED F-104 STARFIGHTER

During its career, the F-104 Starfighter has undergone the remarkable metamorphosis from a relatively simple day air superiority fighter to a complex all-weather strike and reconnaissance aircraft, and although the subject of controversy since the time of its début, it is unquestionably one of the most outstanding combat planes of its era. Its development initially paralleled that of the MiG-21, its design being engendered by an essentially similar requirement—a relatively light day interceptor in which all criteria were subordinated to flight performance. The first of two XF-104 prototypes flew on February 7, 1954, but major changes were incorporated in the YF-104A, 15 examples of which were ordered for evaluation and development, and the first production model, the F-104A, incorporated all the features successively introduced in these aircraft.

F-104A: Deliveries of the F-104A to the U.S.A.F.'s 83rd Fighter-Interceptor Wing began on January 26, 1958, but by the beginning of 1960 the type had been withdrawn from the U.S.A.F.'s active combat inventory as a result of its lack of all-weather capability which prevented its operation within the SAGE (Semi-Automatic Ground Environment) system, and of the 155 F-104As built, 24 were converted to QF-104 target drones, three became NF-104As for use by the Aerospace Research Pilot's School, 25 were transferred to the Chinese Nationalist Air Force, and 12 were passed to the Pakistan Air Force. Most of those remaining were passed to the Air National Guard, but early in 1963, as a result of the Cuban crisis, the F-104s were withdrawn from A.N.G. service and returned to the U.S.A.F.'s active inventory, subsequently serving with the 319th and 331st Fighter-Interceptor Squadrons, these currently being the only Starfighters serving with the Air Defence Command.

Powered by a J79-GE-3B turbojet rated at 9,600 lb.s.t. boosted to 14,800 lb. with full afterburning, the F-104A has ASG-14TI fire control radar, and the pilot is equipped with a *downward*-firing ejector seat. Weights range from 11,660 lb. empty to 17,320 lb.

loaded in clean configuration, and armament comprises one 20-mm. M-61 Vulcan rotary cannon and a pair of AIM-9B Sidewinder infra-red homing AAMs. The Vulcan cannon was removed shortly after the F-104A's service début, the gun bay and ammunition tank space being employed to house auxiliary fuel, but in mid-1964, the threat of MiG-21s entering U.S. airspace, bringing with it the possibility of close-in air-to-air combat for which the Sidewinder AAM is not ideally suited, resulted in the Vulcan being reinstated. The Chinese Nationalist F-104As were phased out of service with the arrival of the first F-104Gs on Taiwan from December 8, 1963 onwards, and although the Pakistani F-104As were employed in the air superiority role during the Indian–Pakistan conflict of September 1965, since the withdrawal of U.S. aid it is unlikely that any fighters of this type are still included in Pakistan's first-line aircraft inventory. A tandem two-seat version of the F-104A, the F-104B first flown on February 7, 1957, was produced for transition training, but only 26 aircraft of this type were manufactured.

F-104C: The first multi-mission version of the basic Starfighter design, the F-104C introduced blown flaps which markedly improved low-speed handling characteristics; was provided with a flight refuelling probe; embodied hard points to permit a range of underwing stores to be carried, and switched to the J79-GE-7A turbojet rated at 10,000 lb.s.t. and 15,800 lb. with afterburning. The first deliveries of the F-104C were made in October 1958, but only 77 aircraft of this model were built, these serving with the 479th Tactical Fighter Wing at George A.F.B., California. Twenty-five F-104C Starfighters from the 479th were deployed to Vietnam in April 1965 to counter the threat posed by MiG fighters. Fifteen were maintained on combat status at Danang, and the F-104Cs flew 2,269 combat sorties, mostly in the ground support role, before being withdrawn at the end of 1965, only to be returned to Vietnam in 1966 following the début of the MiG-21 in North Vietnamese service. A number of ex-T.A.C. F-104Cs are now being refurbished for supply to Jordan's Royal Arab Air Force.

Retaining the M-61 Vulcan rotary cannon and ASG-14 fire control system, the F-104C can carry a pair of 750-lb. or 1,000-lb. bombs or two LAU-3/A pods each housing 19 2.75-in. rockets on underwing pylons with two 160 U.S. gal. (141.5 Imp. gal.) wingtip tanks and a 225 U.S. gal. (187 Imp. gal.) fuselage centreline tank. Normal internal fuel capacity is 896 U.S. gal. (746 Imp. gal.), and for the intercept role a maximum of four AIM-9B Sidewinder AAMs may be carried. A tandem two-seat operational training version of the F-104C was designated F-104D, and 22 examples

(Right) An F-104G Starfighter of the Danske Flyvevåben. Denmark has received 26 F-104Gs which are operated by the 723 and 726 Eskadrillerne in the all-weather intercept role.

were built, and the generally similar F-104F was a tandem two-seat version manufactured specifically for the *Luftwaffe* which acquired 30 aircraft of this type. The equipment of the F-104F is generally similar to that of the single-seat F-104G but the M-61 Vulcan cannon and NASARR system are not installed.

F-104G: Although externally similar to its predecessors, the F-104G, which was the subject of a multi-nation manufacturing programme completed in 1965, embodies extensive structural re-design, the entire airframe having been re-stressed to meet strike fighter strength requirements. Furthermore, it is equipped with the highly sophisticated NASARR (North American Search and Ranging Radar) F-15A-41B optimized in air-to-air and air-to-ground modes to provide airborne target detection and tracking, guidance data, terrain avoidance, contour mapping for navigation, ground mapping for all-weather bombing, and ranging information for bombing computation in visual bombing modes.

European manufacture by a consortium of German, Belgian, Dutch and Italian companies produced 977 F-104Gs, a further 110 being built by Canadair for supply under the Military Assistance Program, and approximately 180 have been built by the parent company. The F-104G is employed in largest numbers by the *Luftwaffe* which has received 600 aircraft of this type, these equipping two interceptor *Geschwader*, JG 71 at Wittmundhaven and JG 74 at Neuburg; five strike fighter *Geschwader*, Jabo G 31 at Norvenich, Jabo G 32 at Lechfeld, Jabo G 33 at Buchel, Jabo G 34 at Memmingen, and Jabo G 36 at Rheine, and two tactical reconnaissance *Geschwader*, Aufkl G 51 at Ingolstadt and Aufkl G 52 at Leck. A further 100 F-104Gs have been delivered to Germany's *Marineflieger*, these equipping *Marinefliegergeschwader* 1 and 2 at Eggebeck and Schleswig-Jagel. The Netherlands has received 120 F-104Gs, these equipping two fighter-bomber squadrons, Nos. 311 and 312 at Volkel, two interceptor squadrons, Nos. 322 and 323 at Leeuwarden, and one tactical reconnaissance squadron, No. 306. Belgium has been the recipient of 100 F-104Gs, these equipping two fighter-bomber *Escadrilles*, Nos. 23 and 31 at Kleine Brogel, and two interceptor *Escadrilles*, Nos. 349 and 350 at Beauvechain. Italy's *Aeronautica Militare* has received 125 F-104Gs which equip the 9° and 10° *Gruppi* for the intercept role, the 101° and 102° *Gruppi* serving in the fighter-bomber role, as does also the 154° *Gruppo*, and the tactical reconnaissance 103° *Gruppo*. The 723 and 726 *Eskadrillerne* of the *Danske Flyvevåben* are both F-104G-equipped, Denmark having received 26 aircraft of this type; Norway's Nr. 331 *Skvadron* operates the F-104G from Bodø; Spain's *Ejercito del Aire* has one F-104G unit, *Escuadron* 161 at Torrejon, and Greece, Turkey, and Nationalist China each have two F-104G-equipped squadrons for the intercept role, the last-mentioned country also possessing one F-104G squadron for tactical reconnaissance.

The F-104G retains the M-61 Vulcan rotary cannon, and for the intercept role missile armament normally comprises two or four AIM-9B Sidewinder AAMs, the NASARR giving radar search, acquisition and automatic tracking for lead-collision or lead-pursuit attack. Up to 4,000 lb of ordnance may be carried externally, attack stores including two AGM-12A Bullpup ASMs, three 700-lb. MLU-10B land-mines, three 1,000-lb. Mk.83 bombs, one 2,000-lb. Mk.84 and two Mk.83 bombs, or a 2,000-lb. nuclear store. The F-104G's bombing computer ties in with the inertial navigator, air data computer and NASARR systems for level release, over-the-shoulder, dive-toss and LABS weapons delivery.

The TF-104G is a tandem two-seater with an essentially similar airframe to the F-104G single-seater and carrying full NASARR equipment, the autopilot and M-61 cannon being deleted, and the electronics and fuel tanks relocated to provide space for the second cockpit.

CF-104: A Canadian-built version of the F-104G, the CF-104 has NASARR R-24A optimised in the air-to-ground mode. The M-61

GENERAL ARRANGEMENT DRAWING: *An F-104G Starfighter (D-8053) of No. 306 Squadron of the Koninklijke Nederlandse Luchtmacht.*

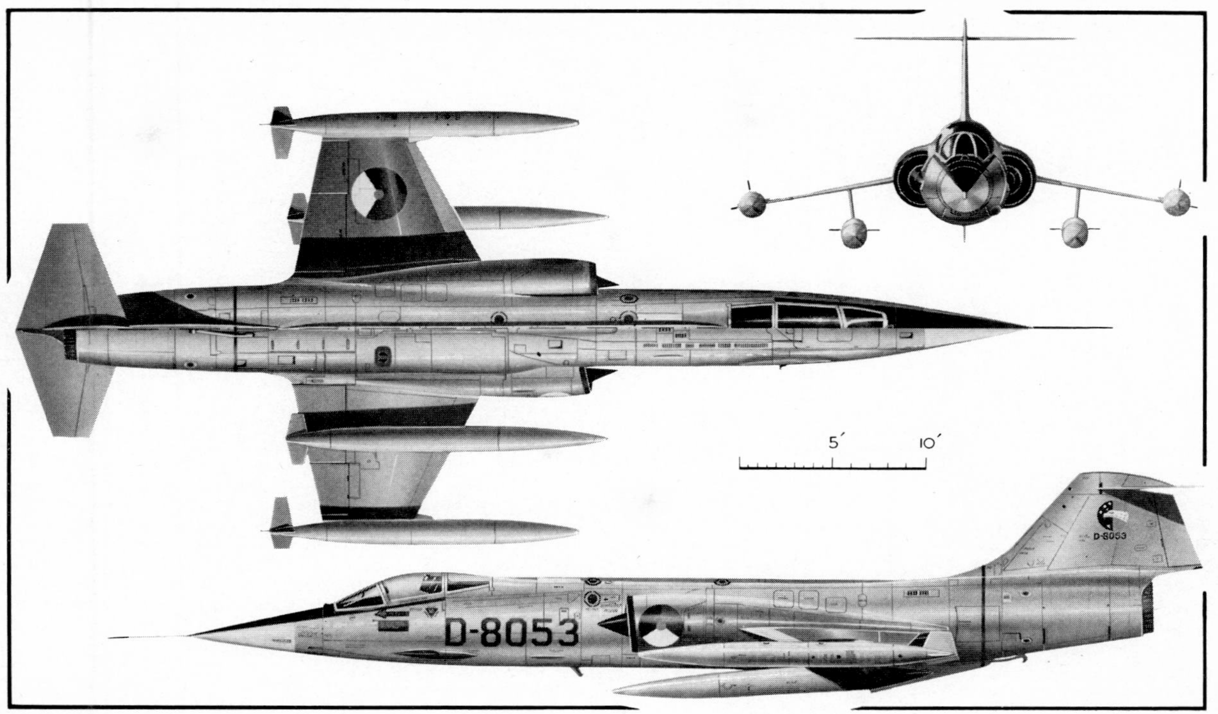
5´
10´
D-8053
D-8053

(*Above*) *A TF-104G Starfighter used by the Koninklijke Nederlandse Luchmacht for weapons trials.*

Vulcan cannon is not installed, rendering unnecessary the lead angle computer, only a simple fixed-reticle sight being fitted, and fuel tanks mounted in the space occupied in the F-104G by the M-61 cannon, its ejector case and ammunition compartments, raise total internal fuel capacity by 122 U.S. gal. (101.5 Imp. gal.). The undercarriage has larger tyres and longer-stroke liquid springs, and performance of the CF-104 is generally similar to that of the F-104G, but empty weight is 13,900 lb., and clean and maximum loaded weights are 21,005 and 28,891 lb. Two hundred CF-104s were manufactured by Canadair for the R.C.A.F., the first flying on May 26, 1961, and this type serves with the No. 1 Air Division in Europe. The CF-104D is a Lockheed-built tandem two-seat trainer generally similar to the TF-104G, and 38 aircraft of this type have been supplied to the R.C.A.F.

F-104J: A licence-manufactured version of the Starfighter basically similar to the F-104G with NASARR F-15J-31 optimized in the air-to-air mode, the F-104J is manufactured for the J.A.S.D.F. by Mitsubishi, and currently equips seven squadrons. Initial contracts for 180 F-104J Starfighters were supplemented during 1966 by an order for a further 30 aircraft for 1967 delivery. The first three F-104Js were built and tested by the parent company which supplied knock-down assemblies for a further 29 aircraft, subsequent aircraft being manufactured completely in Japan. The F-104J has been given the popular name *Eiko* (Glory) in Japan, and the J.A.S.D.F. has also received 20 examples of the tandem two-seat F-104DJ.

F-104S: So far ordered only by Italy's *Aeronautica Militare*, the F-104S is, unlike the F-104G, intended primarily for the all-weather intercept role with AIM-7E Sparrow semi-active radar-homing AAMs and an advanced version of the NASARR system. Powered by a J79-J1Q turbojet providing an afterburning thrust of 17,900 lb., the F-104S is being manufactured under license in Italy by Fiat, the turbojet being assembled by Alfa Romeo, and the NASARR system by FIAR (Fabbrica Italiana Apparechi Radio), and 165 aircraft of this type have been ordered for 1968–70 delivery. By comparison with the F-104G, the F-104S will offer a 16–26 per cent reduction in take-off distance, a 37 per cent improvement in transonic acceleration, a four per cent increase in combat ceiling, a 39–46 per cent reduction in time to intercept, and a 7–12 per cent increase in strike radius. A new flap system will increase manoeuvrability, and placard speed will be raised from the Mach 2.0 limitation of the F-104G to Mach 2.2.

Power Plant: *One General Electric J79-GE-11A turbojet rated at* 10,000 *lb.s.t. and* 15,800 *lb.s.t. with afterburning.*
Performance: *Max. speed*, 1,320 *m.p.h. at* 40,000 *ft.* (*Mach* 2.0), 915 *m.p.h. at* 1,000 *ft.* (*Mach* 1.2)*; tactical radius* (*with two* 120 *U.S. gal./*100 *Imp. gal. and two* 200 *U.S. gal./*162 *Imp. gal. drop tanks*), 690 *mls. at* 610 *m.p.h.* (*Mach* 0.92)*; max ferry range*, 1,988 *mls.; initial climb* (*clean*), 50,000 *ft./min.; time to* 35,000 *ft.*, 1.5 *min.; combat ceiling*, 55,000 *ft.*
Weights: *Empty*, 14,082 *lb.; loaded* (*clean*), 19,841 *lb.; max.*, 28,779 *lb.*
Dimensions: *Span*, 21 *ft.* 11 *in.; length*, 54 *ft.* 9 *in.; height*, 13 *ft.* 6 *in.; wing area*, 196.1 *sq. ft.*
Note: *Specification is applicable to F-104G.*

McDONNELL F-4 PHANTOM II

Widely considered to be the truly outstanding combat aircraft of the present decade and second to none in versatility, the Phantom II, with deliveries approaching 1,700 by mid-1966, is fast becoming the most important warplane in the active inventories of the U.S. Navy, the U.S.A.F., and the U.S. Marine Corps; a position which, once gained, it is likely to retain well into the 'seventies. Conceived to meet a U.S. Navy requirement which, through a succession of changes, finally placed emphasis on all-weather intercept capability with attack as a secondary role, the Phantom II made its début on May 27, 1958 when the first of 23 pre-production examples was flown. The pre-production aircraft and the first 24 production Phantom IIs received the designation F-4A, and 26 of these fulfilled research and development tasks. The remaining 21 F-4As, the first of which was delivered to the U.S. Navy on December 29, 1960, were issued to VF-101 and -121 for training purposes, a role in which they still perform.

F-4B: Equipping two-thirds of the U.S. Navy's 30 Fleet Fighter Squadrons and a similar proportion of the U.S. Marine Corps' 15 Fighter and Fighter-Attack Squadrons by mid-1966, when 29 squadrons were operating this type, the F-4B began to enter the U.S. Navy's inventory in mid-1961, the 500th example being delivered on April 9, 1965, and this model remained in production until supplanted by the F-4J in 1966. Whereas the F-4A was powered by the J79-GE-2 or -2A rated at 10,350 lb.s.t. and 16,150 lb. with afterburning, the F-4B standardised on the J79-GE-8 rated at 10,900 lb.s.t. and 17,000 lb. with afterburning, the improved power plant necessitating an enlarged inlet system and revised intake ramp geometry.

Primarily a shipboard interceptor, the F-4B is crewed by a pilot and radar intercept officer, and for target acquisition and tracking, and the generation of steering information and signals for missile guidance during the attacking phase of an interception, a Westing-

(*Right*) *An F-4B Phantom II* (*Bu. No.* 150996) *of U.S. Marine Corps VMFA-*314. *The first version of the Phantom II to be manufactured in large numbers, the F-4B was serving with 29 U.S. Navy and U.S.M.C. squadrons by mid-*1966 *when it was being phased out of production in favour of the F-4J.*

(Above) An F-4B Phantom II (Bu. No. 150419) *of VF*-143, *one of* 29 *U.S. Navy and U.S. Marine Corps squadrons operating this first major production variant of the aircraft by mid*-1966. *The F-4B is seen here carrying a* 600 *U.S. gal. centreline drop tank, two AIM-7 Sparrow III semi-active radar homing AAMs beneath the fuselage, and two AIM-9 Sidewinder infra-red homing AAMs on underwing pylons. The infra-red sensor beneath the nose, a characteristic feature of the F-4B and its U.S.A.F. equivalent, the F-4C, has been deleted from current production Phantom IIs owing to the mixed success that it has enjoyed in service.*

house APQ-72 (Aero 1A) fire control system with a 32-inch dish antenna is installed in the nose. The APQ-72, which has a ground mapping mode, has a subsidiary AAA-4 infra-red sensor mounted beneath the radome to facilitate detection and tracking of airborne targets. For the intercept task armament comprises up to six AIM-7E Sparrow III semi-active radar homing AAMs or a mix of four Sparrow IIIs and four AIM-9B or -9D Sidewinder 1A or 1C infra-red homers. For its secondary tasks of attack and battle zone interdiction, the F-4B has an AJB-3A bombing system which provides for direct, loft, and timed or instantaneous over-the-shoulder weapons release, and up to 16,000 lb. of stores may be carried externally on five attachments beneath the wings and fuselage. Offensive loads may include 15 Mk.83 1,000-lb. general-purpose bombs, 18 M-117 750-lb. bombs, 24 Mk.82 500-lb. bombs, 15 MLU-10/B 680-lb. land mines, four AGM-12B or -12C Bullpup ASMs, 15 LAU-3A or 13 LAU-10A rocket launchers, or various combinations of these weapons.

Two 315 U.S. gal. (262 Imp. gal.) integral wing tanks combine with six interlinked fuselage tanks to provide a total internal fuel capacity of 2,000 U.S. gal. (1,665 Imp. gal.), and this may be supplemented by a 600 U.S. gal. (500 Imp. gal.) centreline drop tank and two 370 U.S. gal. (308 Imp. gal.) drop tanks to provide an unrefuelled ferry range of 2,300 miles which may be extended with one refuelling to 3,600 miles. Probe-and-drogue flight refuelling is employed, an hydraulically-operated probe extending from the starboard side of the fuselage, fuel transfer rate being up to 1,700 U.S. gal. (1,415 Imp. gal.) per minute. With normal intercept armament, the F-4B can accelerate from Mach 0.92 to Mach 2.05 in 3.5 min. A tactical reconnaissance equivalent to the F-4B, the RF-4B for the U.S. Marine Corps, is described and illustrated on pages 100–103, Vol. II.

F-4C: The F-4C version of the Phantom II, which joined the U.S.A.F.'s strike force in Vietnam in June 1965, now equips the 23 squadrons of the 8th, 12th, 15th, 33rd, 81st and 366th Tactical Fighter Wings, 583 examples of this version of the Phantom II having been delivered to the U.S.A.F. when the last reached the 15th Tactical Fighter Wing on May 4, 1966. Whereas the U.S. Navy's F-4B is primarily an interceptor, the U.S.A.F.'s F-4C combines the air superiority role with broad interdiction and close support capabilities, and U.S.A.F. requirements dictated a number of changes to the basic aircraft, the first production F-4C flying on May 27, 1963, and the first two examples being delivered to the U.S.A.F. in the following November. However, prior to these events, a number of standard U.S. Navy F-4Bs were loaned to the Tactical Air Command for preliminary training purposes, these being delivered to the 836th Air Division at MacDill A.F.B., Florida.

GENERAL ARRANGEMENT DRAWING: *An F-4B Phantom II (Bu. No.* 148396) *of VF*-102 *as flown form the U.S.S. Enterprise. VF*-102 *is home-based at N.A.S. Oceana, and during* 1966 *was operating its F-4Bs from the U.S.S. America in the Mediterranean.*

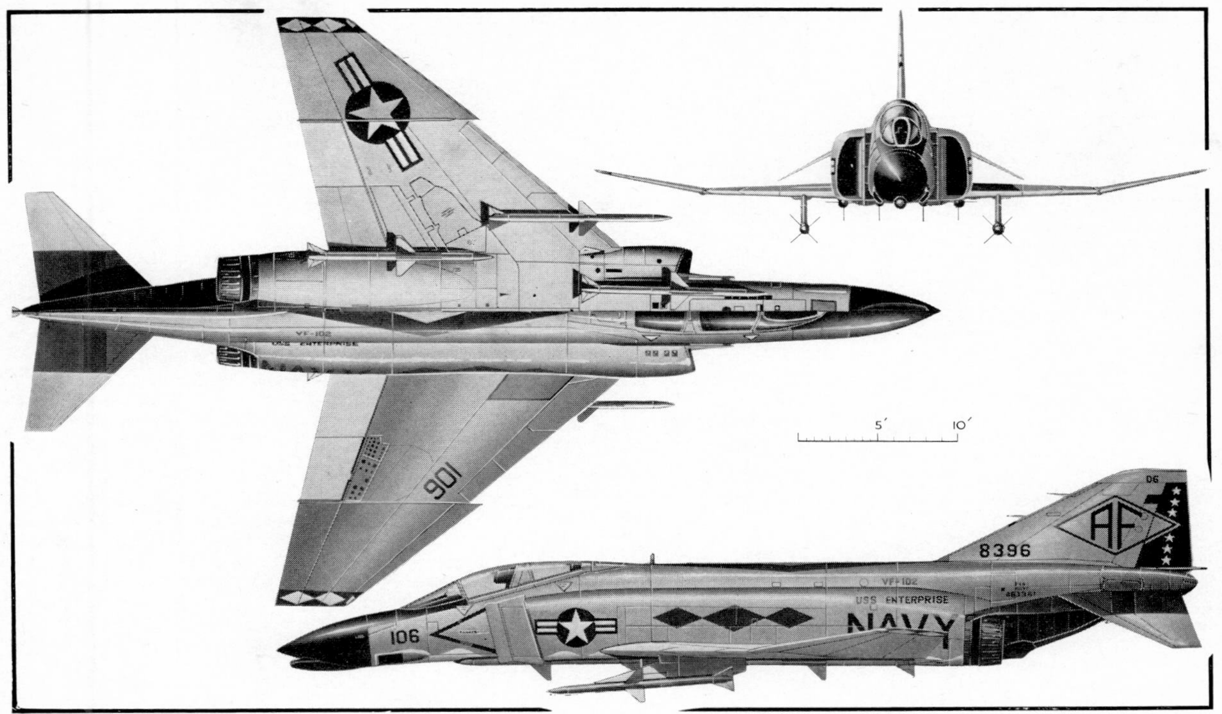
VF-102
USS ENTERPRISE
106
5´
10´
D6
AF
8396
VF-102
USS ENTERPRISE
NAVY
106

(*Left*) *The first F-4J Phantom II* (*Bu. No.*153072) *which began flight trials in May* 1966. *To be delivered to both U.S. Navy and U.S.M.C. squadrons, the F-4J has a Westinghouse AWG-*10 *pulse doppler radar fire control system, J79-GE-*10 *engines, and control surface improvements.*

The principal changes introduced by the F-4C included the slightly modified J79-GE-15 turbojet which, possessing the same thrust ratings as the -8, had provision for a cartridge-pneumatic starter in place of the turbine impingement system employed by the U.S. Navy; the incorporation of a receptacle for boom refuelling behind the second cockpit; the introduction of full dual controls and the rearrangement of the rear cockpit, including the lowering of the instrument panel for improved visibility, and larger wheels and tyres with an anti-skid braking system. A Litton ASN-48 inertial navigation system replaced the F-4B's Eclipse-Pioneer dead-reckoning navigation computer; APQ-100 radar fire control supplanted the APQ-72: improved radar mapping display was provided by the APQ-100 PPI scope, and an improved attitude reference and bombing system (AJB-7) was installed. Provision was made for various U.S.A.F. armament items, and apart from the various ordnance loads carried by the F-4B, the F-4C can carry three Vulpods each containing a 20-mm. Vulcan rotary cannon and 1,100 rounds without changing the standard gunsight and computer. The F-4C was also tested during 1966 with both nine and 15 pod-mounted 7.62-mm. GAU-2B/A Miniguns suspended three from each triple ejector rack. These arrangements are being considered for operational use in Vietnam for suppressive fire against Viet Cong troop concentrations. In Vietnam operating under the 7th Air Force, the F-4C has been employed primarily in the strike role for which it normally carries eight 750-lb. bombs and two 370 U.S. gal. (308 Imp. gal.) drop tanks. It has also served in the reconnaissance, high cover and escort roles, sometimes carrying gun pods for the last-mentioned task, but these are not carried when long range or loiter time is needed owing to their high drag.

F-4D: Basically a modification of the F-4C which it began to succeed on the assembly line late in 1965, the first example flying on December 8th of that year, the F-4D features upgraded air-to-ground weapon delivery capability. An ASQ-91 weapon release computer and an ASG-22 lead computing optical sight have been added, and the APQ-109 radar provides an air-to-ground ranging capability. An ASN-63 inertial navigation system replaces the ASN-48, and the No. 1 fuselage fuel cell has been reduced in

GENERAL ARRANGEMENT DRAWING: *An F-4D Phantom II* (64-0939) *of the* 36*th Tactical Fighter Wing at Bitburg, Germany.*

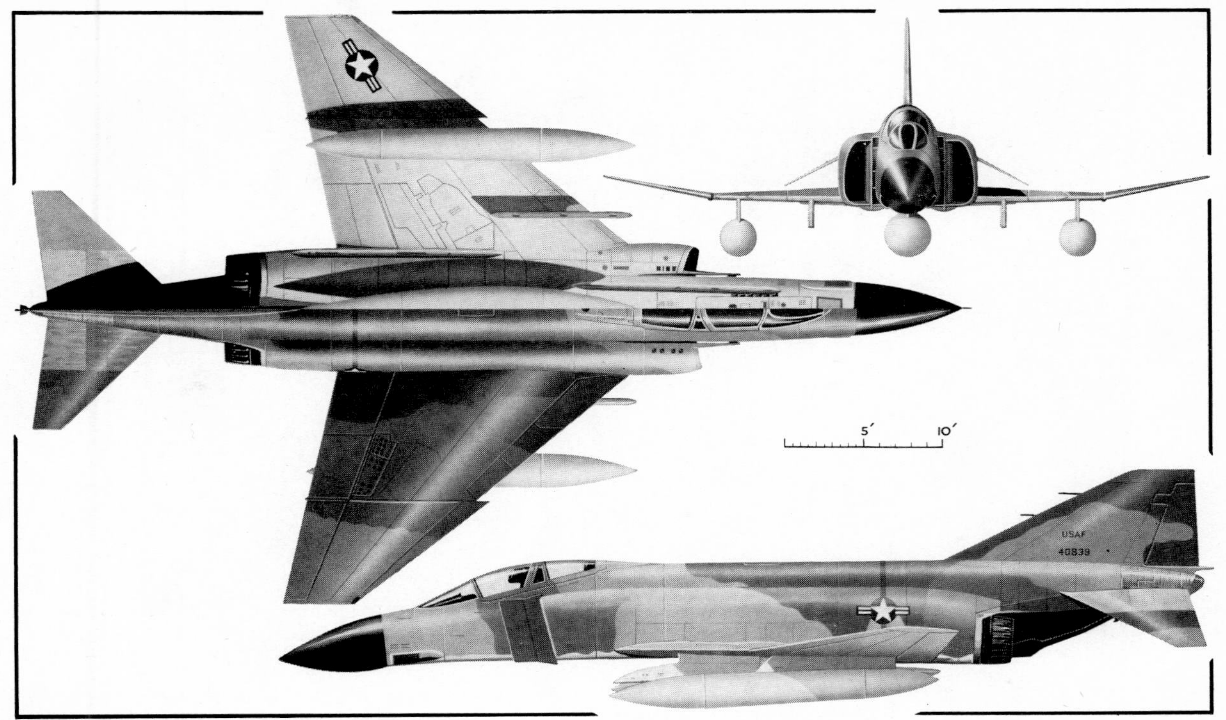
5′
10′
USAF
40839

The F-4D, the current U.S.A.F. production version of the Phantom II, was first flown on December 8, 1965, *and this model followed* 583 *examples of the initial U.S.A.F. variant, the F-4C. The F-4D embodies major systems improvements which enhance its air-to-ground capability. It also possesses the new APQ*-109 *fire control radar system. The first F-4D was delivered to the U.S.A.F. on March* 10, 1966, *and subsequently flown to Bitburg, Federal Germany, for the* 36*th T.F.W., that illustrated* (65–0601) *belonging to the* 53*rd Squadron.*

capacity to provide space for some of the new equipment. The J79-GE-15 turbojets of the F-4C are retained, and the principal external change is to be seen in the enlarged and redesigned radome, the infra-red sensor housing which is a characteristic of the nose of all earlier Phantom IIs having been deleted. The first production F-4D was delivered to the U.S.A.F. on March 10, 1966, and this type has now supplanted the F-105D in the 36th Tactical Fighter Wing with the U.S.A.F.E. in Germany, and is replacing the F-100D in the 50th T.F.W.

F-4E: Scheduled to enter U.S.A.F. service in 1967 and identical to the F-4D apart from a major radar modification to improve performance for the low altitude and ECM environment missions, the F-4E has APQ-117 radar with Hughes CORDS (Coherent On-Receive Doppler System), and places increased emphasis on the intercept task. It is currently proposed to replace the J79-GE-15 engines with the improved -17 model which offers an after-burning thrust of 17,900 lb., this power plant also being proposed for a further U.S.A.F. development of the basic design referred to as the TSF (Tactical Strike Fighter). The desirability of built-in gun armament has been underlined in Vietnam where it has been found that, apart from its value in air-to-ground strike missions, the cannon is important for the close-in, high-*g* manoeuvring type of air-to-air combat in which missiles lose their effectiveness, and the TSF version of the Phantom II has a 20-mm. Vulcan rotary cannon in the extreme nose. In prototype form, the Phantom TSF is a converted YRF-4C tactical reconnaissance aircraft (Vol. II, page 100) with the reconnaissance equipment removed and an M-61 gun capsule taken directly from an F-105D Thunderchief inserted in the space thus made available. It is claimed that the installation of the M-61 Vulcan cannon and uprated engines results in a significant improvement in the Phantom II's tactical fighter capability.

F-4G: During the production run of the F-4B, twelve aircraft were modified to permit the installation of an ASW-21 two-way tactical communications system for automatic vectoring, traffic control and carrier landings, the designation being changed to F-4G. In order to provide space for the added equipment, a new compartment similar to that introduced by the U.S.A.F.'s F-4D was provided in the fuselage by reducing the size of the No. 1 fuel cell, access being through a panel in the top of the fuselage. The F-4G has been issued to one U.S. Navy squadron, VF-213, which was deployed with Carrier Air Wing 11 aboard the U.S.S. *Kitty Hawk* during the autumn of 1965, and saw operational service over Vietnam from November 26, 1965.

F-4J: Successor to the F-4B in production for the U.S. Navy and U.S. Marine Corps, the first example having flown in May 1966, the F-4J is primarily an interceptor but has full attack capability, and embodies a major missile control system performance and reliability improvement resulting from the introduction of the Westinghouse AWG-10 pulse Doppler radar fire control system.

The reduction in internal fuel capacity resulting from the equipment compartment occupying some of the space in the No. 1 fuel bay has been more than compensated for by the provision of a seventh fuselage fuel cell above the engine exhaust nozzles, and an AJB-7 bombing system (similar to that of the F-4C) replaces the AJB-3A. The increased radar, fuel and other equipment weight has raised landing weight to 38,000 lb., this demanding an increase in wheel size (from the 30-in. by 7.7-in. of the F-4B to the 30-in. by 11.4-in. of the U.S.A.F. models), and to maintain low carrier approach speeds at the increased weights flap area has been increased, a drooped (16.5°) aileron configuration has been introduced, and fixed slots are provided on the leading edges of the tailplane, air being bled from the compressors and blown over the leading and trailing edge flaps to enhance boundary layer control. The F-4J standardises on the J79-GE-10 offering an afterburning thrust of 17,900 lb., and this power plant is also proposed for the suggested Phantom FV growth version offered as an alternative to the problematical General Dynamics F-111B.

The Phantom FV, which began life as a $1m. (£357,000) U.S.N.-funded feasibility and preliminary design study completed in August 1966, embodies an increased wing area, is equipped for the air superiority fighter role, and offers significant increases in ferry range, speed and payload over existing F-4 models. An alternative power plant proposed for the Phantom FV is the Rolls-Royce RB.168-27R Spey, a projected development of the RB.168-25R with improved specific fuel consumption.

F-4K: Based on the U.S. Navy's F-4J, the F-4K for the British Navy, the first of the two YF-4K prototypes for which flew on June 27, 1966, embodies changes to make the aircraft compatible with the comparatively small British carriers. The F-4K, deliveries of which are to commence in October 1967, an initial production contract for 26 aircraft having been placed in June 1965, two YF-4K prototypes having been ordered a year earlier, differs from the F-4J primarily in being powered by a pair of Rolls-Royce RB. 168-25R Spey R.Sp.5R Mk.201 turbofans each offering 12,500 lb. s.t.and 21,250 lb. with afterburning. The installation of the Spey with its better specific fuel consumption results in a 15 per cent increase in ferry range and a 10 per cent increase in radius of action. Take-off, unassisted by catapult, is reduced by 30 per cent; time to Mach 2.0 is reduced by one third, and time to climb to 40,000 ft. is cut by 20 per cent. Maximum speed is limited by compressor outlet temperature considerations to approximately Mach 2.1.

In addition to the engine change, the F-4K embodies provision for folding the radome and radar antenna to permit use of the 54-ft. elevators on British carriers, and an extensible nosewheel leg for best incidence catapulting from British Navy catapults. The choice of the Spey engine for the F-4K has necessitated major

(Right) The first YF-4K for the Royal Navy (XT595), the first example of the Phantom to fly with Rolls-Royce Spey turbofans.

(*Above*) *An F-4G Phantom II* (*Bu. No.* 150492) *of VF-*213. *The F-4G is fitted with a two-way data link system, including an automatic carrier landing mode and an approach power compensation system.*

changes in the basic airframe structure, being larger than the J79. It has dictated an enlargement of the engine compartment, an increase in air intake and duct size, and the re-contouring of the aft fuselage. It has also had significant effects on other systems, such as starting provisions, cockpit instrumentation, the bleed air system, and a minor change in the location of the AIM-7E Sparrow missiles which have been adopted for the British model. The AWG-10 fire control radar as fitted to the F-4J with APG-59 Doppler radar has been adopted for the F-4K, and British equipment includes Cossor IFF, Plessey VHF/UHF communications, etc. The British Navy is scheduled to receive a total of 60 F-4K Phantoms, and the first British production example (which will be the 2,534th production Phantom off the line) is currently scheduled for completion in the autumn of 1967.

F-4M: The variant of the Phantom II destined to serve with the R.A.F., the F-4M is based on the F-4K configuration, except for some minor changes such as larger capacity brakes. The basic airframe, undercarriage, power plant and air-to-air armament are identical to those of the F-4K, but major changes have been made to equipment installations to meet R.A.F. air-to-ground weapons delivery requirements, and a Ferranti inertial navigation and attack system is being installed. EMI Electronics is prime contractor for the reconnaissance pod which will be employed by both the F-4K and F-4M, this conforming to the shape of the standard 600 U.S. gal. (500 Imp. gal.) centreline drop tank and containing four forward-, downward- and oblique-looking cameras, optical and infra-red line-scan, and sideways-looking reconnaissance radar. Initial quantities of two YF-4Ms and 20 F-4M Phantoms were ordered in June 1965, and total requirement is for approximately 150 aircraft, deliveries to the R.A.F. commencing in 1968. Initially, the Phantoms will be used to replace a proportion of the R.A.F.'s Hunter F.G.A. Mk.9s, but with the availability of the P.1127 they will be transferred to the intercept role as replacements for the Lightning.

Power Plants: *Two General Electric J*79-*GE*-8 *turbojets each rated at* 10,900 *lb.s.t. and* 17,000 *lb.s.t. with afterburning.*
Performance: *Max. speed* (*clean*), 1,485 *m.p.h. at* 48,000 *ft.* (*Mach* 2.25), (*with four Sparrow III AAMs*), 1,450 *m.p.h.* (*Mach* 2.2), 950 *m.p.h. at* 1,000 *ft.* (*Mach* 1.2)*; low-level tactical radius* (*with* 6,000 *lb. of ordnance*), 400 *mls. at* 420 *m.p.h.; ferry range* (*with one* 600 *U.S. gal.*/500 *Imp. gal. and two* 370 *U.S. gal.*/308 *Imp. gal. drop tanks*), 2,300 *mls. at* 575 *m.p.h. at* 40,000 *ft.* (*Mach* 0.87)*; initial climb* (*clean*), 28,000 *ft./min.; operational ceiling*, 62,000 *ft.*
Weights: *Empty*, 28,000 *lb.; loaded* (*clean*), 44,600 *lb.; max.*, 54,600 *lb.*
Dimensions: *Span*, 38 *ft.* $4\frac{3}{4}$ *in.; length*, 58 *ft.* $3\frac{3}{4}$ *in.; height*, 16 *ft.* 3 *in.; wing area*, 530 *sq. ft.*
Note: *Specification applies specifically to F-4B but is generally applicable to F-4C, D, G, and J variants.*

GENERAL ARRANGEMENT DRAWING: *The first McDonnell YK-4K Phantom II* (*XT595*) *for the Royal Navy.*

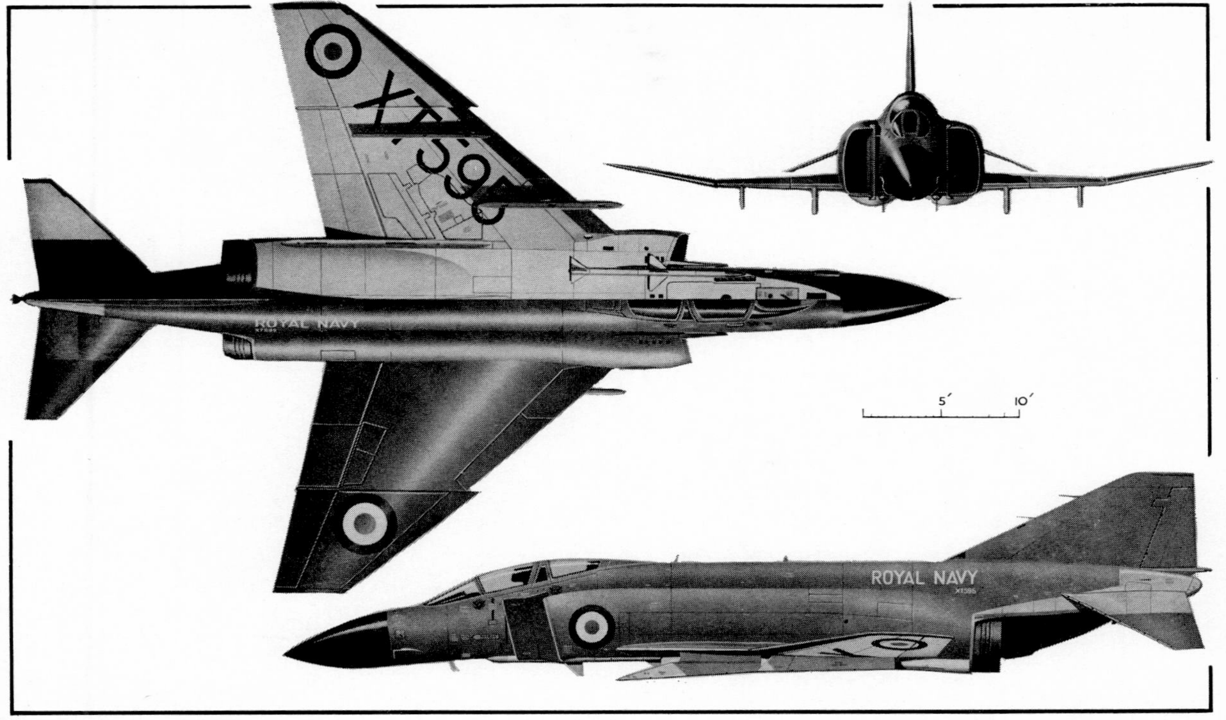
XT596
ROYAL NAVY
5′
10′
ROYAL NAVY

(*Left*) *A CF*-101*B Voodoo* (17447) *of the R.C.A.F. Air Defence Command. The CF*-101*B and the dual-control CF*-101*F currently serve with Nos.* 409, 416 *and* 425 *Squadrons of the R.C.A.F.*

McDONNELL F-101B VOODOO

Together with the F-106A Delta Dart, the F-101B two-seat all-weather interceptor is standard equipment with continental U.S.A.-based Fighter-Interceptor Squadrons of the U.S.A.F.'s Air Defense Command, and also equips three squadrons of the R.C.A.F.'s Air Defence Command. Although dimensionally similar to the single-seat F-101A tactical strike fighter, the F-101B embodies an entirely new forward fuselage accommodating pilot and radar observer in tandem, an MG-13 fire-control system, and a missile bay housing semi-active radar homing or infra-red homing AAMs. Developed as the long-range interceptor system WS-217A, the F-101B flew on March 27, 1957, entering A.D.C. service two years later, and nine Fighter-Interceptor Squadrons had converted to this type when production terminated in March 1961 with the 478th two-seat Voodoo. A small number were completed with full dual controls under the designation TF-101B to combine combat proficiency training and checks with full intercept capability, and from June 1961, 56 late-production F-101Bs and 10 TF-101Bs were transferred to the R.C.A.F. These, initially having nuclear missile capability deleted, were designated F-101F and TF-101F by the Defense Department but in R.C.A.F. service are known as the CF-101B and CF-101F respectively. The F-101B has provision for two AIR-2A Genie nuclear-tipped AAMs which are mounted externally beneath the fuselage. An alternative armament comprises three AIM-4E semi-active radar homing or AIM-4F infra-red homing Super Falcon AAMs mounted on a rotary weapons bay door in the forward fuselage. Sixteen A.D.C. squadrons were operating the Voodoo mid-1966, but some are scheduled for deactivation during 1967.

Power Plants: *Two Pratt & Whitney J*57-*P*-53 *or* -55 *turbojets each rated at* 11,990 *lb.s.t. and* 14,990 *lb.s.t. with afterburning.*
Performance: *Max. speed*, 1,220 *m.p.h. at* 40,000 *ft.* (*Mach* 1.85), 720 *m.p.h. at sea level* (*Mach* 0.95)*; range cruise*, 585 *m.p.h. at* 36,000 *ft.* (*Mach* 0.87)*; max. range*, 1,550 *mls.; initial climb*, 17,000 *ft./min.; service ceiling*, 51,000 *ft.*
Weights: *Empty*, 28,000* *lb.; normal loaded*, 39,900 *lb.; max.*, 46,673 *lb.*
Dimensions: *Span*, 39 *ft.* 8 *in.; length*, 67 *ft.* 4¾ *in.*, (*over probe*), 71 *ft.* 1 *in.; height*, 18 *ft.* 0 *in.; wing area*, 368 *sq. ft.*
*APPROXIMATE

GENERAL ARRANGEMENT DRAWING: *An F*-101*B*-100 *Voodoo* (57-0420) *of the* 2nd *Fighter-Interceptor Squadron, U.S.A.F. Air Defense Command, based at Suffolk County A.F.B., New York.*

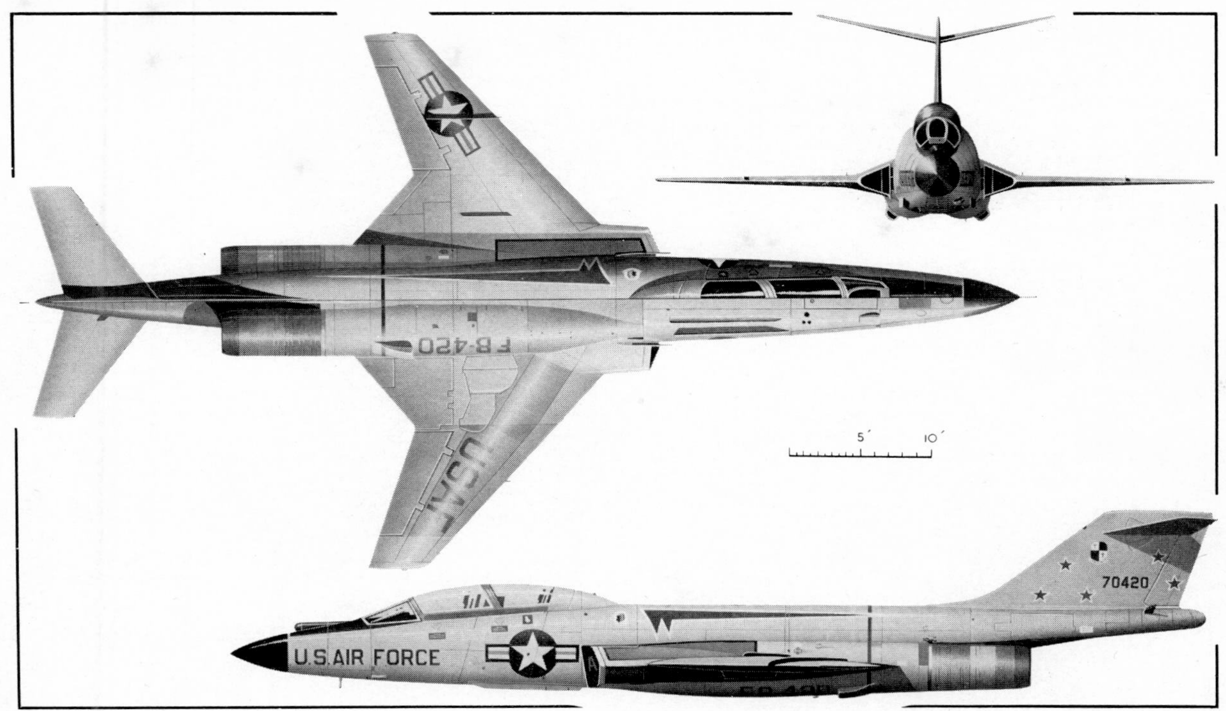

FB-420
USAF
5´ 10´
70420
U.S. AIR FORCE

MIKOYAN-GUREVICH MIG-15 (FAGOT)

No Soviet combat aircraft has exerted a more profound effect on western design thinking than the MiG-15 single-seat fighter. A lightweight high-altitude interceptor, the MiG-15 offered excellent serviceability and ease of handling at low speeds coupled with a speed performance second to none, and although it was to be bested in air-to-air combat over Korea by its American contemporary, the F-86 Sabre, this was largely the result of the low standard of training and experience of the average Chinese pilot flying the Russian fighter, and its lack of radar ranging equipment. Essentially, the MiG-15 offered a superior climb rate, higher ceiling and better acceleration than the American fighter owing to its lower wing loading and better thrust-to-weight ratio, and above 28,000 ft. it was faster than the F-86E, while the latter could outdive its opponent, was better equipped and offered a better gun platform. Today, the MiG-15 is obsolete but, nevertheless, it retains a place in the active aircraft inventories of such countries as Albania, Algeria, Bulgaria, Cambodia, China, and the Democratic People's Republic of Korea.

(*Below*) *A late-production MiG-*15*bis with* 66 *Imp. gal.* (79 *U.S. gal.*) *flush-fitting underwing drop tanks.*

Work on the MiG-15, at that time known as the Type S, began in March 1946 to fulfil a V.-V.S. requirement for a single-seat fighter to intercept bombers at very high altitude under clear weather conditions. A cannon armament and an endurance of at least one hour were specified, and great importance was attached to climb rate and manoeuvrability above 33,000 ft. All the leading fighter design bureaux initiated projects aimed at fulfilling this requirement, and negotiations were initiated with the U.K. for the supply of a number of Rolls-Royce Derwent and Nene centrifugal-flow turbojets, no adequately powerful engines at that time being available in the Soviet Union. With the arrival of the first of these engines early in 1947, the Mikoyan-Gurevich, Lavochkin and Yakovlev bureaux finalised their interceptor designs, utilising the more powerful Nene, although both Lavochkin and Yakovlev simultaneously evolved Derwent-powered back-up designs which, in the event, were to attain production as the La-15 and Yak-23 respectively. Neither the Lavochkin La-168 or Yakovlev Yak-30* attained flight test status until mid-1948, and their similarly-powered competitor, the Mikoyan-Gurevich bureau's Type S, which had flown for the first time on December 30, 1947, had already been ordered into quantity production (in March 1948) as the MiG-15.

Production deliveries of the MiG-15 began late in 1948, and powered by a copy of the Nene designated RD-45 and rated at 4,960 lb.s.t., the fighter was extremely simply equipped, its only electronic equipment consisting of an RSI-6M-1 high-frequency radio and navaid, and an RPKO-10M low-frequency homing receiver. A simple gyro-type gun sight with a maximum range

**It should be noted that the designation "Yak-*30" *was also applied* 12 *years later to a tandem two-seat light jet trainer, the re-use of designations applied to abandoned projects being common practice in the Soviet aircraft industry.*

GENERAL ARRANGEMENT DRAWING: *A MiG-*15*bis of China's Air Force of the People's Liberation Army.*

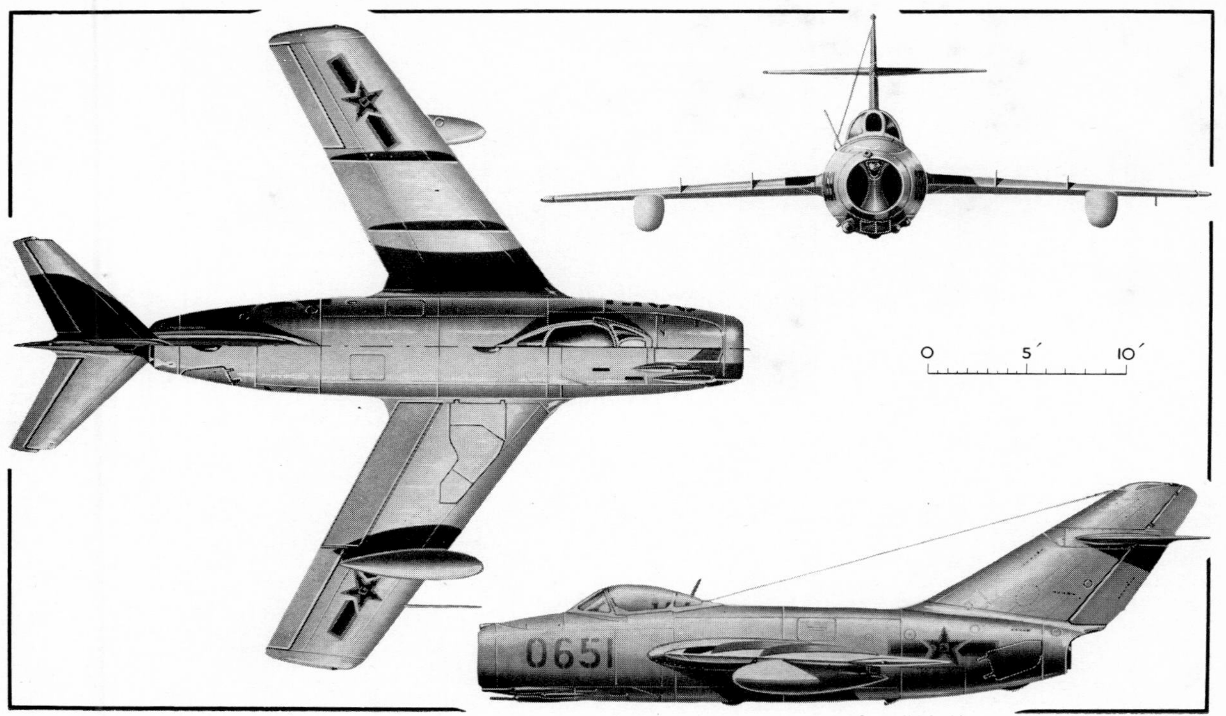
0 5´ 10´
0651

(Left) A MiG-15bis adapted for the fighter-bomber role with a heavy beam introduced into the wing just outboard of the undercarriage main attachment points and projecting forward to enable two 225-lb. class bombs or two rocket pods to be carried in tandem on each wing in addition to two 88 Imp. gal. (106 U.S. gal.) drop tanks. On the example illustrated, the forward pod houses eight 55-mm. rockets.

setting of 2,650 ft. was accompanied by an armament of two 23-mm. Nudelmann-Rikter VYa (NR-23) cannon, although the inadequacy of this pair of weapons was realised at an early stage and they were augmented by a single 37-mm. Nudelmann cannon which was mounted to starboard, the smaller weapons being provided with 80 r.p.g. and the larger weapon with 40 rounds. Redlined at Mach 0.92, the MiG-15 began to experience buffeting at Mach 0.91, and compressibility characteristics were such that the fuselage-mounted air brakes automatically opened at the redlined speed. Internal fuel capacity was 275 Imp. gal. (330 U.S. gal.) housed in a fuselage tank extending between the wing spar frames, and loaded weight at 10,595 lb. was extremely low by contemporary standards. Indeed, it was lighter than any of the first generation of swept-wing fighters, but its only "unconventional" feature was its mid-wing configuration. Licence manufacture of the MiG-15 was initiated in Poland and Czechoslovakia as the LIM-1 and S-102 respectively, and, in the meantime, the quest for improved performance had resulted in the MiG-15bis.

MiG-15bis: Vladimir Klimov's engine design bureau devoted much energy to improving the performance of the basic Nene engine, this work resulting in the RD-45FA, later redesignated VK-1. Able to handle greater mass flow as a result of enlarged combustion chambers, turbine blades and jet pipe, and embodying refinements to the combustion system, the VK-1 gave a take-off thrust of 5,952 lb.s.t. boosted to 6,750 lb. with water injection without any increase in the maximum diameter of the engine. Fuel capacity was boosted by the introduction of two small tanks at the rear which raised internal capacity to 310 Imp. Gal. (372 U.S. gal.), this being supplemented by two 66 Imp. Gal. (79 U.S. gal.) drop tanks; equipment was improved, an RSIU-3M VHF radio transceiver was installed, feeding a blade antenna behind the cockpit, an MRP-48P beacon receiver assisted navigation, an ARK-5 radio compass was provided, an RV-2 or -10 radio altimeter was fitted, and in addition an SRO IFF set made its appearance, and the airframe and systems were subjected to a critical weight analysis which resulted in a reduction of some 200 lb. in empty weight, despite the heavier engine and additional equipment.

The new variant was designated Type SD or MiG-15bis (the "bis" suffix being one of many French words adopted into the Russian vocabulary and roughly equivalent to "Mark Two"), and licence-manufactured examples produced in Poland and Czechoslovakia were known as the LIM-2 and S-103. Licence manufacture was also undertaken in China. The MiG-15bis appeared over Korea in 1951, shortly before the début of the F-86F Sabre, and some reconnaissance capability was provided in some aircraft by the addition of a vertical camera aft of the gun pack. Flying close to their absolute ceiling, MiG-15bis reconnaissance fighters were extremely difficult to counter, and probing over Germany by this model led to the R.A.F. stripping some Venoms for high altitude interception. Gun armament remained the same as that of the late production MiG-15, and two 550-lb. or 1,100-lb. bombs or small rocket projectiles could be carried underwing.

MiG-15UTI: Produced almost simultaneously with the MiG-15bis, the tandem two-seat MiG-15UTI, which received the appellation *Midget* under the NATO naming system, and LIM-3 and CS-102 designations in Poland and Czechoslovakia respectively, was manufactured both with and without armament, the former version having two 23-mm. cannon. The second cockpit was inserted at some expense to fuel capacity, and in terms of speed performance the two-seater was rather inferior to its single-seat counterpart owing to the poor canopy shape, maximum speed being reduced to Mach 0.83 at sea level. The MiG-15 UTI conversion trainer remains in service with more than a score of air arms.

Power Plant: *One Klimov VK-*1 (*RD-*45*FA*) *centrifugal-flow type turbojet rated at* 5,952 *lb.s.t.*
Performance: *Max. speed,* 668 *m.p.h. at sea level* (*Mach* 0.876), 650 *m.p.h. at* 20,000 *ft.* (*Mach* 0.89), 620 *m.p.h. at* 40,000 *ft.; tactical radius in clean condition,* 240 (200) *mls., with two* 66 *Imp. gal./*79 *U.S. gal. drop tanks,* 340 (300) *mls.; initial climb,* 10,827 (10,433) *ft./min.; ceiling,* 51,800 (49,215) *ft.*
Weights: *Empty,* 8,320 (8,200) *lb.; normal loaded,* 11,085 (11,288) *lb.; max.,* 13,889 (14,253) *lb.*
Dimensions: *Span,* 33 *ft.* 1½ *in.* (33 *ft.* 0¾ *in.*)*; length,* 36 *ft.* 5 *in* (33 *ft.* 1½ *in.*)*; height,* 12 *ft.* 1¾ *in.; wing area,* 255.1 (254.028) *sq. ft.*
Note: *Specification applies specifically to standard MiG-*15*bis, data in parentheses relating to the late production MiG-*15.

*The MiG-*15*UTI tandem two-seat trainer, seen right in service with an Indonesian squadron, is widely used for advanced and conversion training, being operated by some* 20 *air arms. It is now in process of replacement in the V.-V.S. and the Czechoslovak, Polish, and several other air arms by the MiG-*21*UTI. The MiG-*15*UTIs illustrated retain full armament for secondary operational tasks.*

(Left) A MiG-17F day fighter of the Iraqi Air Force; this service currently possess three squadrons which still operate this type.

MIKOYAN-GUREVICH MIG-17 (FRESCO)

The MiG-17 single-seat fighter, which has participated in desultory combat over Vietnam during 1965-66, is today, despite its age, one of the world's most widely used combat aircraft, and currently serves with the air arms of Afghanistan, Albania, Cambodia, China, Czechoslovakia, the German Democratic Republic, Hungary, Indonesia, Iraq, the Korean Democratic People's Republic, Morocco, Poland, Rumania, Syria, the United Arab Republic, and the Democratic Republic of Vietnam, as well as with the Soviet Union's V.-V.S. The MiG-17, or Type SI as it was originally known, appeared in 1949, and was in essence an aerodynamically refined MiG-15. It was destined to be manufactured in larger numbers than any post-war combat aircraft. Retaining the VK-1 turbojet of the MiG-15bis, the MiG-17 introduced a wing of thinner section and greater sweep angle (leading edge sweep ranging from 47° inboard to 43° outboard), a third wing fence being provided to reduce the harmful effects of the new wing on low speed stability, the rear fuselage was extended, increasing the fineness ratio, the span of the tailplane was increased, and the air brake geometry was revised.

The MiG-17 entered V.-V.S. service in 1952, and followed the MiG-15bis into production in Poland as the LIM-5, in Czechoslovakia as the S-105, and in China. Allocated the identification name *Fresco* by NATO, the MiG-17 soon appeared in a variety of modified versions which necessitated the addition of suffix letters to the identification name. Thus, the initial production day fighter MiG-17 became the *Fresco-A*, armament of this model comprising two 23-mm. and one 37-mm. cannon which was used with a simple lead pursuit optical gyro gunsight. Some difficulties were evidently experienced with the narrow air brakes mounted low on the rear fuselage of the initial production model, and therefore enlarged rectangular air brakes were introduced and mounted on the fuselage sides aft of the wings (*Fresco-B*). The decision to introduce a short afterburner on the MiG-17's engine may have been another factor influencing the repositioning of the air brakes, as it was obviously desirable to move the hydraulic actuators for the brakes from the vicinity of the afterburner itself. However, when the definitive MiG-17F (*Fresco-C*) with afterburning engine made its début, the air brakes had reverted to their original position on the rear fuselage,

GENERAL ARRANGEMENT DRAWING: *A MiG-17F all-weather interceptor of the Ceskoslovenské letectvo*

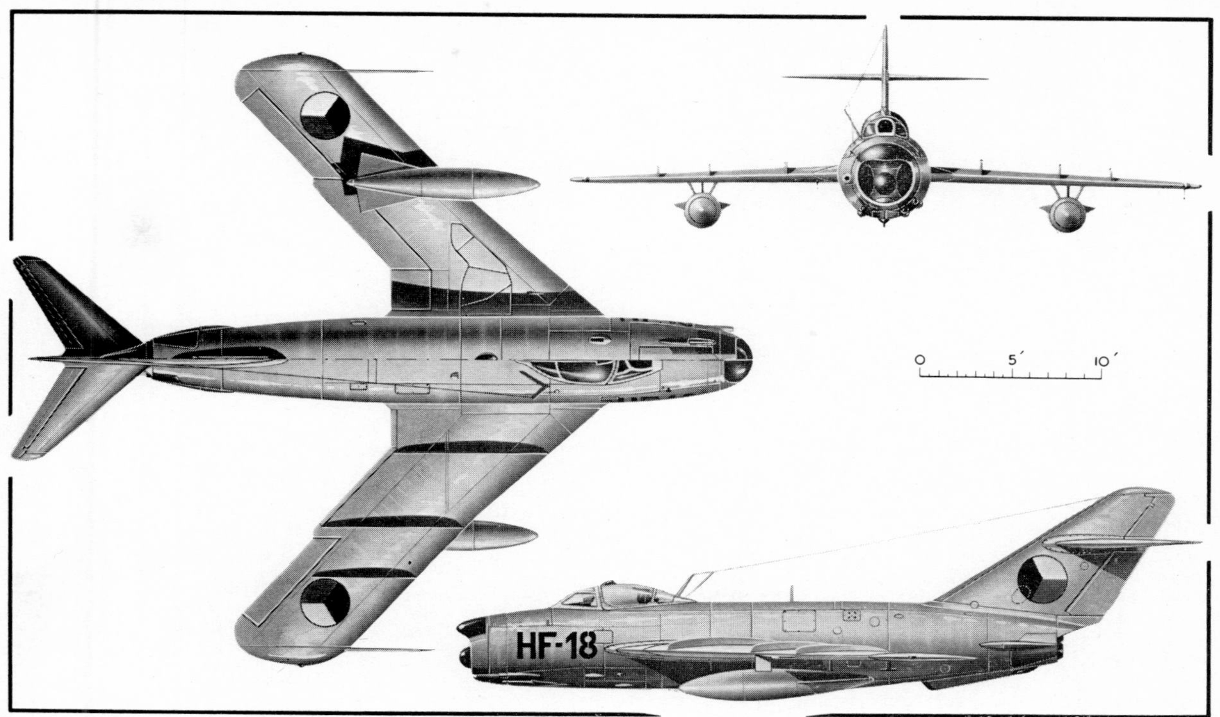
0
5´
10´
HF-18

although these were of revised shape, being shorter and deeper. The MiG-17F (the "F" suffix indicating *Forsazh*, or "boosted") is currently the most widely used version of the basic design.

The MiG-17F differs externally from the original MiG-17 in having the previously-mentioned redesigned air brakes and the tail cone cut back, exposing the end of the afterburner nozzle of the VK-1A engine which offers a maximum thrust of 6,990 lb. Initially, the built-in armament was similar to that of earlier models, but the slow-firing (400 r.p.m.) 37-mm. weapon was eventually replaced by a third 23-mm. gun, and underwing loads could include four pods each housing eight 55-mm. rockets, two 210-mm. rockets, or two 550-lb. bombs. Since 1955, and the progressive replacement of the MiG-17 by supersonic aircraft for the day intercept role, this aircraft has been gradually relegated to the low-level ground attack role, a task for which it is not very well suited, and various attempts have been made to improve its capabilities in this capacity. One of the principal shortcomings of the MiG-17 in the attack role was the strict limitation on underwing ordnance when drop tanks were carried, and radius of action without such tanks for the low-level role was something less than inadequate.

In the Soviet Union a similar modification to that previously carried out on some MiG-15s was applied to the MiG-17, this consisting of the introduction of a heavy beam which extended forward from the wing leading edge immediately outboard of the undercarriage wells. This enabled two rocket pods or 550-lb. bombs to be carried in tandem under each wing with drop tanks further outboard. In Poland, a more extensive conversion was undertaken, the under surface of the inboard wing being lowered to almost twice its original depth and the thick section's effect on speed performance being partly offset by a highly swept extension of the inboard leading edge, this providing accommodation for twin-wheel main undercarriage members with low-pressure tyres and additional fuel tankage, bombs or rockets being carried on shackles under the outboard panels.

For the limited all-weather intercept role, a modified version of the MiG-17F began to appear in 1955 (*Fresco-D*). This featured a radar scanner in the central intake bullet and a second radar in an extended upper intake lip. The combat camera was moved from the top of the intake to the starboard side, the fuselage nose was lengthened slightly, and in order to provide room for the pilot's radar scope the windscreen was moved forward and the quarter-lights modified. The radar ranging operated through a horizontal dielectric strip in the intake splitter, the ranging unit being housed in the intake lip, and the A.I. scanner being mounted in the hemispherical radome. Like the MiG-17F day fighter, the all-weather model was powered by the afterburning VK-1A, and initially carried a trio of 23-mm. cannon. However, the cannon armament of some aircraft was later deleted, and four small beam-riding missiles – apparently early versions of the *Alkali* – mounted on rails beneath the inboard wing sections, these being carried in addition to a pair of 88 Imp. gal. (106 U.S. gal.) drop tanks.

Power Plant: *One Klimov VK-1A centrifugal-flow type turbojet rated at* 5,952 *lb.s.t. and* 6,990 *lb.s.t. with afterburning.*
Performance: *Max. speed,* 635 *m.p.h. at* 39,370 *ft.* (*Mach* 0.96), 692 *m.p.h. at sea level; tactical radius* (*with two* 66 *Imp. gal./*79 *U.S. gal. drop tanks*), 465 *mls. at* 508 *m.p.h. at* 36,000 *ft.* (*Mach* 0.8)*; time to* 40,000 *ft.*, 6.8* *min.; service ceiling,* 57,500 *ft.*
Weights: *Loaded* (*clean*), 11,465 *lb.; max.*, 14,000* *lb.*
Dimensions: *Span,* 31 *ft.* 6 *in.; length,* 36 *ft.* 4 *in.; height,* 11 *ft.* 0 *in.; wing area,* 233.264 *sq. ft.*
*APPROXIMATE
Note: *Specification applies to day fighter model of MiG-17F known in the West as Fresco-C.*

MIKOYAN MIG-19 (FARMER)

The lineal successor to the MiG-17, the MiG-19 single-seat day interceptor was the first Soviet warplane capable of attaining speeds in excess of Mach 1.0 in level flight to attain quantity production, development having begun in 1952, and the first flight being made late in 1953. In addition to serving with the V.-V.S. in both day and limited all-weather interceptor forms, the MiG-19 is operated by the air arms of China, Cuba, Czechoslovakia, the German Democratic Republic, Indonesia, Iraq, Poland and the United Arab Republic, and a small number of aircraft of this type have been supplied to Pakistan by China.

The initial production model, a simply-equipped day fighter with the by then traditional Russian fighter armament of one 37-mm. and two 23-mm. cannon, entered service with the V.-V.S. in 1955, power being provided by two RD-5 axial-flow turbojets mounted side by side in the rear fuselage and each offering 4,800 lb.s.t. dry and 6,700 lb. with afterburning. Allocated the identification name *Farmer* by NATO, the MiG-19 featured a three-spar wing swept 55° at the leading edge and having 4.5° of anhedral. All fuel was housed in the fuselage, the tailplane had conventional elevators, and underwing loads could comprise four rocket pods

(*Below*) *This MiG-*19 *of the Ceskoslovenské letectvo, like that illustrated on page* 134, *is an early limited all-weather version, the radar ranging unit being housed in the upper lip of the intake with the A.I. scanner in the small radome on the intake splitter.*

(Left) An early production example of the limited all-weather variant of the MiG-19 interceptor. This version has the extended forward fuselage but retains the wing-root-mounted cannon deleted from later production all-weather models.

each with eight 55-mm. missiles, two pods of 19 55-mm. missiles, two 220-mm. or 325-mm. rockets, or two 550-lb. or 1,100-lb. bombs. Two 88, 132 or 176 Imp. gal. (105, 158 or 301 U.S. gal.) drop tanks could be carried.

The MiG-19 was progressively developed for both day and limited all-weather roles, the definitive day fighter version (*Farmer-C*) introducing a slab-type tailplane, RD-9 turbojets rated at 6,170 lb.s.t. dry and 7,850 lb. with afterburning, an additional air brake under the forward fuselage, and an armament of three 30-mm. cannon. A limited all-weather counterpart (*Farmer-D*) in which cannon armament was reduced to two 30-mm. weapons and the fuselage nose was lengthened by approximately 1.8 ft., appeared in 1958. This featured two radar antennae in the nose, the conical scan dish being housed in a central radome carried on the intake splitter, and the range measurement antenna being incorporated in an enlarged air intake upper lip. The cannon armament was subsequently deleted from most aircraft of this type, the guns being replaced by four *Alkali* beam-riding AAMs mounted on special pylons inboard of the drop tanks, and well forward of the wing in order to clear the inward-retracting undercarriage members.

Power Plants: *Two Klimov RD-9F(VK-9) axial-flow turbojets each rated at* 6,170 *lb.s.t. and* 7,850 *lb.s.t. with afterburning.*
Performance: *Max. speed,* 902 *m.p.h. at* 32,810 *ft.* (*Mach* 1.33), 740 *m.p.h. at* 50,000 *ft.* (*Mach* 1.12), 685 *m.p.h. at sea level* (*Mach* 0.95)*; tactical radius* (*clean*), 280* *mls.; ferry range* (*with two* 176 *Imp. gal.*/211 *U.S. gal. drop tanks*), 1,365 *mls.; climb to* 32,810 *ft.* (*clean*), 1.1 *min.; ceiling,* 55,775 *ft.*
Weights: *Empty,* 12,132 *lb.; loaded* (*clean*), 18,630 *lb.; max.,* 22,500* *lb.*
Dimensions: *Span,* 29 *ft.* 6 *in.; length,* 41 *ft.* 4¾ *in.; height,* 12 *ft.* 5½ *in.; wing area,* 269.1 *sq. ft.*
*APPROXIMATE
Note: *This specification apparently applies to the definitive day fighter model known in the West as Farmer-C.*

GENERAL ARRANGEMENT DRAWING: *A MiG-19 (Farmer-C) day interceptor of the Voenno-Vozdushny Sily.*

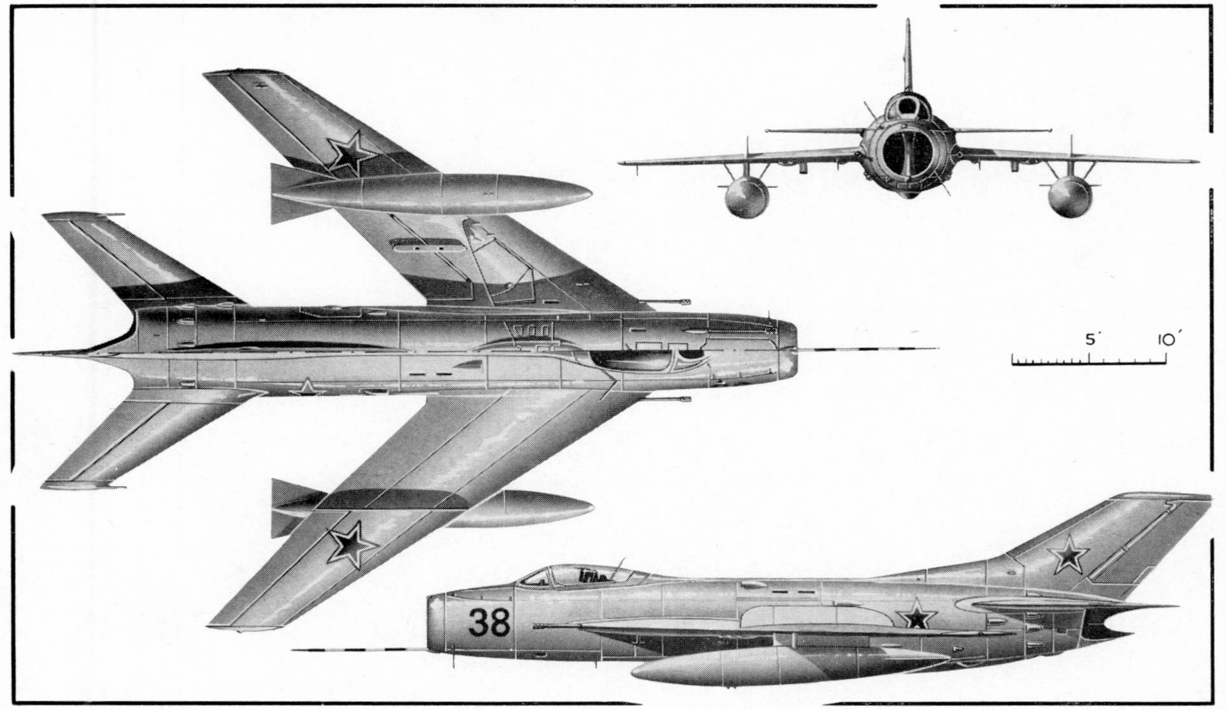
5′
10′
38

MIKOYAN MIG-21 (FISHBED)

There are today few fighters designed solely for the air superiority role; aircraft intended for point defence and the provision of top cover to enable close-support aircraft to perform their task with impunity. Most major aircraft-manufacturing countries have concluded that the air superiority task does not, in itself, warrant the cost of development, and in endeavouring to combine this function with strike and reconnaissance plus all-weather capability have evolved complex and highly expensive machines, and air superiority fighters have become *rarae aves* indeed. The appearance of the MiG-21, almost the sole current representative of the air superiority fighter category, over Vietnam in 1966 served to underline the dangers of ignoring such simple combat aircraft, for the Russian fighter possesses much the same speed performance as the Phantom II by which it has been challenged in combat, coupled with superior manoeuvrability affording it a distinct advantage under conditions of close-in fighting, and its manufacturing cost is less than a quarter of that of the infinitely more sophisticated multi-purpose American fighter.

The success of the MiG-21 is indisputable. It has been criticised on the score of armament, avionics, poor engine response, and short radius of action, but it is universally praised on the score of handling ease, performance, servicing and maintenance simplicity, and ability to operate from relatively poor surfaces and short runways. What is more, it is relatively inexpensive to manufacture. The MiG-21 has been in service for more than seven years, its début in V.-V.S. squadrons having taken place in 1959. It has been progressively improved over the decade that has elapsed since its first true prototype was flown, and it continues in large-scale production, both in the Soviet Union and Czechoslovakia, currently serving with 17 national air arms.

Development of the MiG-21 began in the early 'fifties with the formulation of a specification calling for a small and simple fighter with modest internal fuel capacity, capable of attaining the maximum possible speed which was to be combined with good manoeuvrability, climb rate and ceiling. Simple radar ranging was to be combined with cannon armament, and the aircraft had to be able

(Left) Two MiG-21 point-defence day interceptors of the Ceskoslovenské letectvo. Licence manufacture of a version of the later MiG-21F is being undertaken in Czechoslovakia.

GENERAL ARRANGEMENT DRAWING: *A Mikoyan MiG-21F of Cuba's Fuerza Aérea Revolucionaria.*

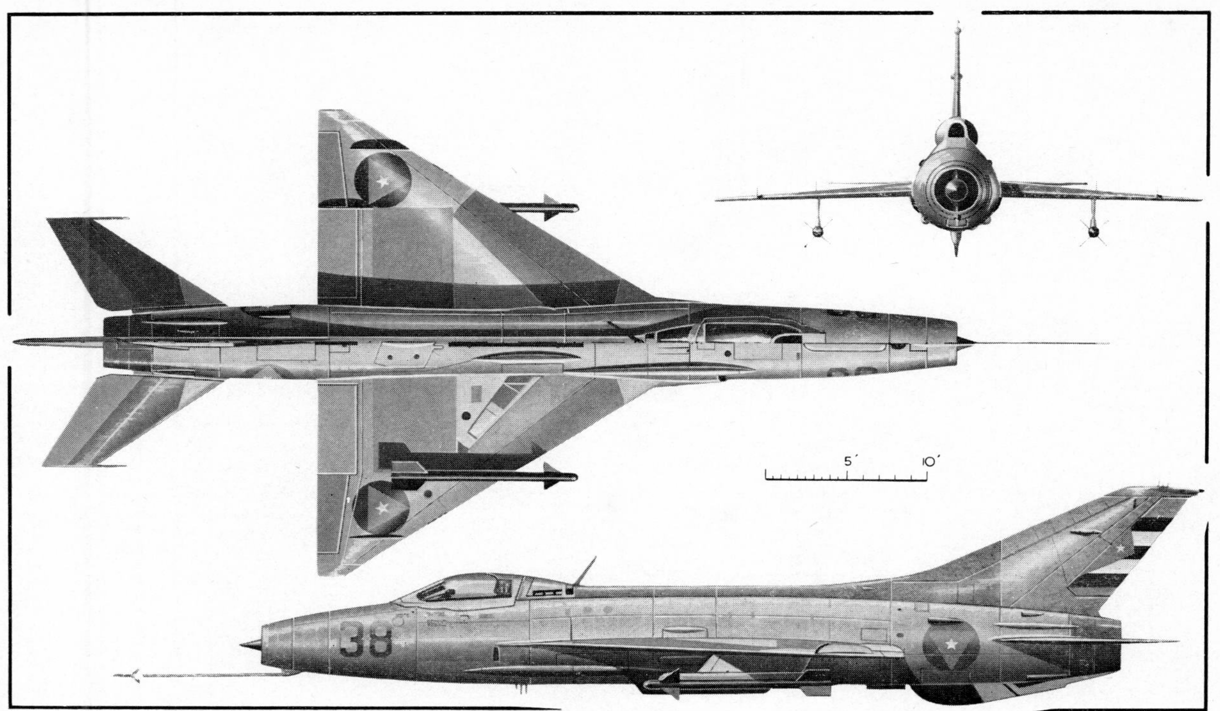
5′
10′
38

(*Above*) *A MiG-21F of the Ceskoslovenské letectvo flying with both fore and aft air brakes extended. The additional pair of brakes beneath the forward fuselage were first introduced on this version of the MiG-21.*

to operate from small frontline airfields. Simultaneously, in the U.S.A. the shortcomings of the first generation of U.S.A.F. jet fighters had resulted in a requirement for a similar day superiority fighter in which all criteria were subordinated to flight performance, and the result was the Lockheed F-104 Starfighter which, in its initial form, possessed much the same power as the contemporary MiG-21 and had generally similar empty and loaded weights, but these were the *only* similarities, for the Lockheed design team, not overly worried by short-field performance which figured largely in the specification to which the MiG-21 was evolved, selected a radical configuration embodying a long, needle-nosed fuselage with unusually small anhedralled trapezoidal wings, and a narrow-track undercarriage. Mikoyan's team, on the other hand, elected to adopt the "tailed delta" configuration in which some interest was being shown in the U.K.

Combining low wave drag and structural weight with good supersonic manoeuvrability, the "tailed delta" arrangement was ideal for a supersonic interceptor, although its poor subsonic lifting capacity limited any secondary ground attack role, and despite extensive research at the TsAGI, the Mikoyan team was still not entirely convinced of the superiority of the delta over more orthodox swept surfaces. Finally, two aerodynamic prototypes were built, these being identical in every respect apart from their wings, one being a delta and the other featuring sharply swept wings. Like the F-104, these aerodynamic test vehicles flew in 1955, both being demonstrated over Tushino on June 24, 1956, by which time the "tailed delta" arrangement had clearly demonstrated its superiority and had been selected for the production fighter, the first true prototype of which flew in 1957.

The initial production version of the MiG-21, dubbed *Fishbed-B* in the West, began to leave the assembly line in early 1959. With radar ranging in a small intake diffuser cone and a pair of 30-mm. cannon which could be supplemented by two pods each housing 19 55-mm. rockets, the MiG-21 accommodated some 500 Imp. gal. (600 U.S. gal.) internally, a 132 Imp. gal. (158 U.S. gal.) drop tank normally being carried on a ventral pylon, and its performance was high by contemporary standards despite an engine rated at only some 9,500 lb.s.t. boosted to about 12,500 lb. with afterburning, this being achieved by carrying the bare minimum of armament and equipment, and biasing the design towards low drag even, in some cases, at the cost of some structural problems. Diminutive air brakes were mounted under the fuselage just aft of the centreline pylon, and a drogue parachute housing was provided under the extreme rear fuselage.

MiG-21F: Efforts to boost available thrust resulted in a 5–6 per cent increase, and the slightly more powerful engine with a dry rating of about 10,000 lb.s.t. and an afterburning thrust of 13,200 lb. was installed in a MiG-21 which, under the designation Ye-66 and flown by G. Mosolov, established a world speed record of 1,571 m.p.h. over a distance of 9.3–15.5 mls. on October 31, 1959. On September 16, 1960, the same aircraft flown by Konstantin Kokkinaki established a 100-km. closed-circuit speed record of 1,335 m.p.h., or Mach 2.02, a maximum speed of 1,553 m.p.h. (Mach 2.35) being attained over part of the course. The uprated engine was duly incorporated in the production model of the fighter which received the designation MiG-21F, the suffix letter indicating *Forsazh*, or "boosted", and presumably referring to the increased power available.

The MiG-21F appeared in V.-V.S. service in 1961, the normal intercept armament comprising a pair of infra-red homing AAMs known in the West by the code-name *Atoll* and obviously inspired, at the very least, by the AIM-9 Sidewinder, the 19 rocket pods providing an alternative underwing armament. Owing to the critical weight factor, the port cannon was usually removed and faired over, the space previously occupied by its ammunition tank being used for an auxiliary fuel tank. The MiG-21F, which is manufactured under license in Czechoslovakia, has been supplied to the air arms of Algeria, Cuba, Finland, the German Democratic Republic, Hungary, India, Indonesia, Iraq, the Korean Democratic People's Republic, Poland, Rumania, Syria, the U.A.R., the Democratic Republic of Vietnam, and Yugoslavia. Licence production of the all-weather version of the MiG-21F is being undertaken in India where the first aircraft scheduled for delivery in 1967 are being assembled from imported components, with deliveries of aircraft assembled from components of indigenous manufacture following two years later, the Indian Air Force planning to acquire a total of some 450 MiG-21 fighters by 1972 to equip seven–nine wings. The Sino-Communists received a few examples of the early production MiG-21 immediately prior to the disruption of Sino-Russian relations in 1960, and a copy of the Russian fighter is now being manufactured in China.

By 1961, the MiG-21F, known as the *Fishbed-C* in the West, had received a number of modifications. The engine air suction relief doors just ahead of the wing had been enlarged, and the small aft-mounted air brakes had been augmented on some aircraft by two larger brakes beneath the wing leading-edge roots and incorporating part of the cannon fairings. One aircraft was fitted with a 6,615 lb. thrust rocket motor in a faired ventral housing, and, as the Ye-66A, was flown by Colonel Mosolov to an altitude of 113,891 ft. in a zoom climb to establish a new world record. The Ye-66A, which was evidently participating in an aerodynamic drag reduction programme, embodied a cockpit canopy of improved contour

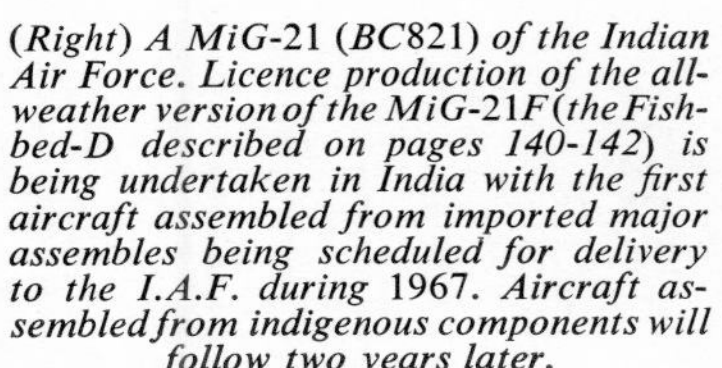

(*Right*) *A MiG-21* (*BC*821) *of the Indian Air Force. Licence production of the all-weather version of the MiG-21F* (*the Fishbed-D described on pages 140-142*) *is being undertaken in India with the first aircraft assembled from imported major assembles being scheduled for delivery to the I.A.F. during* 1967. *Aircraft assembled from indigenous components will follow two years later.*

with a large fairing extending well back over the spine to improve wave drag and resulting in a marginal performance improvement. This feature was subsequently adopted as standard for the A.I.-equipped all-weather derivative of the MiG-21 known as the *Fishbed-D* in the West.

MiG-21UTI: A tandem two-seat conversion training derivative of the basic single-seat MiG-21, and intended as the successor to the MiG-15UTI, the MiG-21UTI has a fixed windscreen, that of the single-seater being attached to the canopy and hinged at the forward edge for access, and separate starboard-hinging glazed sections over the two cockpits, the standard cockpit being occupied by the pupil, and the second cockpit, which has been inserted aft at some expense to fuel capacity and is equipped with duplicated basic controls and instruments, is occupied by the instructor. Possessing a generally similar performance to the MiG-21F, the MiG-21UTI has been delivered to the Czech, Finnish and Polish air arms, and also to those of several other countries operating the single-seat model. The MiG-21 UTI has been allocated the identification name of *Mongol* in the West.

Power Plant: *One axial-flow turbojet rated at* 10,000* *lb.s.t. and* 13,200* *lb.s.t. with afterburning.*
Performance: *Max. speed* (*clean*), 1,320* *m.p.h. at* 36,000 *ft.* (*Mach* 2.0), (*with two Atoll AAMs and one* 132 *Imp. gal.*/158 *U.S. gal. drop tank*), 990* *m.p.h.* (*Mach* 1.5)*; tactical radius* (*clean at subsonic cruise*), 375* *mls.; ferry range* (*with one* 132 *Imp. gal.*/158 *U.S. gal. drop tank*), 1,260* *mls.; initial climb* (*with two AAMs*), 30,000* *ft./min.*
Weights: *Normal loaded*, 17,000* *lb.; max.*, 18,800* *lb.*
Dimensions: *Span*, 25 *ft.* 0 *in.**; *length*, 47 *ft.* 0 *in.**; *height*, 14 *ft.* 6 *in.**; *wing area*, 250* *sq. ft.*
*APPROXIMATE

MIKOYAN MIG-21 (FISHBED-D)

Although conceived as a small, inexpensive clear-weather interceptor, the basic MiG-21 design has proved amenable to adaptation for the all-weather role, and in this form has been manufactured in some considerable numbers since 1962 for use by air forces of the Warsaw Pact countries and other recipients of Soviet aid. Currently operated by the air arms of, among others, Czechoslovakia, the German Democratic Republic, Indonesia, Poland and Syria, the A.W. MiG-21, although limited in capability, is appreciably less expensive than the larger, more powerful and more comprehensively equipped Sukhoi Su-9 which is the standard V.-V.S. single-seat all-weather interceptor.

Allocated the identification name *Fishbed-D* all-weather, the MiG-21 differs from the MiG-21F day fighter primarily in having a completely redesigned forward fuselage of lengthened and less tapered form, the engine air intake, although possessing a similar throat area to that of the day fighter, having been substantially enlarged in diameter to permit the installation of a centrally-mounted A.I. radome which produces a double shock to improve high speed thrust. The new forward fuselage is accompanied by a similar fairing aft of the cockpit canopy to that first seen on the record-breaking Ye-66A, and these changes, together with the deletion of the cannon armament and more minor aerodynamic improvements, result in a performance increase of the order of Mach 0.2. A supplementary pair of air brakes are mounted in a similar position to those of some MiG-21F day fighters, although of redesigned configuration, and armament normally comprises a pair of *Atoll* infra-red homing AAMs mounted on launching shoes attached to the standard underwing weapons pylons, although this rather ineffective and dated armament may now be in process of replacement by more sophisticated AAMs such as the two-stage *Awl* which has a longer range and more potent warhead.

GENERAL ARRANGEMENT DRAWING: *MiG*-21 (*Fishbed-D*) *of the III Pulk Lotnictwa Mysliwskiego of the Polskie Lotnictwo Wosjkowe.*

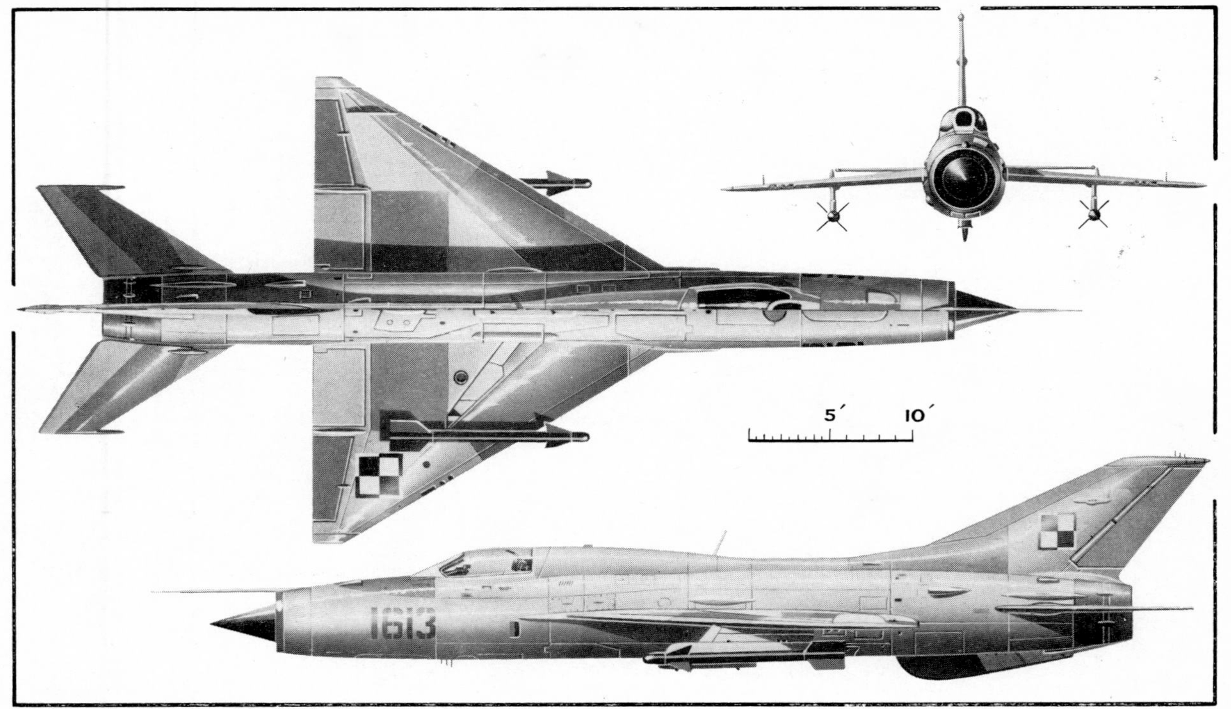
5´
10´
1613

(Left) A MiG-21 all-weather interceptor with two Atoll infra-red homing AAMs mounted on underwing pylons. The additional pair of air brakes under the forward fuselage can be seen partly extended. A forward pair of air brakes was also introduced on the MiG-21F.

The designation "MiG-23" has previously been applied in the West prematurely to a further derivative of the MiG-21 line which, demonstrated during the 1961 Aviation Day display, received the NATO identification name *Flipper*, and of which there is no evidence of quantity production or service introduction. Retaining the standard MiG-21 wing, tail surfaces and undercarriage married to a new, lengthened fuselage with a similar but rather larger A.I. radar cone in the air intake and two turbojets installed in a fashion reminiscent of that of the MiG-19, this aircraft is reputedly that which, as the Ye-266, established a new 1,000-km. closed-circuit record of 1,441.5 m.p.h. (Mach 2.19) in April 1965 with Alexander Fedotov at the controls. Previously, what is believed to be an essentially similar aircraft but powered by a single turbojet with an afterburning thrust of 22,046 lb., had established a 100-km. closed-circuit record of 1,491.9 m.p.h. (Mach 2.26) on October 7, 1961 with the same pilot at the controls, had averaged 1,665.9 m.p.h. (Mach 2.52) over a 15–25 km. course on July 7, 1962, when flown by Col. Mosolov, and had established a sustained altitude record of 74,276 ft. on September 11, 1962 with Pyotr Ostapenko at the controls.

Power Plant: *One axial-flow turbojet rated at* 10,000* *lb.s.t. and* 13,200* *lb.s.t. with afterburning.*
Performance: *Max. speed* (*clean*), 1,520* *m.p.h. at* 36,000 *ft.* (*Mach* 2.3), (*with two AAMs*), 1,320* *m.p.h.* (*Mach* 2.0)*; tactical radius* (*clean at subsonic cruise*), 350* *mls.; initial climb* (*with two AAMs*), 25,000* *ft./min.; time to* 40,000 *ft.*, 4.5* *min.*
Weights: *Loaded*, 18,700* *lb.; max.*, 20,500* *lb.*
Dimensions: *Span*, 25 *ft.* 0 *in.**; *length*, 49 *ft.* 0 *in.**; *height*, 15 *ft.* 0 *in.**; *wing area*, 250* *sq. ft.*
*APPROXIMATE

NORTH AMERICAN F-86 SABRE

The F-86 Sabre and its Russian contemporary, the MiG-15, are assured places in aviation history among the truly great warplanes of all time. Conceived almost simultaneously and flown in prototype form within three months of each other, they met in combat over Korea within two years of their service début, and today, 19 years after their initial flights, they still provide important items in the active inventories of many air arms. The Sabre line was a prolific one, and although no longer serving with the U.S.A.F. in any of its multifarious versions, it is operated in day fighter-bomber and all-weather interceptor forms by the air forces of no fewer than 21 countries.

The first XP-86 Sabre prototype was flown on October 1, 1947, and the initial production model, the F-86A-1 day interceptor, flew less than eight months later on May 20, 1948. Carrying six 0.5-in. M-3 machine guns with 267 r.p.g. and a Mk.18 lead computing gun sight, the F-86A attained 677 m.p.h. at sea level (Mach 0.885) and 595 m.p.h. at 34,500 ft. (Mach 0.895), and the type attained service early in 1949 with the U.S.A.F.'s 1st Fighter Group. The 554th and last F-86A was completed in December 1950, by which time production of the initial model had given place to the F-86E which was identical to the late production F-86A (the last 24 of which had been fitted with an A-1CM gun sight coupled with APG-30 radar) apart from introducing an all-flying tail. Like its predecessor, the F-86E was powered by a J47-GE-13 turbojet rated at 5,200 lb.s.t., and 336 aircraft of this model were manufactured by the parent company and, in the meantime, licence manufacture had been initiated in Canada by Canadair. The Canadian company applied the designation CL-13 to the licence-built F-86E, the first 351 (of which 60 were supplied to the U.S.A.F. as F-86E-6-Can Sabres) being known as Sabre Mk.2s, and the next 438 as Sabre Mk.4s, these incorporating modifications to the air conditioning, pressurization controls and canopy release. A number of Canadair-built Sabre Mks.2 and 4 were later updated and fitted with extended wing leading edges, and from July 1954, 104 were supplied to the Royal Hellenic Air Force, 105 to the Turkish Air Force, 180 to Italy's *Aeronautica Militare* and 121 to the Yugoslav Air Force. Known as F-86E(M) Sabres, these still equip three day interceptor squadrons of the Turkish Air Force's Air Defence Command, and one Air Division of Yugoslavia's air arm. The definitive day interceptor version of the Sabre was, however, the F-86F, which was destined to be produced in larger numbers than any other day fighter version of the basic aircraft, and remains in extremely widespread service with the world's air arms.

F-86F: Flown on March 19, 1952, the F-86F switched to the 5,910 lb.s.t. J47-GE-27 turbojet which raised maximum speed to 688 m.p.h. at sea level and 604 m.p.h. at 35,000 ft. The 79th and subsequent aircraft had the underwing shackles modified to take 200 U.S. gal. (166.5 Imp. gal.) drop tanks in place of the 120 U.S. gal. (100 Imp. gal.) tanks previously fitted, these boosting combat radius from 330 to 463 miles, and modifications introduced progressively on the production line included provision of the simpler A-4 gun sight and additional wing strongpoints providing for two pylons beneath each wing, the inboard pair of pylons carrying a 120 U.S. gal. (100 Imp. gal.) drop tank or a 1,000-lb. bomb, and the outboard pair each carrying a 200 U.S. gal. (166.5 Imp. gal.) tank. The deletion of the leading-edge slats and the extension of the wing leading edge were found to delay the onset of buffet, providing the pilot with an increase in usable *g*'s, and with the F-86F-35 production batch a LABS (Low Altitude Bombing System) computer was installed, and provision made for a 1,200-lb. tactical nuclear store to be carried under the port wing, more conventional loads comprising two 750-lb. or 1,000-lb. bombs, two 750-lb. Napalm tanks, or eight 5-in. HVARs.

From 1954 the export of surplus U.S.A.F. F-86F Sabres to

(*Above*) *Two Mitsubishi-assembled F-86F Sabres photographed at Hamamatsu. Seven J.A.S.D.F. squadrons currently operate this type.*

Allied nations began under the MDAP (Mutual Defense Assistance Program), one of the first foreign recipients being the Chinese Nationalist Air Force which, between November 1954 and June 1958, took delivery of 320 F-86Fs and seven RF-86Fs, the latter each carrying one K-17 and two K-22 cameras in a special compartment beneath the cockpit. Of these, 150 of the survivors still equip the C.N.A.F.'s 2nd and 3rd Day Fighter Wings, these having been modified from September 1958 to carry a pair of AIM-9 Sidewinder infra-red homing AAMs. Spain received 244 F-86Fs from April 1956, these currently equipping *Escuadrones* 101, 102, 112, 121, 151 and 981 of the *Ejercito del Aire*; Norway received 90 F-86Fs, the sole remaining R.No.A.F. unit to operate this type, Nr.338 *Skvadron*, being scheduled to convert to the F-5A during 1967; Peru received 14 F-86Fs which still equip one *Escuadron de Caza* of the *Fuerza Aérea del Peru*; the *Fuerzas Aéreas Venezolanas* acquired 22 F-86Fs which equip *Escuadrones de Caza* 37 and 38, and 28 F-86Fs delivered to the *Fuerza Aérea Argentina* are operated by the I Fighter-Bomber Group. Forty-seven F-86Fs were delivered to the Royal Thai Air Force. The *Forca Aérea Portuguesa* received 50 F-86Fs which equip Nos. 10 and 11 Squadrons, and the Republic of Korea Air Force's 11th Fighter Wing comprises three squadrons of F-86Fs, 112 examples of which were delivered, together with 10 RF-86Fs.

Production of the F-86F had terminated in 1954, but the U.S. government was soon to discover that it could not fulfil its enormous MDAP Sabre commitments from surplus U.S.A.F. aircraft alone and, accordingly, on June 27, 1955, a contract for 215 additional F-86F Sabres was placed with the parent company, a further 65 being added on March 27, 1956 to bring total production of the F-86F by the parent company to 1,539, the last being flown on December 28, 1956. The new orders were for the F-86F-40 which reverted to leading-edge slats which were modified to combine their low-speed handling benefits with the high-speed advantages offered by the extended wing leading edge. Simultaneously, the wing span and area were increased from 37 ft. 1 in. to 39 ft. 1 in. and 302.3 to 313.4 sq. ft., these changes being applied retrospectively to all F-86F-25s and -30s.

In the meantime, the resuscitated Japanese air arm, the J.A.S.D.F., had received 28 F-86Fs for training purposes (18 of these later being converted to RF-86F configuration), and the first F-86F-40s manufactured by the parent company were shipped to Japan in 1956, the J.A.S.D.F. having received 180 aircraft by mid-1957, although 45 of these were not used and were subsequently returned to the U.S.A.F. Mitsubishi assembled a total of 300 F-86F-40s from imported components, the first of these being

GENERAL ARRANGEMENT DRAWING: *An F-86F-30 Sabre* (52-4461) *of the 3rd Fighter Wing of the Chinese Nationalist Air Force.*

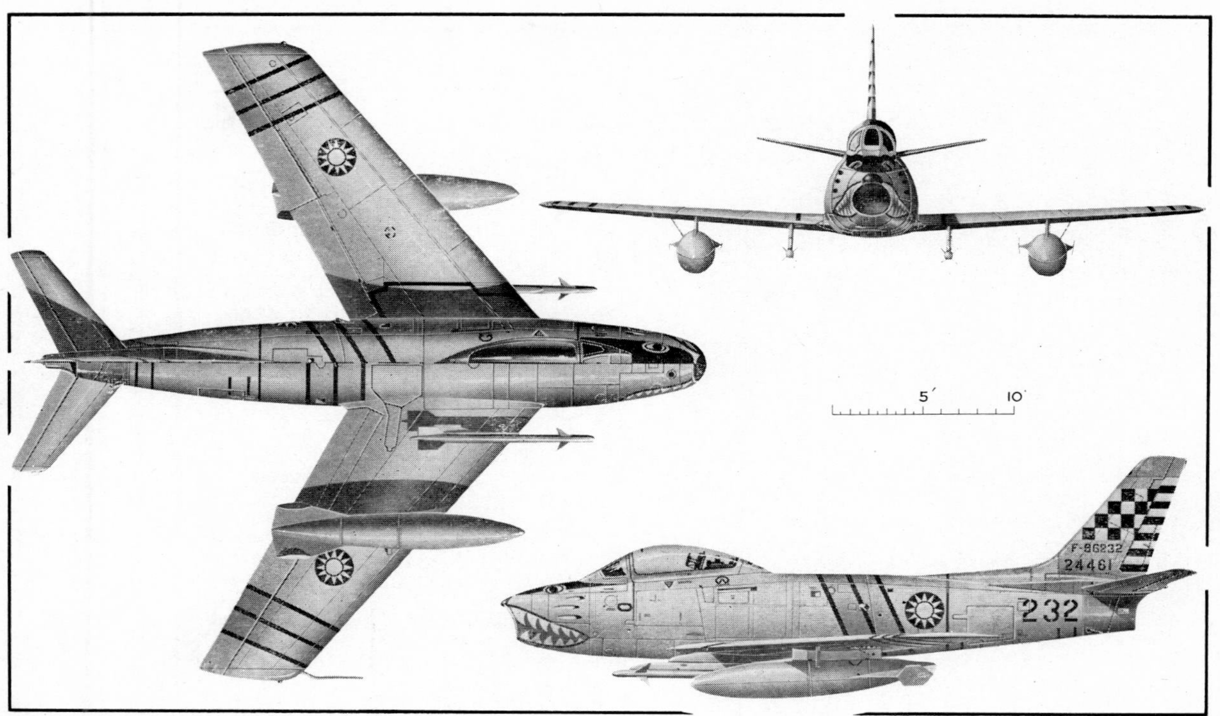
5′ 10′
F-86232
24461
232

(*Left*) *F-86F Sabres of Spain's Ala de Caza No.*1 *at Manises-Valencia. A total of* 244 *F-86F Sabres was delivered to Spain in* 1956–7.

Power Plant: *One General Electric J47-GE-27 turbojet rated at* 5,910 *lb.s.t.*
Performance: *Max. speed* (*at* 15,532 *lb.*), 678 *m.p.h. at sea level* (*Mach* 0.89), 599 *m.p.h. at* 35,000 *ft.* (*Mach* 0.9), (*at* 14,212 *lb.*), 687 *m.p.h at sea level* (*Mach* 0.9), 604 *m.p.h. at* 35,000 *ft.* (*Mach* 0.902)*; tactical radius* (*with two* 200 *U.S. gal./*166.5 *Imp. gal. drop tanks*), 463 *mls. at* 529 *m.p.h.; ferry range* (*with two* 120 *U.S. gal./*100 *Imp. gal. and two* 200 *U.S. gal./*166.5 *Imp. gal. drop tanks*), 1,525 *mls.; initial climb* (*at* 15,532 *lb.*), 8,100 *ft./min.*, (*at* 14,212 *lb.*), 9,800 *ft./min.; service ceiling* (*at* 15,532 *lb.*), 47,000 *ft.*, (*at* 14,212 *lb.*), 49,600 *ft.*
Weights: *Empty*, 11,125 *lb.; loaded* (*clean*), 15,198 *lb.; max.*, 20,611 *lb.*
Dimensions: *Span*, 39 *ft.* 1 *in.; length*, 37 *ft.* 6½ *in.; height*, 14 *ft.* 8¾ *in.; wing area*, 313.4 *sq. ft.*
Note: *Specification applies specifically to the F-*86*F-*40.

flown on August 9, 1956 and the last being delivered on February 25, 1961, these currently equipping the 3rd, 4th, 5th, 6th, 7th, 8th and 10th Squadrons of the J.A.S.D.F. One hundred and twenty North American-built F-86F-40s were delivered to the Pakistan Air Force during 1956–58, and approximately 80 of these remain in service with six Pakistani squadrons.

CL-13B: During 1953, while production of the F-86F was in full swing with the parent company, the Canadian licensee had initiated production of a new Sabre variant which, embodying the extended wing leading edges and wing fences of the F-86F-30, switched from the J47-GE-13 engine to the indigenous Orenda 10 of 6,355 lb.s.t. Slightly larger than the J47, the Orenda necessitated enlarging the frame openings over the engine bay, some local structural changes and the provision of different pick-up points, and as the CL-13A Sabre Mk.5, the modified fighter flew on July 30, 1953. The Sabre Mk. 5 could attain an altitude of 40,000 ft. in half the time taken by the Mk.4, and 370 examples were manufactured (75 of these later being presented to the *Luftwaffe*) before production of the definitive Canadian model, the CL-13B Sabre Mk.6, began.

Flown on November 2, 1954, the Sabre Mk.6 differed from its predecessor primarily in having the 7,275 lb.s.t. two-stage Orenda 14 turbojet. Empty weight was reduced from the Mk.5's 11,365 lb. to 11,143 lb., and performance was markedly improved, maximum speed (at 14,044 lb.) ranging from 710 m.p.h. at sea level (Mach 0.933) to 620 m.p.h. at 36,000 ft. (Mach 0.94), initial climb rate being 11,800 ft./min., and an altitude of 40,000 ft. being attained in six minutes. Tactical radius was 363 mls. in clean condition, and with two 200 U.S. gal. (166.5 Imp. gal.) drop tanks, range was 1,495 mls. The majority of Sabre Mk.6s built had a similar wing to that of the F-86F-40 without the tip extensions, and 382 aircraft of this model were built of which six were supplied to the Colombian

Air Force, these currently being operated alongside a small number of MAP-supplied F-86F Sabres; 34 were supplied to the South African Air Force, and the last 225 were built for the *Luftwaffe* which phased the last of them out of service during 1965. Ninety of the ex-*Luftwaffe* Sabre Mk.6s were sold to the Pakistan Air Force in 1966.

F-86D: The all-weather F-86D interceptor, which, for its time, was an extraordinarily sophisticated combat aircraft, had, despite its designation, nothing in common with other members of the Sabre family apart from its wing. Virtually a new machine, its concept was unprecedented in that for the first time the second crew member standard in all aircraft of this category was supplanted by complex electronic systems, and the classic gun armament was relinquished in favour of rockets. Two YF-86D prototypes and 122 production F-86Ds were contracted for on October 7, 1949, and the first YF-86D was flown on December 22, 1949. Production contracts eventually brought total orders for the F-86D to 2,504 aircraft, but as was perhaps to be expected with so advanced a warplane, it suffered numerous teething troubles, and these prevented service introduction until 1953.

The E-4 fire control system was a particular source of trouble, but its teething problems were eventually overcome, and the F-86D became an effective interceptor, offering radar target location, electronically computed aiming, and an extremely destructive armament of 24 2.75-in. rockets in a retractable missile tray. The APG-37 radar, the scanner for which was housed in a radome above the air intake, located the target at distances up to 30 mls., and after locking-on, the APA-84 computer determined a lead collision course and launched the missiles, the pilot electing whether to fire six, 12 or all 24 rockets. Various changes were introduced in each successive production block, and with the F-86D-40 the J47-GE-17 turbojet, which offered 5,000 lb.s.t. dry and 6,650 lb.s.t. with afterburning, gave place to the -17B rated at 5,425 lb.s.t. boosted to 7,500 lb. with afterburning, while the 239th F-86D-45 was the first D-model to receive the J47-GE-33 of 5,550 lb.s.t. and 7,650 lb. with afterburning. The delivery of ex-U.S.A.F. F-86Ds to Allied nations did not commence until 1958

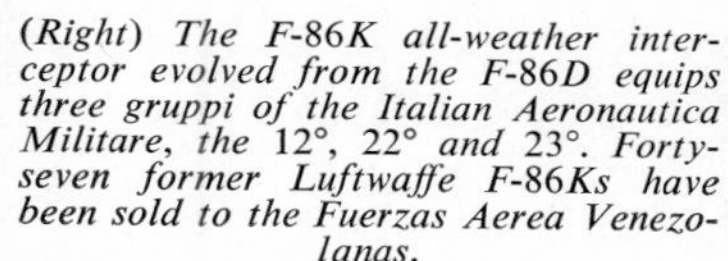
(*Right*) *The F-86K all-weather interceptor evolved from the F-86D equips three gruppi of the Italian Aeronautica Militare, the 12°, 22° and 23°. Forty-seven former Luftwaffe F-86Ks have been sold to the Fuerzas Aerea Venezolanas.*

(Left) An F-86D Sabre (52-9994) *of the Republic of Korea Air Force which possesses two squadrons operating all-weather interceptors of this type. Primary armament is now a pair of Sidewinder AAMs.*

when the security classification of the E-4 fire control system was modified, and some of these were later fitted for Sidewinder AAMs.

Fifty-six F-86Ds were delivered to Denmark, but the last R.Dan.A.F. unit equipped with this type was disbanded on March 31, 1966; 106 were supplied to the J.A.S.D.F. and equip the 101st, 102nd, 103rd and 105th Squadrons but are scheduled to be phased out during Fiscal 1967; the Republic of Korea received sufficient to equip two squadrons of the R.O.K.A.F.; the Chinese Nationalist Air Force has one F-86D-equipped squadron; 50 were supplied to the Royal Hellenic Air Force but will be phased out in 1967; 50 were delivered to the Turkish Air Force and currently remain the equipment of two squadrons; 18 were provided to the Philippine Air Force and are operated by one of that service's four combat squadrons, and 130 transferred to Yugoslavia's air arm equip one Fighter Division.

F-86K: Evolved from the D-model for supply to NATO forces under the MDAP, the F-86K differed from its predecessor primarily in having a simpler fire control system and cannon armament. The APG-37 radar was retained in the nose, but an MG-4 fire control supplanted the E-4, and four 20-mm. M-24A-1 cannon with 132 r.p.g. supplemented by two AIM-9B Sidewinder AAMs replaced the retractable missile tray. Internal fuel tankage remained unchanged at 610 U.S. gal. (508 Imp. gal), this being supplemented by two 120 U.S. gal. (100 Imp. gal.) drop tanks.

Development of the F-86K had begun on May 14, 1953, two F-86D-40 Sabres being modified as YF-86K prototypes, and the first of these flying on July 15, 1954. An agreement previously reached with the Italian Fiat company on May 18, 1953 provided for the assembly of the F-86K in Italy, and in order to accelerate deliveries of the fighter. 120 were assembled by North American, all being completed by the end of 1955, and 221 were assembled by Fiat, the first of these flying on May 23, 1955. The two YF-86Ks were sent to Italy as pattern aircraft, and the U.S.-assembled aircraft were divided between Norway and the Netherlands. Sixty-three Fiat-assembled aircraft were supplied to the *Aeronautica Militare*, and the remaining Fiat-assembled machines were divided between France (60), Germany (88), Netherland (6), and Norway (4). The F-86K possessed a slightly longer nose than the F-86D, and the last 45 Fiat-assembled aircraft had the extended wing leading edges and tips of the F-86F-40, others being modified retrospectively to similar standards.

The F-86K was phased out of *Luftwaffe* service in 1965, and 47 former *Luftwaffe* aircraft of this type were sold to the *Fuerzas Aérea Venezolanas* in 1966. The F-86K has also been phased out of *Armée de l'Air* and *Nederlandse Luchtmacht* service, but those remaining of the 65 delivered to the latter air arm were overhauled by Fiat in 1963–64 and passed to the Turkish Air Force with which they currently serve. Italy's *Aeronautica Militare* retains three F-86K-equipped *Gruppi*, the 12°, 22° and 23°, and the R.No.A.F.

GENERAL ARRANGEMENT DRAWING: *An F-86D-35 Sabre* (51-8490) *of the Republic of Korea Air Force.*

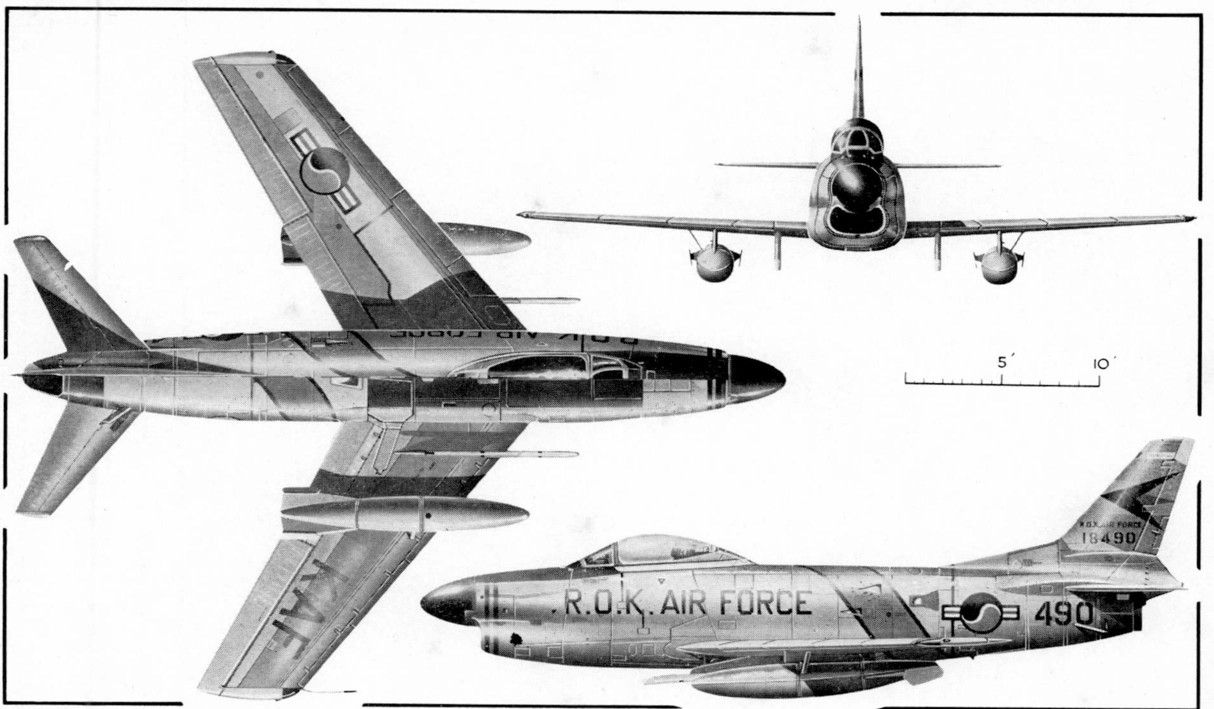
5′
10′
R.O.K. AIR FORCE
490
R.O.K. AIR FORCE
18490

which received 63 F-86Ks operates this type in its Nrs. 334, 337 and 339 squadrons, the first of these being scheduled to convert to the Northrop F-5A during 1967.

F-86L: During 1956, work began on a programme of reconditioning and modernising the F-86D, and adapting it for operation with the SAGE (Semi-Automatic Ground Environment) system. The modernisation of the electronics included the installation of an ARR-39 Data Link receiver, a new command radio and glide slope receiver, and APX-25 identification radar. Similar wing extensions to those introduced on the F-86F-40 were applied, and 981 F-86D Sabres were so modified under the designation F-86L. The F-86L Sabres were passed by the U.S.A.F. to the Air National Guard, and the last A.N.G. unit to operate this type, the 196th Fighter Interceptor Squadron, converted to F-102A Delta Daggers in the summer of 1965, although 17 F-86L Sabres supplied to the Royal Thai Air Force still equip one squadron of that air arm.

Power Plant: *One General Electric J47-GE-33 (-17B) turbojet rated at 5,550 (5,425) lb.s.t. and 7,650 (7,500) lb.s.t. with afterburning.*
Performance: *Max. speed, 693 m.p.h. at sea level (Mach 0.92), 616 (612) m.p.h. at 40,000 ft. (Mach 0.934/0.925); tactical radius, 270 (272) mls. at 550 m.p.h.; ferry range (with two 120 U.S. gal./100 Imp. gal. drop tanks), 769 (744) mls.; initial climb, 12,000 ft./min.; service ceiling, 49,600 ft.*
Weights: *Empty, 13,498 (13,367) lb.; loaded (point intercept), 18,160 (18,379) lb.; max., 19,952 (20,171) lb.*
Dimensions: *Span, 37 ft. 1½ in. (39 ft. 1¼ in.); length, 40 ft. 3¼ in. (40 ft. 11 in.); height, 15 ft. 0 in.; wing area, 287.9 (313.37) sq. ft.*
Note: *Specification applies to the F-86D-45, data in parentheses being applicable to the F-86K.*

NORTH AMERICAN F-100 SUPER SABRE

The first of the U.S.A.F.'s "Century-series" fighters, the F-100 Super Sabre has provided the backbone of the Tactical Air Command for a number of years, and has seen extensive service in Vietnam, but only some nine Tactical Fighter Wings (3rd, 20th, 27th, 31st, 48th, 354th, 401st, 405th and the 474th) were still operating this type by the autumn of 1966, and the Super Sabre will have been largely phased out of first-line T.A.C. service by the end of 1967, and transferred to the Air National Guard.

The F-100, development of which was initiated on February 3, 1949, was destined to become the world's first fighter capable of genuine supersonic performance, and the first of two YF-100A prototypes was flown on May 25, 1953, the first production F-100A following barely five months later, on October 29, 1953. The F-100A carried four Pontiac-built M-39E cannon, an APX-6 radar gunsight, and 1,020 U.S. gal. (850 Imp. gal.) of fuel internally. Power was provided by a 9,700 lb.s.t. J57-P-7 turbojet, and various modifications and improvements were introduced during the manufacture of 203 of the initial model, including the installation of the J57-P-39 on the last 36 machines, delivery of which was completed in March 1954. Six years later, in 1960, 80 ex-U.S.A.F. F-100As were brought up to the later F-100D standards and delivered to the Chinese Nationalist Air Force, but only some 45 of these remained on C.N.A.F. strength by mid-1966. In order to increase the versatility of the basic F-100 in the fighter-bomber role, the wing was structurally strengthened, enabling eight underwing pick-up points for a maximum stores load of 7,500 lb. to be introduced, and simultaneously flight-refuelling facilities were provided, the modified model being placed in production as the F-100C.

GENERAL ARRANGEMENT DRAWING: *An F-100D Super Sabre (54-2134) of No. 727 Eskadrille of the Kongelige Danske Flyvevåben at Karup.*

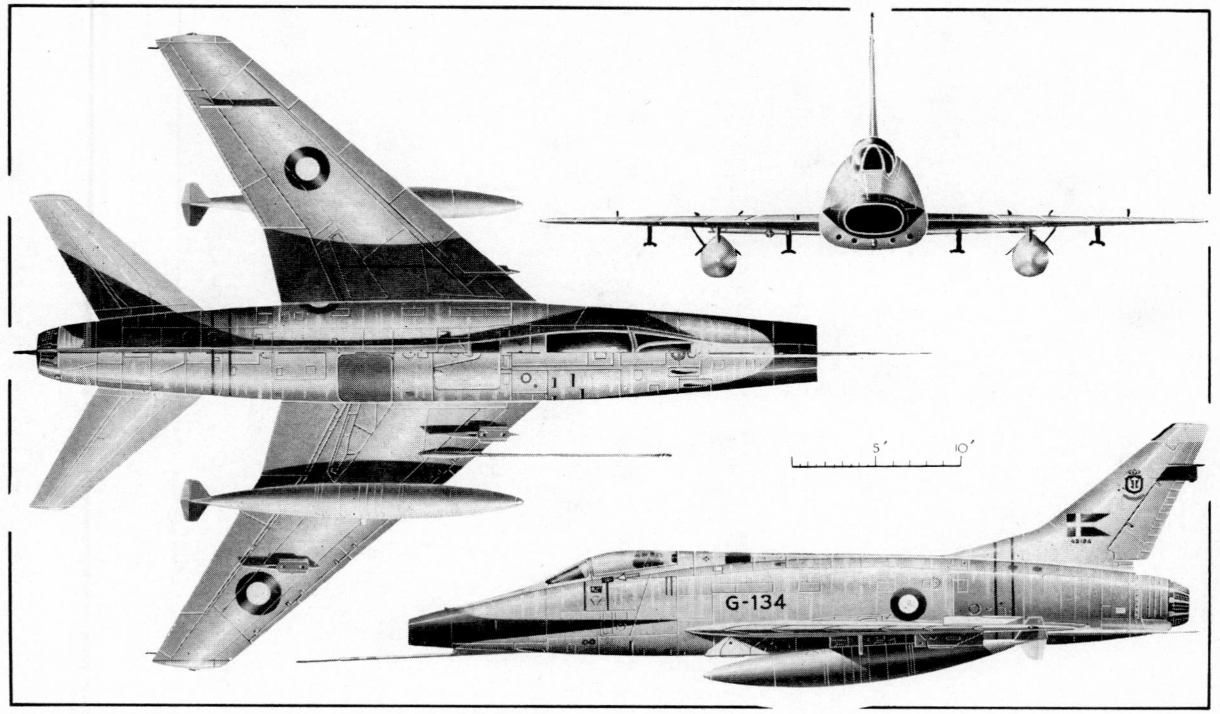
5′
10′
G-134

Although now giving place to the F-4C and -4D Phantom II as the backbone of the U.S.A.F. Tactical Air Command, the F-100D Super Sabre is still serving with some nine U.S.A.F. Tactical Fighter Wings. The F-100D illustrated (left) has the camouflage finish now applied to most aircraft of this type, and belongs to the 79th Tactical Fighter Squadron based at Woodbridge, Suffolk.

F-100C: Carrying an armament of four 20-mm. M-39E cannon with 200 r.p.g. like its predecessor, the F-100C was fitted with an APG-30 radar gunsight, and internal fuel capacity was increased to 1,195 U.S. gal. (995 Imp. gal.) in the fuselage and wings, giving a combat radius of 550 miles or a sortie time of 1.5 hr. Weighing 28,000 lb. in clean condition, the F-100C attained an altitude of 35,000 ft. within four minutes of brakes off, and supersonic performance was maintained down to 8,000 ft. at which altitude maximum speed was 810 m.p.h. (Mach 1.1). Production of the F-100C totalled 476 machines, and these were progressively phased out of the U.S.A.F. and passed to the Air National Guard with which they currently serve in five Tactical Fighter Wings, and to the Turkish Air Force which, recipient of 260 aircraft of this type, currently operates the F-100C in 10 squadrons of the 1st and 3rd Tactical Air Forces.

Power Plant: *One Pratt & Whitney J57-P-21A turbojet rated at* 11,700 *lb.s.t. and* 16,950 *lb.s.t. with afterburning.*
Performance: *Max. speed,* 864 *m.p.h. at* 35,000 *ft.* (*Mach* 1.3), 810 *m.p.h. at* 8,000 *ft.* (*Mach* 1.1)*; range cruise,* 565 *m.p.h. at* 36,000–45,000 *ft.* (*Mach* 0.86)*; combat radius* (*clean*), 550 *mls.; range* (*with two* 450 *U.S. gal.*/375 *Imp. gal. drop tanks*), 1,500 *mls.; initial climb,* 16,000 *ft./min.; time to* 32,300 *ft.* (*clean*), 2.5 *min.*
Weights: *Empty,* 21,000 *lb.; normal loaded,* 29,762 *lb.; max.,* 34,832 *lb.*
Dimensions: *Span,* 38 *ft.* 9⅓ *in.; length* (*over probe*), 54 *ft.* 3 *in.; height,* 16 *ft.* 2⅔ *in.; wing area,* 385.2 *sq. ft.*

F-100D: The definitive single-seat production model of the Super Sabre, the F-100D differs from the C-model in having a Minneapolis-Honeywell autopilot, revised vertical tail surfaces, jettisonable cantilever underwing stores pylons and, for the first time on any F-100 model, inboard landing flaps. The first F-100D flew on January 24, 1956, and 1,274 examples were subsequently produced, a substantial number of these being delivered to NATO air arms, and in addition to serving with the T.A.C., the Pac.A.F., and the U.S.A.F.E., the F-100D equips Nos. 725, 727 and 730 *Eskadrillerne* of the Royal Danish Air Force, and the *Armée de l'Air's* 11e *Escadre.*

Retaining the four Pontiac M-39E cannon, the F-100D can

(Right) The tandem two-seat F-100F (56-3827) photographed taking-off from Yokota carries the detachable refuelling probe which projects from beneath the starboard wing.

carry four AIM-9 Sidewinder AAMs for the intercept role, and for the attack mission six 1,000-lb. bombs, twenty-four 5-in. HVARs, or two AGM-12A Bullpup ASMs, two 1,000-lb. bombs and two 225 U.S. gal. (187 Imp. gal.) drop tanks may be carried.

F-100F: A tandem two-seat derivative of the F-100D combining the tactical fighter-bomber role with that of combat proficiency training, the F-100F first flew on March 7, 1957, and 333 examples were built, the last being delivered in October 1959. Serving with the U.S.A.F., the A.N.G., and the air arms of Nationalist China, Denmark, France and Turkey, the F-100F has a 36-in. additional section inserted in the fuselage for the second cockpit. Built-in armament is restricted to two M-39E cannon, but an external stores load of up to 6,000 lb. may be carried, empty and normal loaded weights being 22,300 lb. and 30,700 lb. respectively.

NORTHROP F-5

Serving with the U.S.A.F.'s 10th Fighter Commando Squadron in Vietnam, and the likely subject of additional U.S.A.F. procurement as a result of accelerated aircraft attrition rates suffered in South-East Asia, the F-5 was originally designed to meet the needs of smaller foreign air arms rather than a specialised U.S. military requirement. Currently being manufactured in substantial quantities for supply under the Military Assistance Programme to the air forces of countries militarily aligned with the U.S.A., the F-5 was initiated in 1954 as a private venture under the company designation N-156F. A U.S. Department of Defense contract was subsequently awarded for three prototypes, the first of which flew on July 30, 1959, and in April 1962, the N-156F was selected as the new MAP all-purpose fighter, and ordered in both single-seat and tandem two-seat forms as the F-5A and F-5B respectively, 180 having been delivered by the beginning of 1966 when production rate had attained 10 per month.

F-5A: The single-seat F-5A, the first MAP production example of which flew on May 19, 1964, currently serves with the air arms of Nationalist China, Greece, Iran, Morocco, South Korea, the Philippines, Thailand and Turkey, the first F-5-equipped squadron to attain combat readiness belonging to the Imperial Iranian Air Force and achieving this status in June 1965. MAP deliveries of the F-5 to Thailand and South Vietnam were scheduled to commence during 1966, Norway began taking delivery of the F-5 in March 1966, about two-thirds of the cost of the Norwegian aircraft coming from MAP funds, and Spain will begin to receive the F-5 in 1967 as a largely national purchase. Current plans call for the manufacture of 750–800 MAP F-5s through 1968–69.

The standard MAP F-5A, which combines second generation supersonic aerodynamics with a high degree of functionability and maintenance demands lower than those of the subsonic fighters of the last decade, is capable of fulfilling the attack, reconnaissance and air superiority roles. Able to operate from unpaved fields, the F-5A can deliver 1,500 lb. of ordnance and

(Above) An F-5A of the U.S.A.F.'s 10th Fighter Commando Squadron. The fixed flight refuelling probe may be seen projecting ahead of the cockpit. The F-5As employed by the 10th embody several modifications over standard MAP aircraft, such as 200 lb. of additional armour on the underside of the fuselage to reduce vulnerability to groundfire.

20-mm. cannon fire at ranges over 575 miles, and for short radius missions operating from grass fields in forward areas it can carry 2,500 lb. of ordnance, maximum external ordnance load being 6,200 lb. This is carried on five ground-removable external pylons and at two wingtip stations. The centreline pylon will take a 2,000-lb. class store, the two inboard wing pylons will each take a 1,000-lb. class store, the two outboard pylons will take a 750-lb. class store, and the wingtip stations can each carry a single AIM-9B Sidewinder AAM. Typical loads include four AGM-12B Bullpup ASMs, sixteen 5-in. HVAR missiles, or four pods each with nineteen 2.75-in. FFAR missiles, but for short-range missions the F-5 can carry such loads as nine 250-lb. Mk.81 bombs plus two AGM-12B Bullpups, or a combination of two Sidewinders, one 2,000-lb. Mk.84 bomb, two 1,000-lb. Mk.83 bombs and two 750-lb. BLU-1/B napalm tanks. Loiter time in the direct support mission may be increased by single-engine cruise on station, and the F-5 enjoys outstanding low-altitude manoeuvrability; turning radius with flaps up at 260 m.p.h. pulling 1.81 *g* is only 3,045 ft. at an altitude of 1,000 ft., while at 20,000 ft. at military power it can maintain more than 3 *g* at constant IAS for over 350° of turn.

Built-in armament consists of two 20-mm. M-39 cannon with 280 r.p.g. mounted in the upper decking of the nose, and internal

GENERAL ARRANGEMENT DRAWING: *An F-5A* (63-8399) *of the* 105*th Fighter Squadron of the R.O.K. Air Force* 10*th Fighter Wing at Suwon A.F.B.*

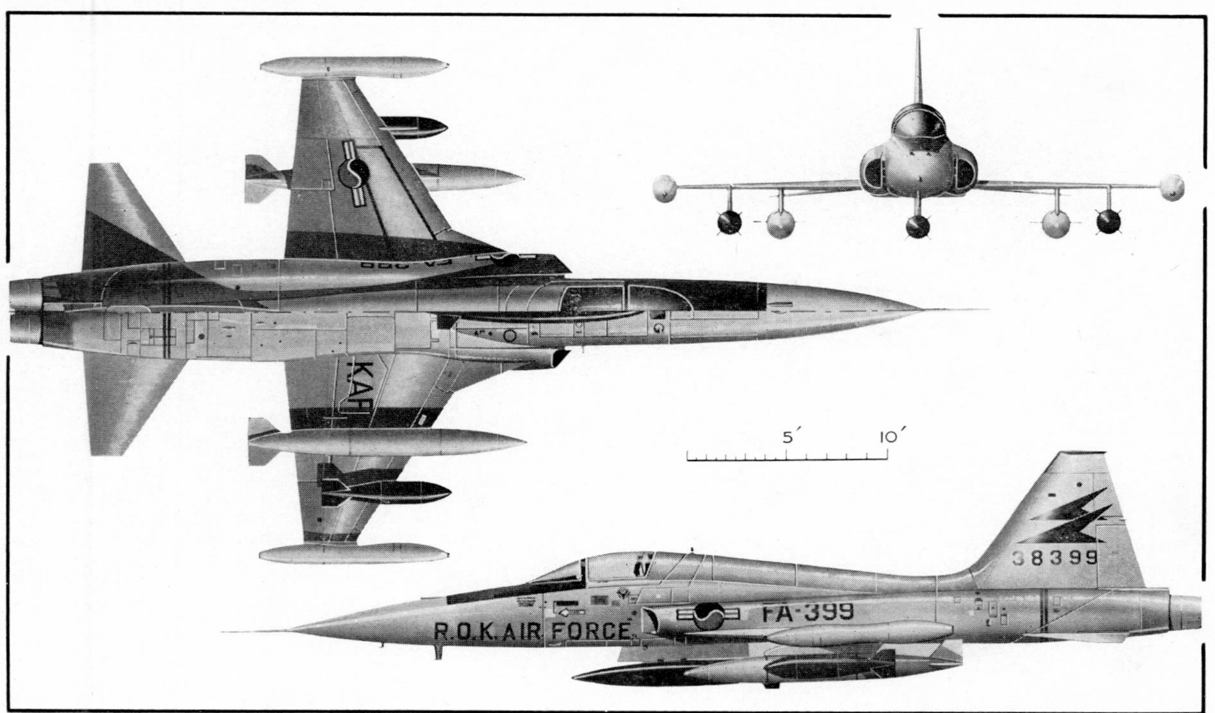
5′
10′
38399
FA-399
R.O.K. AIR FORCE
KAF

(*Left*) *Three Northrop F-5A fighters of the U.S.A.F.'s* 10*th Fighter Commando Squadron photographed over Vietnam.*

fuel capacity is 585 U.S. gal. (487 Imp. gal.), and the auxiliary supply system can comprise one 275 U.S. gal. (230 Imp. gal.), two 150 U.S. gal. (125 Imp. gal.) drop tanks plus two 50 U.S. gal. (41 Imp. gal.) removable wingtip tanks, or two 275 U.S. gal. tanks plus the wingtip tanks.

The 12 F-5As employed by the 4503rd Tactical Fighter Squadron (subsequently brought up to full squadron strength as the 10th Fighter Commando Squadron) formed for the evaluation of the fighter in Vietnam and which joined operations in October 1965, received aircraft diverted from the MAP production line, these being modified by the introduction of a fixed flight refuelling probe, some 200 lb. of armour on the fuselage underside, a two-gyro platform for the attitude indicator, and by the removal of the rudder-travel limit, and the F-5As supplied to Norway differ from the standard MAP aircraft in having a tail hook for arrested airfield landings, and intake lip and windshield de-icing.

F-5B: Possessing similar ordnance-lifting capabilities as the single-seat F-5A, the tandem two-seat F-5B adds training capability to its range of operational roles, and apart from the replacement of the cannon armament by a second cockpit, there are few differences between the two versions. Manufactured on the same line as the F-5A, the F-5B accounts for roughly one-tenth of MAP orders so far placed, the ratio of two-seaters to single-seaters being about 1 : 9.

F-5C: Originally proposed for the U.S.A.F. Tactical Air Command, an improved development of the F-5A evolved as part of a manufacturer-sponsored programme has been tentatively designated F-5C, a prototype with the company designation F-5-15 having begun flight trials in May 1965. The principal differences between the F-5C and the MAP F-5A are the introduction of 4,300 lb.s.t. J85-GE-15 turbojets in place of the lower-powered -13s; 'take-off doors' to increase engine air and improve efficiency during take-off, and a two-position nosewheel leg raising the take-off attitude by 3° and permitting earlier lift-off with a forward c.g. Added to these changes tested on the F-5-15 will be the barrier engagement tail hook and anti-icing provisions already incorporated in the Norwegian F-5A. The modifications result in a 33 per cent improvement in take-off ground roll which, at 14,000 lb., is reduced from 2,650 ft. to 1,890 ft., while, with a 2,500-lb. combat load, take-off roll is reduced from 4,200 ft. to 3,300 ft. In the intercept

(Right) The first Northrop F-5A for the Royal Norwegian Air Force which is in process of receiving 68 F-5As and F-5Bs, and (below, right) F-5As of the Imperial Iranian Air Force at the 1st Fighter Air Base at Mehrabad.

Power Plants: *Two General Electric J85-GE-13 turbojets each rated at* 2,720 *lb.s.t. and* 4,080 *lb.s.t. with afterburning.*
Performance: *(F-5A) Max. speed (with clean wingtips at* 11,000 *lb.),* 924 *m.p.h. at* 36,860 *ft. (Mach.* 1.4*), (with a Sidewinder at each wingtip at* 14,000 *lb.),* 870 *m.p.h. (Mach* 1.32*), (at* 11,000 *lb. at sea level),* 745 *m.p.h. (Mach* 0.98*); range cruise (max. fuel configuration),* 554 *m.p.h. at* 36,000–40,000 *ft. (Mach* 0.84*); tactical radius (supersonic intercept mission with Mach* 1.24 *cruise to intercept point,* 5 *min. max. power and Mach* 0.84 *cruise return),* 167 *mls., (attack mission with* 550 *U.S. gal. auxiliary fuel and* 1,500 *lb. ordnance),* 635 *mls.; ferry range,* 1,865 *mls.; initial climb (clean),* 29,800 *ft./min.; combat ceiling (at* 11,100 *lb.),* 50,000 *ft. (F-5B) Max. speed (clean condition with one pilot),* 884 *m.p.h. at* 36,000 *ft. (Mach* 1.34*); initial climb,* 28,700 *ft./min.*
Weights: *(F-5A) Empty,* 7,860 *lb.; max. loaded,* 20,040 *lb. (F-5B) Empty,* 8,227 *lb.; max. loaded,* 19,800 *lb.*
Dimensions: *(Figures in parentheses relate to F-5B) Span,* 25 *ft.* 3 *in.; length,* 47 *ft.* 2⅓ *in.* (46 *ft.* 4 *in.); height,* 13 *ft.* 2 *in.* (13 *ft.* 1 *in.); wing area,* 173.82 *sq. ft.*

configuration initial climb rate is boosted by some 7,000 ft./min. to 37,000 ft./min., maximum speed also being increased marginally from Mach 1.4 to Mach 1.42.

CF-5: Being manufactured under licence for the R.C.A.F. by Canadair, the CF-5 embodies the improvements tested on the F-5-15, anti-icing equipment and flight refuelling capability. The CF-5 will enter service the with R.C.A.F. Mobile Command in 1967, and current proposals call for the inclusion of some 20 tandem two-seat models designated CF-5B in the quantity of 125 aircraft programmed.

(*Left*) *An F-84F Thunderstreak* (*FU*-155) *of the* 31*ème Escadrille—the operational training unit—of the* 10*ème Wing of the Force Aérienne Belge at Petit-Brogel. The F-84F currently remains in first-line operational service with Belgium's* 1*ème and* 2*ème Escadrilles.*

REPUBLIC F-84F THUNDERSTREAK

It may be stated with complete justification that the F-84F Thunderstreak single-seat tactical fighter-bomber which, for so many years, provided the backbone of NATO, owes its existence solely to a conflict that took place on the other side of the globe—the Korean War. Until North Korean forces crossed the 38th parallel, funds available to the U.S.A.F. for the acquisition of new aircraft were strictly limited, and it was in this atmosphere of strict economy that the F-84F was conceived. Essentially the fuselage of the existing F-84E Thunderjet married to new swept wing and tail surfaces to increase the limiting Mach number, the F-84F was intended to utilise almost 60 per cent of the tooling used for the earlier fighter, but the prototype, the YF-84F, which flew on June 3, 1950, three weeks before the Korean conflict began, proved a mediocre aircraft indeed, offering only a marginal performance gain over the existing F-84E. There can be no doubt that but for the additional funds made available as a result of the fighting in Korea which made possible the decision to completely rework the design, further development of the F-84F would have been abandoned.

The more powerful Wright J65 turbojet supplanted the 5,800 lb. s.t. Allison J35-A-29, and to cater for the increased airflow necessary, an additional seven-inch section was spliced into the fuselage along the horizontal plane, resulting in an elliptical air intake. With these and other changes, a second YF-84F flew on February 14, 1951, the first production F-84F following on November 22, 1952. Like the second prototype, the initial production F-84Fs had the J65-W-1, this being supplanted by the J65-W-3 in the F-84F-5-RE and subsequent production batches. Later aircraft, commencing with the F-84F-25-RE batch, introduced an all-moving slab-type tailplane, and during the mid 'fifties deliveries of the F-84F to NATO air arms began, this aircraft equipping the bulk of the tactical fighter-bomber elements until re-equipment with the F-104G Starfighter began in 1963. In fact, almost half the 2,711 F-84F Thunderstreaks built (1,301) were for NATO forces with which it rapidly built up a reputation for being tank-like in construction and capable of absorbing a lot of punishment and staying

GENERAL ARRANGEMENT DRAWING: *An F-84F Thunderstreak* (52-7022) *of the Türk Hava Kuvvetleri.*

5´ 10´
7022
27022

in the air. It also proved itself thoroughly reliable and offered a relatively smooth ride through low-level turbulence.

Today, the F-84F Thunderstreak remains in service with the *1ème* and *2ème Escadrilles* of the *Force Aérienne Belge* at Florennes and Nos. 314 and 315 Squadrons of the *Koninklijke Nederlandse Luchtmacht* at Eindhoven, and is scheduled to remain operational with these units until 1969–70; with the 4e Escadre of the *Armée de l'Air* although expected to be phased out of service with this air arm by 1967; with the *Luftwaffe's* Jabo G 35 at Husum which is expected to re-equip during 1967; with the 102°, 155° and 156° *Gruppi* of the *Aeronautica Militare Italiano* which are expected to re-equip during 1968–70 with the F-104Gs transferred from the intercept elements with the availability of the F-104S; with two squadrons of the Royal Hellenic Air Force which expect to re-equip with the F-5A during 1967–68, and with five squadrons of the Turkish Air Force which will progressively re-equip with the F-5A during 1966–69. The F-84F was temporarily restored to the U.S.A.F.'s active inventory to equip additional T.A.C. wings established in 1962–63, but has now been re-assigned to the Air National Guard.

The F-84F has an A-4 radar gunsight for use with a battery of six 0.5-in. Colt-Browning M-3 machine guns, four of which are mounted in the fuselage and two in the wing roots, and up to 6,000 lb. of ordnance or fuel tanks may be carried on external pylons in 22 different combinations, a typical load comprising two 1,000-lb. bombs, eight 5-in. HVARs, and two 230 U.S. gal. (191.5 Imp. gal.) drop tanks to give a take-off weight of 26,030 lb. The total internal fuel capacity is 570 U.S. gal. (475 Imp. gal.), but two 230 U.S. gal. (191.5 Imp. gal.) drop tanks are normally carried, while for ferry purposes two 450 U.S. gal. (375 Imp. gal.) or four 230 U.S. gal. (191.5 Imp. gal.) tanks may be carried, giving a maximum fuel load of 1,490 U.S. gal. (1,241 Imp. gal.), and for overload take-off assistance a solid-fuel rocket motor is mounted beneath the tailpipe.

(*Below*) *An F-84F Thunderstreak* (53-6970) *of the* 155° *Gruppo of the Italian* 6ª *Aerobrigata. Italy's Aeronautica Militare still possesses three F-84F-equipped Gruppi.*

Power Plant: *One Wright J65-W-3 turbojet rated at* 7,220 *lb.s.t.*
Performance: *Max. speed (clean),* 695 *m.p.h. at sea level (Mach* 0.91), 658 *m.p.h. at* 20,000 *ft.* (*Mach* 0.94); *combat radius (clean),* 450 *mls. at* 528 *m.p.h. at* 36,000–40,000 *ft.* (*Mach* 0.8), *with two* 230 *U.S. gal./*191.5 *Imp. gal. drop tanks,* 790 *mls.; ferry range (with four* 230 *U.S. gal./*191.5 *Imp. gal. drop tanks),* 2,140 *mls.; initial climb (clean),* 8,200 *ft./min.,* (*at* 25,190 *lb.*), 3,620 *ft./min.; service ceiling,* 46,000 *ft.*
Weights: *Loaded (clean),* 19,340 *lb.; normal loaded,* 26,000 *lb.; max.,* 28,000 *lb.*
Dimensions: *Span,* 33 *ft.* 7¼ *in.; length,* 43 *ft.* 4¾ *in.; height,* 14 *ft.* 4¾ *in.; wing area,* 325 *sq. ft.*

(Right) An F-105D Thunderchief (62-4370) of the U.S.A.F. Tactical Air Command. During 1966, the Republic Aviation Division of the Fairchild Hiller Corporation was installing more advanced avionics packages in F-105Ds for use in Vietnam, and proposals were being made to reinstate the Thunderchief in production to meet the attrition of the Vietnam conflict. Proposed changes include the provision of 750 lb. of additional armour beneath the cockpit and around the fuselage accessory section.

REPUBLIC F-105 THUNDERCHIEF

Largest and heaviest single-seat fighter in the world, the F-105D version of the Thunderchief has been responsible for the major share of the U.S.A.F.'s strike missions against targets in North Vietnam. Although designed primarily for the delivery of nuclear weapons at supersonic speeds, the F-105D's Mach 2.0 performance capability has proved to be of no value over Vietnam where it flies subsonically in the conventional ordnance delivery role against bridges, railways and other targets to inhibit the flow of men and supplies destined for the Viet Cong, the weapons bay designed to house a nuclear store being occupied by fuel.

The F-105D currently serves with the 4th (Seymour Johnson A.F.B.), 18th (Kadena, Okinawa), 23rd (McConnell A.F.B.), 35th (Da Nang), 49th (Spangdahlem, Germany), 355th (McConnell A.F.B.), and 6441st (Yokota, Japan) Tactical Fighter Wings, with a total of 21 Squadrons, and in its initial production and rather less sophisticated F-105B form, the Thunderchief equips the Air National Guard's 108th (New Jersey) Tactical Fighter Wing.

The F-105 was originally conceived as a private-venture successor to the F-84F Thunderstreak, and the first of two J57-P-25-powered YF-105A prototypes flew on October 22, 1955. The third aircraft, designated F-105B and flown on May 26, 1956, was only superficially similar to its predecessors, having been largely redesigned in detail as a result of the availability of new aerodynamic data on supersonic aircraft design, and employing the very much more powerful J75-P-3 turbojet. This was the first of 12 pre-production machines for development purposes, deliveries of the production F-105B to the U.S.A.F. commencing on May 27, 1958, the 4th Tactical Fighter Wing re-equipping with this type. The 4th was destined to be the only U.S.A.F. unit to fly the F-105B as, on June 9, 1959, an appreciably more advanced model, the F-105D, had flown, and this supplanted the B-model on the assembly line with the 79th Thunderchief. The 4th continued to operate the

F-105B until 1964 when it re-equipped with the F-105D and passed the earlier aircraft to the Air National Guard's 108th Tactical Fighter Wing.

F-105D: Possessing much improved mission electronics to permit all kinds of offensive strike and reconnaissance operations in all weather, the F-105D introduced the APN-131 Doppler airborne navigation system which, automatically and independently of ground installations, supplies the pilot with continual present-position co-ordinates, ground speed, track, heading and distance to target, wind direction and velocity, and alternative destination selection. The NASARR R-14A all-purpose monopulse radar is optimized in both air-to-ground and air-to-air modes, and for both low-level and high-level missions, providing air search, automatic tracking, ground and contour mapping, and terrain avoidance, irrespective of visibility, ceiling or target-area condition, and this, the Doppler and the General Electric FC-5 flight control system and autopilot, are tied together to form an automatic navigation system which, at the time of its introduction, was the most sophisticated extant. The ASG-19 Thunderstick fire control system, which includes the NASARR, provides automatic or manual and blind or visual weapons delivery, with automatic or manually-controlled weapons release in all the various modes, from over-the-shoulder toss to retarded lay-down.

Whereas the J75-P-5 engine of the interim F-105B offered a maximum afterburning thrust of 23,500 lb., the J75-P-19W standardised for the F-105D affords 17,200 lb.s.t. dry and a maximum thrust of 26,500 lb. with afterburning and water injection. Built-in armament of both models comprises a 20-mm. M-61 Vulcan rotary cannon with 1,029 rounds, and this weapon has proved singularly accurate and effective in Vietnam. An internal weapons bay is provided, this being intended for a nuclear store and permitting the Thunderchief to bomb in clean configuration for maximum speed delivery, but with the F-105D-25 and subsequent production batches increased emphasis was placed on conventional capability, and an exceptionally wide range of stores can be lifted up to a maximum of 12,000 lb. There are 17 store-carrying stations, and such loads as 16 250-lb., 500-lb., or 750-lb. bombs, nine 1,000-lb. bombs, or four AGM-12 Bullpup ASMs may be carried. In Vietnam all missions are flown with a 390 U.S. gal. (325 Imp. gal.) fuel tank in the internal weapons bay to supplement the 1,160 U.S. gal. (966 Imp. gal.) internal fuel, and with external fuel in one of two configurations—either two 450 U.S. gal. (375 Imp. gal.) drop tanks on inboard pylons or one 650 U.S. gal. (541 Imp. gal.) drop tank on the fuselage centreline. Normal offensive load with the two drop tanks is six 750-lb. M-117 bombs or five 1,000-lb Mk.83 bombs, and with the centreline tank two 2,000-lb. or 3,000-lb. bombs may be carried.

F-105F: The F-105F tandem two-seat dual-purpose mission trainer

Power Plant: *One Pratt & Whitney J75-P-19W turbojet rated at 17,200 lb.s.t. and 24,500 lb.s.t. with afterburning (boosted to 26,500 lb.s.t. for 60 sec. with water injection).*
Performance: *Max. speed (clean), 855 m.p.h. at sea level (Mach 1.11), 1,390 m.p.h. at 36,000 ft. (Mach 2.1), 1,122 m.p.h. at 50,000 ft. (Mach 1.7); tactical radius (with two AGM-12 ASMs, one 650 U.S. gal./541 Imp. gal. and two 450 U.S. gal./375 Imp. gal. drop tanks), 920 mls., (with 16 750-lb. bombs), 230 mls.; ferry range (max. external fuel), 2,390 mls. at 584 m.p.h.; initial climb (clean), 34,400 ft./min.*
Weights: *Empty, 28,000 lb.; normal loaded (clean), 38,034 lb.; max. overload, 52,546 lb.*
Dimensions: *Span, 34 ft. 11¼ in.; length, 67 ft. 0⅓ in.; height, 19 ft. 8⅓ in.; wing area, 385 sq. ft.*

GENERAL ARRANGEMENT DRAWING: *An F-105D Thunderchief (60-0428) of the 6441st Tactical Fighter Wing at Yokota, Japan.*

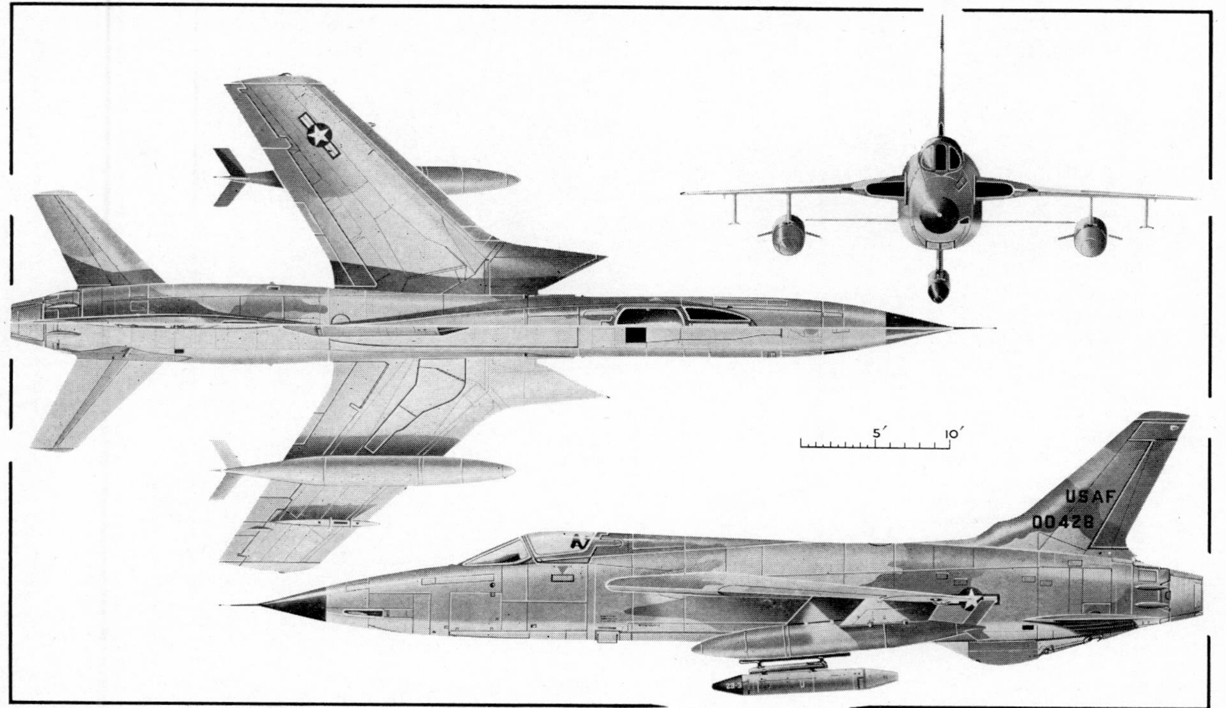
5′
10′
USAF
00428

(Left) A tandem two-seat F-105F Thunderchief (63-8349) at Andrews A.F.B. The F-105F retains the full mission capability of the single-seat F-105D, performance being within three per cent of that of the single-seater.

and tactical fighter version of the F-105D flew on June 11, 1963, and some 140 aircraft of this type were ordered in lieu of a similar number of the single-seat model, these being distributed among the 21 U.S.A.F. and three A.N.G. Thunderchief squadrons. The F-105F differs from the D-model primarily in having an additional section inserted in the forward fuselage to provide space for the second cockpit, increasing overall length to 69 ft. 7⅛ in., and slightly taller vertical tail surfaces to compensate for the increased forward side area, overall height being 20 ft. 2 in. Normal loaded weight (clean) is increased to 40,073 lb., maximum overload weight being 54,027 lb., and performance is within three per cent of that of the single-seater. Production of the Thunderchief was phased out during 1964, between 800 and 900 aircraft of all models having been manufactured.

SAAB 32B LANSEN

A two-seat night and all-weather interceptor derived from the basic Saab 32 attack aircraft (see pages 201–204), the Saab 32B entered the design development phase in 1955, the prototype flying for the first time on January 7, 1957, and the production model entering *Flygvapnet* service in 1959 as the J 32B, some 150 having been built when the final example was delivered on May 2, 1960. Currently equipping two interceptor wings, F 1 at Västerås and F 12 at Kalmar, and one *Division* of F 21 at Luleå, the J 32B differs little externally from other Lansen variants, but embodies extensive internal redesign dictated by the installation of the more powerful RM 6A (RB.90 Mk.47A Avon) engine, a heavier internal cannon armament of four 30-mm. Aden M/55 weapons, and the introduction of intercept avionics. In addition to some enlarging and redesigning of the air intake ducting for compatibility with the more powerful engine with its larger SFA afterburner, local structural strengthening was undertaken, and modifications were introduced in the control system to improve transonic speed handling qualities.

Carrying some 220 lb. more avionic equipment than the A 32A,

GENERAL ARRANGEMENT DRAWING: *A J 32B Lansen of F 1, the Västmanlands Flygflottilj, at Hässlö, Västerås.*

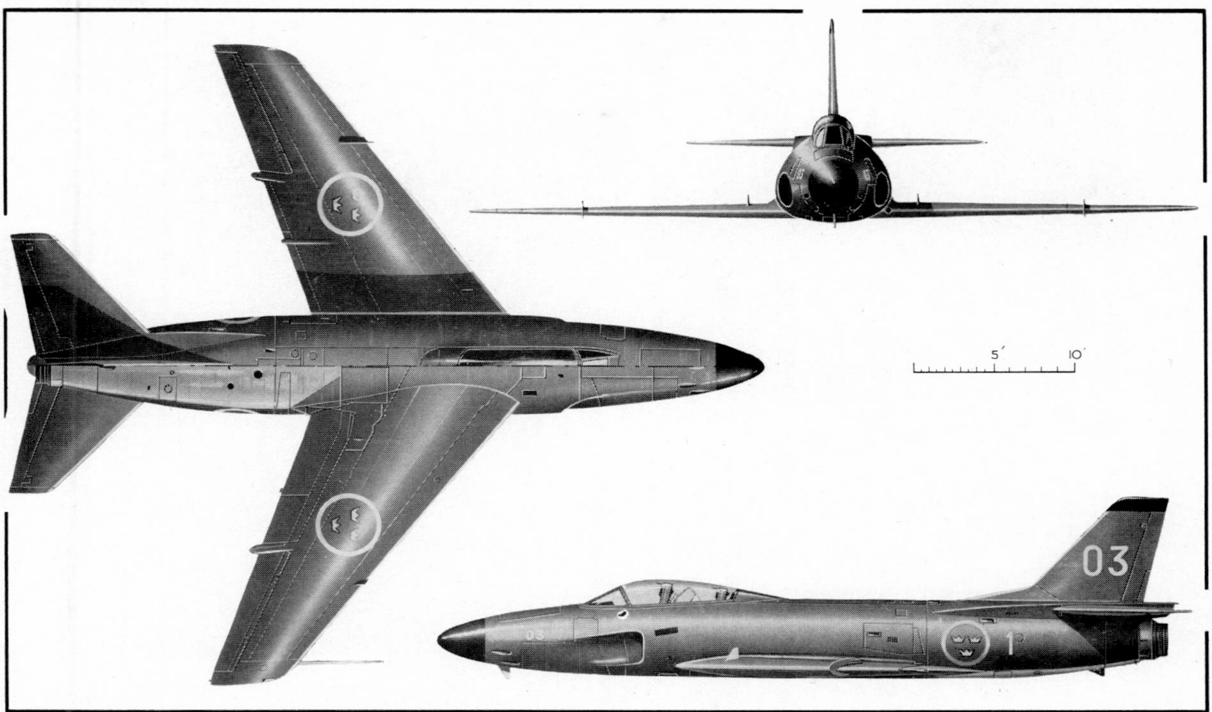
5'
10'
03
1

(*Above*) *Two J 32B Lansens of the Flygvapnet's F* 1.

the J 32B has PN-50/A and PN-51 radar navaids, a PH-11/A radar altimeter, L.M. Ericsson PS-42 radar ranging, the Saab S6 all-weather gun sight and general-purpose type fire control system for all-weather lead-pursuit interception, and a Lear basic attitude-holding autopilot. A Hughes-type infra-red sensor is currently being introduced primarily for use at night. Internal fuel capacity is similar to that of the A 32A at 770 Imp. gal. (925 U.S. gal.), and this may be supplemented by a flush-fitting 121 Imp. gal. (146 U.S. gal.) ventral auxiliary tank. The primary intercept armament now comprises four *Robot* 24 (Sidewinder) infra-red homing AAMs mounted on underwing launching shoes, but alternative external ordnance loads include four pods each housing 19 7.5-cm. rockets, 24 13.5-cm. rockets or 12 18-cm. rockets.

Some consideration has been given to the possibility of re-manufacturing a number of J 32B interceptors for the attack role to supplement the ageing A 32As pending availability of the AJ 37 Viggen in the early 'seventies, but no decision had been taken at the time of closing for press.

Power Plant: *One Svenska Flygmotor RM 6A* (*Rolls-Royce RB.*90 *Mk.*47*A Avon*) *turbojet rated at* 11,025 *lb.s.t. and* 14,330 *lb.s.t. with afterburning.*
Performance: *Max. speed* (*at* 24,679 *lb.*), 710 *m.p.h. at sea level* (*Mach* 0.93), 630 *m.p.h. at* 36,000 *ft.* (*Mach* 0.95)*; normal cruise*, 528 *m.p.h. at* 36,000–40,000 *ft.* (*Mach* 0.8)*; range* (*with four Rb* 24 *missiles and* 121 *Imp. gal./*146 *U.S. gal. ventral tank*), 900–1,000* *mls.; initial climb* (*clean at* 24,679 *lb.*), 19,685 *ft./min.; service ceiling*, 52,490 *ft.*
Weights: *Empty*, 16,535 *lb.; loaded* (*clean*), 24,679 *lb.; max. loaded*, 29,760 *lb.*
Dimensions: *Span*, 42 *ft.* $7\frac{3}{4}$ *in.; length*, 49 *ft.* $0\frac{1}{4}$ *in.; height*, 15 *ft.* 3 *in.; wing area*, 402.57 *sq. ft.*
*APPROXIMATE

SAAB 35 DRAKEN

With a primary intercept role and a secondary strike role, and unique in employing a wing planform of double-delta configuration, the Saab 35 Draken (Dragon) has displayed considerable development potential since first introduced into service by the *Flygvapnet* in 1960, and the current production model, the Saab 35F, has little in common with initial versions other than its external appearance. Integrated with the STRIL 60 ground environment, it is claimed to provide the most modern and efficient manned all-weather air defence system in Europe. The Saab 35 fighter is currently serving with the *Flygvapnet* in four versions: the J 35A which has now been almost entirely supplanted by later models but is still operated by F 16 at Uppsala; the J 35B which equips part of F 16 and F 18 at Tullinge; the J 35D operated by F 3 at Malmslätt and F 10 at Ängelholm, and the J 35F which began to enter service with F 13 at Norrköping in 1965. Approximately half the 550 Drakens ordered for the *Flygvapnet* had been delivered by mid-1966, and production is scheduled to continue until at least 1969, the J 35F having been ordered in more substantial numbers than any other Draken version.

Detail design of the Saab 35 was initiated in December 1951, a contract for three prototypes and three pre-production aircraft being awarded in August 1953, and the first prototype flew on October 25, 1955. Eight months later, in August 1956, an initial production order was awarded Saab which delivered the first two production aircraft to F 13 on March 8, 1960.

J 35A: Powered by an RM 6B (S.F.A.-built RB.90 Mk.48A) turbojet rated at 11,250 lb.s.t. and boosted to some 15,190 lb. by an S.F.A. Model 65 afterburner, the initial service Draken, the J 35A, was a fairly basic aircraft in terms of armament and control systems, with a Saab S 6B fire control system, a plain intercept radar built under CSF licence by L. M. Ericsson (offering search, lock-on and break-away modes), and Lear basic attitude-holding auto-pilot for conventional lead-pursuit attack with cannon or unguided rockets. Armament comprised two 30-mm. Aden M/55 cannon with 90 r.p.g. which could be supplemented by four Saab rocket launchers each housing 19 7.5-cm. unguided missiles, and the internal fuel capacity of 493 Imp. gal. (592 U.S. gal.) could be supplemented for ferry purposes by four 66 Imp. gal. (79 U.S. gal.) drop tanks. Weighing 14,528 lb. empty and some 19,800 lb. in

(Below) A J 35D Draken of F 3 *in the camouflage scheme adopted by the Flygvapnet in* 1966 *for all tactical aircraft. The J35D serves with F* 3 *at Malmslätt and F* 10 *at Ängelholm.*

The J 35D was the first version of the Draken to receive the RB.146 Mk.60 Avon which supplanted the RB.90 Mk.48A of the earlier production models. The example illustrated (left) is operated by F3 at Malmslätt.

normal loaded condition, the J 35A attained a maximum climb rate of the order of 39,400 ft./min. and Mach 1.8 in level flight, but was somewhat short on range in clean condition.

The 63rd and subsequent production J 35A fighters introduced a lengthened rear fuselage with a Model 66 afterburner. The longer aft fuselage eradicated some slight longitudinal instability at both high and low speeds, simultaneously making possible greater air brake extension without buffet, and the improved fineness ratio reducing drag at high speed. A solid-tyred diabolo tailwheel was fitted to permit pilots to use the maximum nose-up attitude for aerodynamic braking on the ground. The fuselage extension increased overall length, including pitot head, from 49 ft. $10\frac{3}{4}$ in. to 52 ft. 5 in. or, excluding pitot, 43 ft. 7 in. to 46 ft. $1\frac{1}{4}$ in. Most early production J 35A Drakens have been converted to Sk 35C tandem two-seat trainers or brought up to later J 35B standards. The Sk 35C, which is used alongside the J 35A by the operational conversion unit at Uppsala, embodies a new front fuselage in which the instructor is seated slightly above the pupil, his cockpit having the minimum of instrumentation, virtually all systems, navigation equipment, undercarriage, etc. being controlled exclusively from the front cockpit. The instructor is provided with a periscopic sight for landing, and the Sk 35C carries neither radar nor armament, additional fuel tanks supplanting the 30-mm. cannon, and maximum speed is of the order of Mach 1.5.

J 35B: The second production version of the single-seat Draken, the J 35B, differs little from late production J 35As apart from the introduction of the Saab S7 collision-course gunsight and fire control system and more advanced instrumentation. The J 35B first flew on November 29, 1959, and despite its collision-course radar retained the lead-pursuit weapons of its predecessor. At an early service stage provision was made for a quartette of *Robot* 24 (Sidewinder) infra-red homing AAMs which currently provide the principal intercept armament of both this and the later J 35D. As the J 35B has the dual interceptor and strike role, provision is made for such alternative external ordnance loads as two 1,100-lb. bombs, four 550-lb. bombs, nine 220-lb. bombs, or eighteen 13.5-cm. HVAR missiles.

J 35D: Essentially an interim model of the Draken pending the introduction of the definitive J 35F, the J 35D carries a similar array of weapons to that of its immediate production predecessor, but introduces the substantially more powerful RM 6C (RB.146

GENERAL ARRANGEMENT DRAWING: *A J 35D Draken of F* 10, *the Skånska Flygflottilj, based at Ängelholm,*

5´ 10´
21
10

Mk.60 Avon) turbojet with an S.F.A. Model 67 afterburner with a consequent benefit to all-round performance. The installation of the RM 6C was accompanied by a 115 Imp. gal. (138 U.S. gal.) increase in internal fuel capacity, and increases in empty and maximum loaded weights from 14,528 lb. and 19,800 lb. to 16,017 lb. and 22,663 lb. respectively. The Lear flight control system was supplanted by the Saab FH5 system with air data system, stick-steering, and various following modes, and vertical tape instruments were tied in with the data link system integrating the aircraft with the STRIL 60 ground environment.

The prototype J 35D, a converted J 35A airframe, was flown on December 27, 1960, and production deliveries began to F 13 in 1963.

J 35F: Currently considered to be the definitive model of the basic Draken design, the J 35F which now serves with F 13 was under continuous development for some five years prior to its service début, the Swedish Air Staff decision to adopt a mix of infra-red and radar-homing Falcon missiles as the Draken's definitive intercept armament having been taken in March 1959, and the first prototype airframe being flown in 1961. The first variant of the basic design to carry collision-course attack armament, which is particularly necessary in view of Sweden's very short warning time, the J 35F normally carries a mix of two *Robot* 27 semi-active radar homing and two *Robot* 28 infra-red homing AAMs which are modified versions of the Hughes Falcon manufactured by Saab, the former being carried beneath the fuselage and the latter beneath the wings. The infra-red homers are carried because of the limitations of the radar homers in conditions of heavy countermeasures and close to the ground, and they thus complete the intercept capability over the full band of heights and tactical situations.

Equipment includes the Saab S 7B collision-course fire-control system, L. M. Ericsson's PS-01/A search and ranging radar, PN-594/A and PN-793/A navaids, the Saab FH5 automatic flight control system, and a Hughes infra-red sensor which, mounted beneath the nose of the J 35F, improves sighting and maintains weapon effectiveness during countermeasures activity. Only the port 30-mm. Aden cannon is retained, that in the starboard wing having been removed to provide space for an electronics package, but the attachment points for other ordnance loads are retained. The J 35F introduces a zero-zero rocket ejection seat to the Draken for the first time, this having also been adopted for the S 35E reconnaissance version (see Vol. II, page 110), and a single-piece blown hood replaces the framed and pannelled canopy fitted to previous models. Internal fuel capacity is 630 Imp. gal. (757 U.S. gal.), and this may be supplemented by two 115 Imp. gal. (138 U.S. gal.) drop tanks.

Power Plant: *One Svenska Flygmotor RM* 6C (*Rolls-Royce RB.*146 *Mk.*60 *Avon*) *rated at* 12,710 *lb.s.t. and* 17,260 *lb.s.t. with afterburning.*
Performance: *Max. speed* (*clean*), 1,320–1,390* *m.p.h. at* 36,000–40,000 *ft.* (*Mach* 2.0–2.1), (*with four AAMs*), 1,190* *m.p.h.* (*Mach* 1.8)*; range cruise*, 590 *m.p.h. at* 36,000 *ft.* (*Mach* 0.9)*; range* (*internal fuel*), 700 *mls.*, (*with two* 115 *Imp. gal./*138 *U.S. gal. drop tanks*), 895 *mls.; initial climb* (*clean*), 39,510 *ft./min.*, (*with four AAMs*), 32,000 *ft./ min.; combat ceiling*, 55,000 *ft.*
Weights: *Empty*, 16,370 *lb.; loaded* (*with four AAMs*), 22,830 *lb.; max. loaded*, 26,600* *lb.*
Dimensions: *Span*, 30 *ft.* 10¾ *in.; length* (*including probe*), 50 *ft.* 4 *in.*, (*excluding probe*), 46 *ft.* 10¼ *in.; height*, 12 *ft.* 8⅓ *in.; wing area*, 529.8 *sq. ft.*
*APPROXIMATE
Note: *Specification applicable to J 35F.*

GENERAL ARRANGEMENT DRAWING: *A J 35F Draken of* F 13, *the Bråvalla Flygflottilj, based at Norrköping.*

5´
10´
09
13

SUKHOI SU-7 (FITTER)

A single-seat close-support and ground attack fighter, the Su-7 was the first design of Pavel Osipovich Sukhoi to attain quantity production after the re-establishment of his design bureau in 1953, the bureau having previously been disbanded in 1949. The Su-7, evolved in parallel with the Su-9 all-weather interceptor with which it shares limited "commonality" of major components, is a relatively unsophisticated warplane capable of operating from short, rough strips but lacking in flexibility owing to the strict limitation in underwing loads imposed by the sharp sweepback selected for its wing. Extensively used by the *Frontovaya Aviatsiya*, the tactical component of the V.-V.S., and equipping the ground attack elements of the *Ceskoslovenské letectvo* and The *Polskie Lotnictwo Wojskowe*, the Su-7 has been in service since 1959–60, and has been progressively developed during its production life, current models having an uprated engine and other modifications.

(*Above and below*) *Sukhoi Su-7MB close-support fighters of the Ceskoslovenské letectvo, that above carrying twin drop tanks.*

The basic design, allegedly designated Su-1, made its public début over Tushino in June 1956, at which time it was presumably being evaluated against a contemporary Mikoyan design, a smaller swept-wing aircraft having some "commonality" of structure with the prototype MiG-21 and dubbed *Faceplate* in the West. The initial production model of the Su-7 was powered by a turbojet with an afterburning thrust of 19,840 lb., suggesting a dry thrust of the order of 14,500 lb., but the later production Su-7M has an

GENERAL ARRANGEMENT DRAWING: *A Sukhoi Su-7MB of the Ceskoslovenské letectvo.*

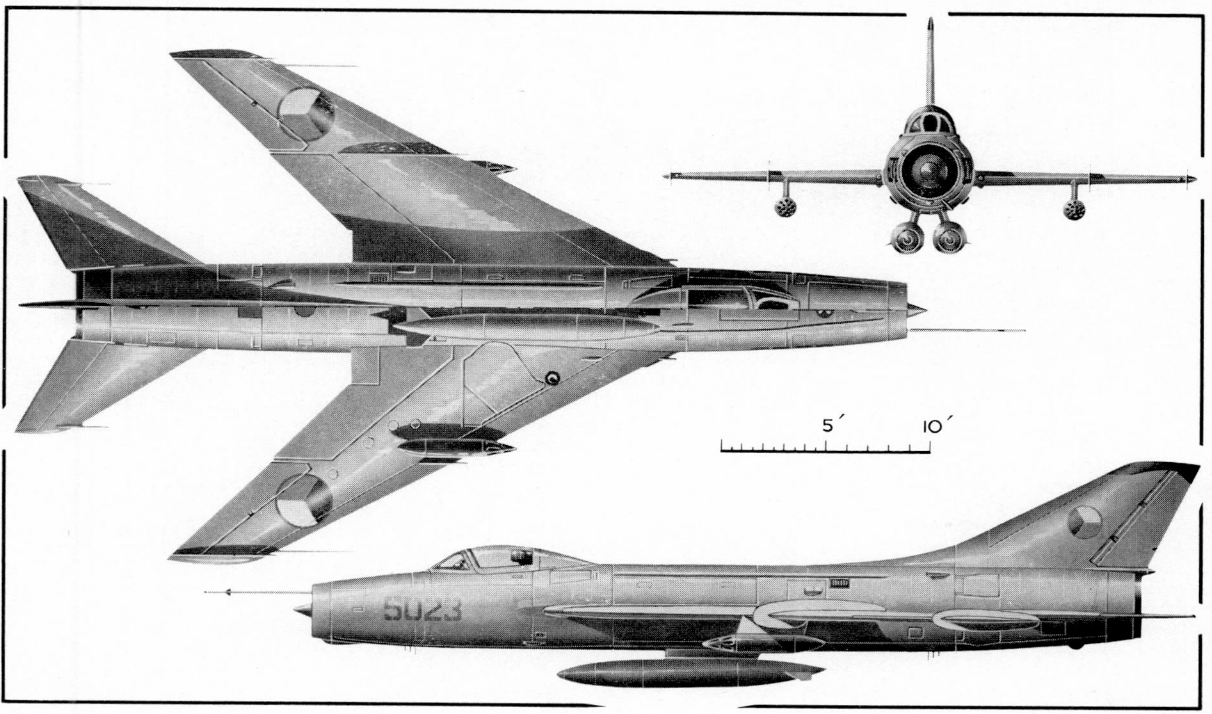
5′
10′
5023

(Left) The Sukhoi Su-7 close-support and ground attack fighter is widely used by the Frontovaya Aviatsiya, and exists in tandem two-seat version for the conversion trainer role. The sharp sweepback of the Su-7's wing places a strict limitation on underwing stores, but the type is of rugged construction and can operate from grass strips.

uprated engine similar to that employed by current Su-9 fighters and which, according to data released to the F.A.I., has an afterburning thrust of 22,050 lb., its installation being accompanied by some enlarging of the air intake. Other modifications introduced since the Su-7's service début include external cable ducts which run along the back of the centre fuselage, and the transfer of the pitot head from a central position above the air intake to a position to starboard.

The Su-7's wing, which features large area-increasing flaps extending from the roots to almost 50° span, is swept 62° at the leading edge, and offers useful fuel volume but strictly limits the number of weapons pylons that can be fitted. Internal fuel capacity may be supplemented by a pair of 132 Imp. gal. (158 U.S. gal.) tanks mounted side by side on stores pylons beneath the fuselage, and flight refuelling facilities are provided. Radar ranging is provided, but equipment is relatively unsophisticated in keeping with the overall design concept, and the nearest Western equivalent is the appreciably lighter and smaller Northrop F-5A. The array of weapons that can be carried by the Su-7 is far less impressive than that of the F-5A owing to pylon limitations. The installation of the twin 30-mm. cannon in the wing roots avoids pitching when the guns are fired, providing a stable platform, but there is probably considerable interference drag between the stores on the ventral pylons which can each lift a 1,000-lb. bomb. The two underwing pylons appear to be restricted to relatively light loads, such as a single bomb up to 550 lb. weight or a pod housing 19 unguided rockets of 55-mm. calibre. The version of the Su-7 serving with the *Ceskoslovenské letectvo* has been referred to both as the Su-7MB and Su-7B, and may be presumed to be identical to models operated by the *Frontovaya Aviatsiya* of the V.-V.S. A tandem two-seat training version, the Su-7UTI, is also in service.

Power Plant: *One axial-flow turbojet of* 15,500* *lb.s.t. and* 22,050* *lb.s.t. with afterburning.*
Performance: *Max. speed (clean),* 1,056* *m.p.h. at* 36,000 *ft.* (*Mach* 1.6), (*with two* 132 *Imp. gal./*158 *U.S. gal. drop tanks and two rocket pods*), 790* *m.p.h.* (*Mach* 1.2)*; initial climb (clean),* 30,000 *ft./min.,* (*high drag configuration*), 23,500 *ft./min.*
Weights: *Loaded (clean),* 27,000* *lb.; max. loaded,* 30,500* *lb.*
Dimensions: *Span,* 32 *ft.* 3 *in.**; length,* 55 *ft.* 0 *in.**; height,* 16 *ft.* 0 *in**.
*APPROXIMATE

SUKHOI SU-9 (FISHPOT)

During the late 'forties and early 'fifties, combat aircraft designers in all the principal aircraft-manufacturing countries began, after a brief flirtation with the tailless configuration, to evince marked interest in the delta wing planform. While the delta configuration was not to prove the panacea that many believed, this type of wing was adopted by many warplanes evolved during this period, and the Soviet Union largely pioneered the "tailed delta" for relatively small fighters. The "tailed delta" configuration had been adopted by the Lavochkin and Yakovlev design bureaux for competing tandem two-seat twin-jet all-weather interceptors that appeared in 1951 under the design bureau designations La-250 and Yak-1000, these being in a broadly similar category to the Gloster Javelin, but the lack of success of these relatively large aircraft is indicated by the preference shown for the rather more orthodox Yak-25 that made its début two years later. More success attended smaller aircraft of this configuration, however, the MiG-21 point-defence day interceptor being an outstanding example. A rather larger but still relatively small contemporary of the MiG-21 was the Sukhoi-designed Su-9 intended to fulfil the single-seat all-weather interceptor role, and since manufactured in substantial numbers for the (*Istrebitilnaya*) *Aviatsiya Protivo-vozdushnoi Oborony Strany*, or (Fighter) Aviation of the Air Defence of the Country, the V.-V.S.'s equivalent of the U.S.A.F.'s Air Defence Command.

Evolved in parallel with the Su-7 ground attack fighter on the basis of limited "commonality" of components, the Su-9 has an essentially similar fuselage and similar tail surfaces to those of its stablemate, these being married to a rather highly loaded 57° delta

(Right) The Su-9 single-seat all-weather interceptor provides one of the principal weapons in the armoury of the so-called Fighter Aviation of the Air Defence of the Country, its closest Western equivalent being the F-102A Delta Dagger.

wing to result in an interceptor possessing no direct western counterpart—the closest equivalent being the heavier and lower-powered F-102A Delta Dagger. Two aerodynamic prototypes of the Su-9 were seen at Tushino in 1956, one having a housing for A.I. radar over the air intake and wing root-mounted cannon, this receiving the appellation *Fishpot-A* in the West, and the other having a more orthodox circular air intake with a central cone for the A.I. radar, and being dubbed *Fishpot-B*. The latter configuration was subsequently adopted for the production version of the Su-9 which began to appear in V.-V.S. service late in 1959.

Increases in engine power evidently paralleled those applied to the Su-7, for shortly after its service début, the Su-9 (labelled T-431 for record-breaking purposes) established a zoom climb altitude record of 94,657 ft., data furnished the F.A.I. indicating that the afterburning thrust of the engine was 19,840 lb., but when a sustained altitude record of almost 70,000 ft. was established by an aircraft of the same type three years later, the engine, which was referred to as a "TRD-31", was then quoted as having an afterburning thrust of 22,046 lb. As later Su-9s have a slightly larger air intake than early production examples, it may be assumed that the uprated engine was applied to the standard interceptor. Having no cannon armament, the Su-9 has been seen most frequently with four AAMs, which, known as *Alkalis* in the West, appear to be employed with an A.I. radar modulated for beam riding, although this missile is now rather dated and may well have been supplanted by a more effective weapon. The Su-9 has a similar ventral pylon arrangement for two 132 Imp. gal. (158 U.S. gal.) drop tanks.

Experimental derivatives of the Su-9 have been seen with such modifications as a two-shock intake resulting from moving the centre body forward, but there has been as yet no indication that such developments have achieved production status.

Power Plant: *One axial-flow turbojet of* 15,500* *lb.s.t. and* 22,050* *lb.s.t. with afterburning.*
Performance: *Max. speed* (*clean*), 1,190* *m.p.h. at* 40,000 *ft.* (*Mach* 1.8), (*with four AAMs*), 990* *m.p.h.* (*Mach* 1.5)*; range cruise*, 595* *m.p.h. at* 36,000–40,000 *ft.* (*Mach* 0.9)*; initial climb*, 27,000* *ft./min.; service ceiling*, 55,000* *ft.*
Weights: *Loaded* (*clean*), 25,500* *lb.; max.*, 29,000* *lb.*
Dimensions: *Span*, 31 *ft.* 0 *in.**; *length*, 55 *ft.* 0 *in.**; *height*, 16 *ft.* 0 *in.**; *wing area*, 425* *sq. ft.*
*APPROXIMATE

GENERAL ARRANGEMENT DRAWING: *A Sukhoi Su-9 of the* (*Istrebitilnaya*) *Aviasiya Protivo-vozdushnoi Oborony Strany.*

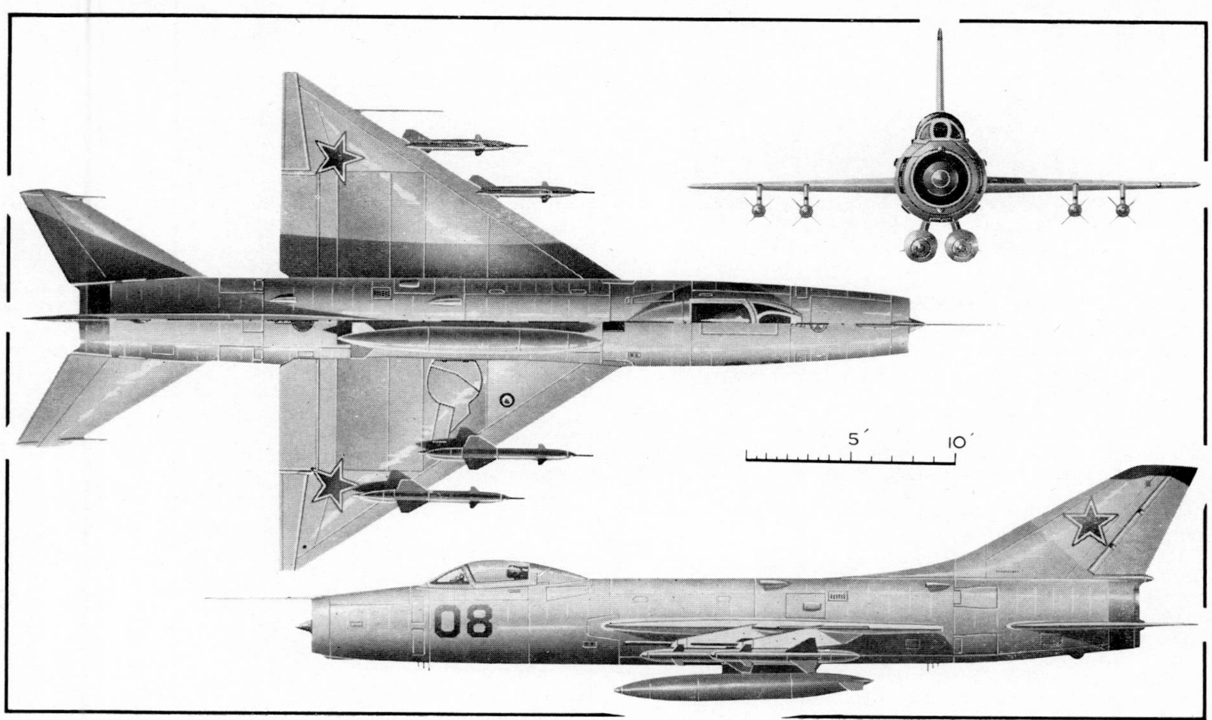
5´
10´
08

Although now obsolescent, the Yak-25 (left) remains in service in some numbers with the all-weather intercept elements of the V.-V.S.

* *The designation "Yak-25" had previously been applied in 1947 to a variant of the Yak-19 experimental single-seat jet fighter from which it differed primarily in having swept tail surfaces. As this type had been abandoned, the designation was re-allocated in 1953.*

YAKOVLEV YAK-25 (FLASHLIGHT-A)

The Yak-25, the first Soviet jet all-weather interceptor to attain service status, is the progenitor of a line of military aircraft which, manufactured over more than a decade, have embraced roles ranging from long-range high-altitude strategic and short-range low-level tactical reconnaissance, to tactical strike and training. Now obsolescent after serving the V.-V.S. as its principal night and all-weather interceptor for 12 years, the Yak-25 nevertheless remains in service in some numbers in its original role, although a proportion of the aircraft of this type have now been converted for all-weather fighter pilot and navigator instruction, this conversion being dubbed *Mangrove* in the West.

Intended to intercept such targets as the Vickers Valiant and Boeing B-47, the Yak-25* was flown for the first time in 1953, entering service with the (*Istrebitilnaya*) *Aviatsiya Protivo-vozdushnoi Oborony Strany* in 1955. Powered by non-afterburning RD-5 turbojets of 4,800 lb.s.t., the performance of the Yak-25 in its original form was unspectacular, although some improvement resulted some eighteen months after the initial service début of the fighter when the original turbojets were supplanted by RD-9s of 6,170 lb.s.t. The Yak-25 relied heavily on the relatively long search range radar which employed a large dish scanner, and as the Soviet Union was a late starter in the field of airborne fire control, it was forced to use the stern chase, visual contact method of interception. The two crew members were seated in tandem ejector seats, and the most unusual feature of the design was its novel undercarriage which was of zero-track tricycle arrangement,

Power Plants: *Two Klimov RD-9 axial-flow turbojets each rated at* 6,170 *lb.s.t.*
Performance: *Max. speed*, 630 *m.p.h. at sea level* (*Mach* 0.83), 594 *m.p.h. at* 36,000 *ft.* (*Mach* 0.9)*; range cruise*, 495 *m.p.h. at* 40,000 *ft.; initial climb*, 9,800 *ft./min.; service ceiling*, 50,000 *ft.*
Weights: *Normal loaded*, 22,000* *lb.*
Dimensions: *Span*, 36 *ft.* 0 *in.**; *length*, 51 *ft.* 0 *in.**; *height*, 12 *ft.* 6 *in.**; *wing area*, 302* *sq. ft.*
*APPROXIMATE

GENERAL ARRANGEMENT DRAWING: *A Yak-25 of the V.-V.S.'s* (*Istrebitilnaya*) *Aviatsiya Protivo-vozdushnoi Oborony Strany.*

5′
10′
067

the fighter being virtually balanced on the twin-wheel aft member of the undercarriage with outrigger units on the wingtips. Built-in armament comprised two 37-mm. N-type cannon mounted semi-externally and forming a pack with a snap-opening missile launcher housing 55-mm. unguided rockets. By detaching the gun barrels, the armament pack could be winched down from the fuselage.

An up-dated version of the basic Yak-25 embodying afterburning engines, similar aerodynamic refinements to those applied to the prototype of the Yak-28 (Vol. II, page 113), and a sharply pointed nose radome to lessen drag and reduce rain erosion, was demonstrated over Tushino in 1956, but no production of this model appears to have been undertaken, possibly owing to the relatively marginal increase in performance that it offered over the basic Yak-25, and the fact that it possessed a short lead time over later all-weather interceptors. One interesting aspect of the Yak-25's development, however, is the fact that this somewhat uninspired, relatively conventional design should have been selected in preference to the more exotic twin-engined all-weather interceptors developed and tested at much the same time by both Yakovlev and Lavochkin design bureaux.

YAKOVLEV FIREBAR

Representing the "third generation" of Yak-25 derivatives, the tandem two-seat all-weather and night fighter code-named *Firebar* by NATO stems from efforts by the Yakovlev design bureau in the late 'fifties to develop the well-proven Yak-25 airframe to permit operation at appreciably higher weights and speeds by means of aerodynamic refinements, increased wing area, and the installation of substantially larger, more powerful turbojets. An all-weather interceptor equivalent of the "second generation" Yak-28 tactical strike and reconnaissance aircraft (the *Flashlight-B*) made its appearance shortly after the service début of the basic Yakovlev design, but this model was not developed to production status, and although possessing a generally similar overall configuration, the later *Firebar* is, to all intents and purposes, a new design.

The *Firebar* differs from earlier Yak-25 derivatives in a number of major respects, and may be distinguished by its fatter engine nacelles with central intake cones, its modified wing planform, and the fact that the wing is mounted higher on the fuselage, simultaneously raising the jet pipes clear of the ground and providing more space for fuel and equipment. The wing of the *Firebar* and that of its tactical attack and reconnaissance equivalent, the *Brewer* (see pages 204–206) has a straight inboard trailing edge and sharp leading edge sweepback inboard of the engine nacelles, increasing gross area by some 60 sq. ft. The vertical tail surfaces have been increased in area, tailplane sweep angle has been increased, and the "zero-track" tricycle undercarriage of earlier Yak-25 developments has given place to a widely-spaced "bicycle" gear, the air-

Power Plants: *Two axial-flow turbojets each rated at* 10,000* *lb.s.t. and* 13,200* *lb.s.t. with afterburning.*
Performance: *Max. speed*, 735* *m.p.h. at* 35,000 *ft.* (*Mach* 1.1), 725* *m.p.h. at sea level* (*Mach* 0.95)*; tactical radius* (*clean*), 575* *mls. at* 570* *m.p.h. at* 35,000 *ft.; range* (*internal fuel*), 1,200* *mls.*, (*auxiliary fuel*), 1,600* *mls.; initial climb*, 28,000* *ft./min.; service ceiling*, 55,000* *ft.*
Weights: *Loaded*, 35,000* *lb.*
Dimensions: *Span*, 38 *ft.* 6 *in.**; *length*, 59 *ft.* 0 *in.**; *height*, 13 *ft.* 0 *in.**; *wing area*, 400* *sq. ft.*
*APPROXIMATE

GENERAL ARRANGEMENT DRAWING: *A Yakovlev Firebar presumably serving with the* (*Istrebitilnaya*) *Aviatsiya Protivo-vozdushnoi Oborony Strany.*

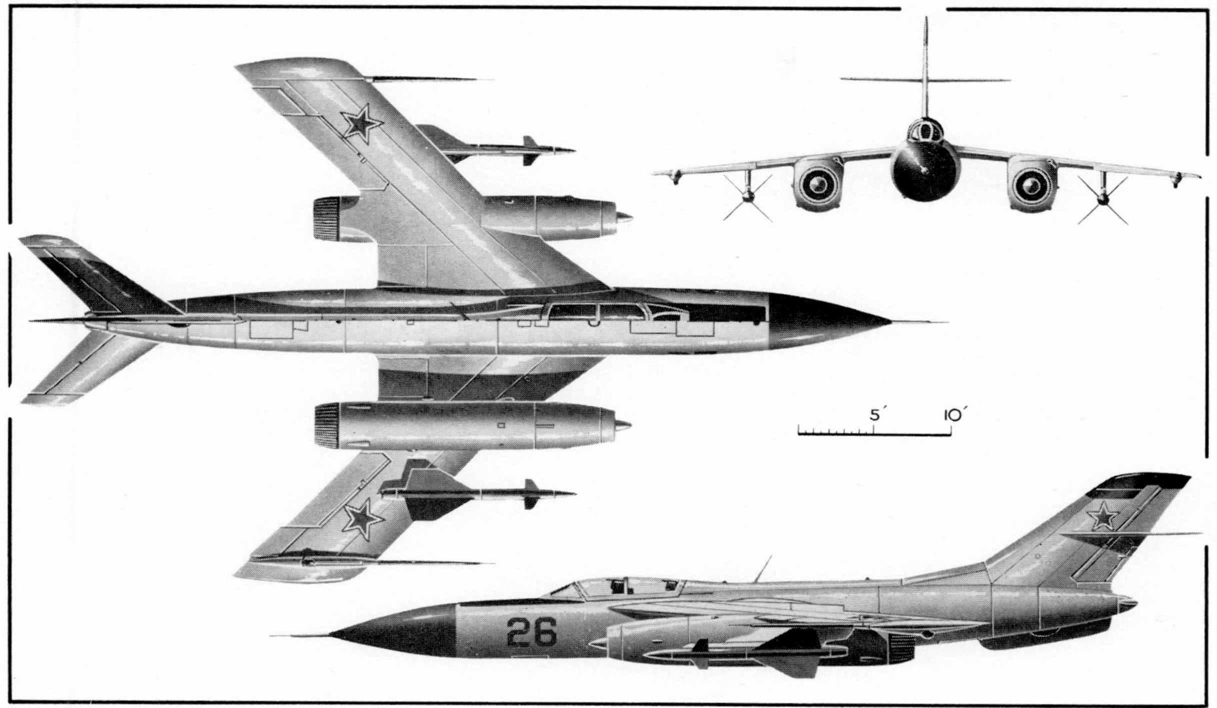
5´
10´
26

craft's weight being divided between the two twin-wheel fuselage-mounted units.

The *Firebar*, which is believed to have entered service with the (*Istrebitilnaya*) *Aviatsiya Protivo-vozdushnoi Oborony Strany* as a successor to the Yak-25 during 1962–63, differs from the *Brewer* primarily in having tandem seating for the two crew members, and an A.I. radar in place of the glazed nose. This A.I. radar is believed to have a range of 35–40 miles, and primary armament appears to comprise two 13 ft. 6 in. missiles which are presumably semi-active radar homing weapons weighing about 500 lb. and possessing a range of six–seven miles. These missiles are carried by launching shoes mounted outboard of the engine nacelles, and these stations can presumably be used, as on the *Brewer*, for long-range fuel tanks. No cannon armament is carried. The *Maestro* is a dual-control training model which currently serves in the systems operator-training role and does not differ from the *Firebar* externally.

YAKOVLEV FIDDLER

A multi-mission two-seat long-range all-weather fighter and reconnaissance-strike aircraft, the machine allocated the name *Fiddler* by NATO, the Soviet designation of which was unknown at the time of closing for press, was evolved during the mid 'fifties, and is believed to have entered V.-V.S. service during 1962–63. Possessing a design biased towards economical high-altitude operation, the *Fiddler* is the largest fighter to have attained service status, the only comparable western aircraft being the very much later and appreciably more advanced General Dynamics F-111. Evidently intended to meet a V.-V.S. requirement for an interceptor capable of dealing with aircraft remaining outside Russian territory, either using electronic counter-measures or launching stand-off weapons, the *Fiddler* appears to carry its own early warning radar to detect low-flying intruders, and its equipment may be presumed to include passive homing devices, frequency-switching A.I., and navigational aids of exceptionally long range. The *Fiddler* also appears to be suitable for attacking surface targets, for which task the ventral electronics are likely to be supplanted by a weapons bay, while the forward-looking radar would operate in a ground-mapping or terrain-clearance mode.

The *Fiddler* is likely to have a normal endurance in the patrol-interceptor role of about 3.5 hours, and this possibly exceeds 5.5

The multi-mission aircraft known in the West as the "Fiddler" is primarily a long-range interceptor but has a secondary reconnaissance-strike role.

GENERAL ARRANGEMENT DRAWING: *A Yakovlev Fiddler long-range interceptor.*

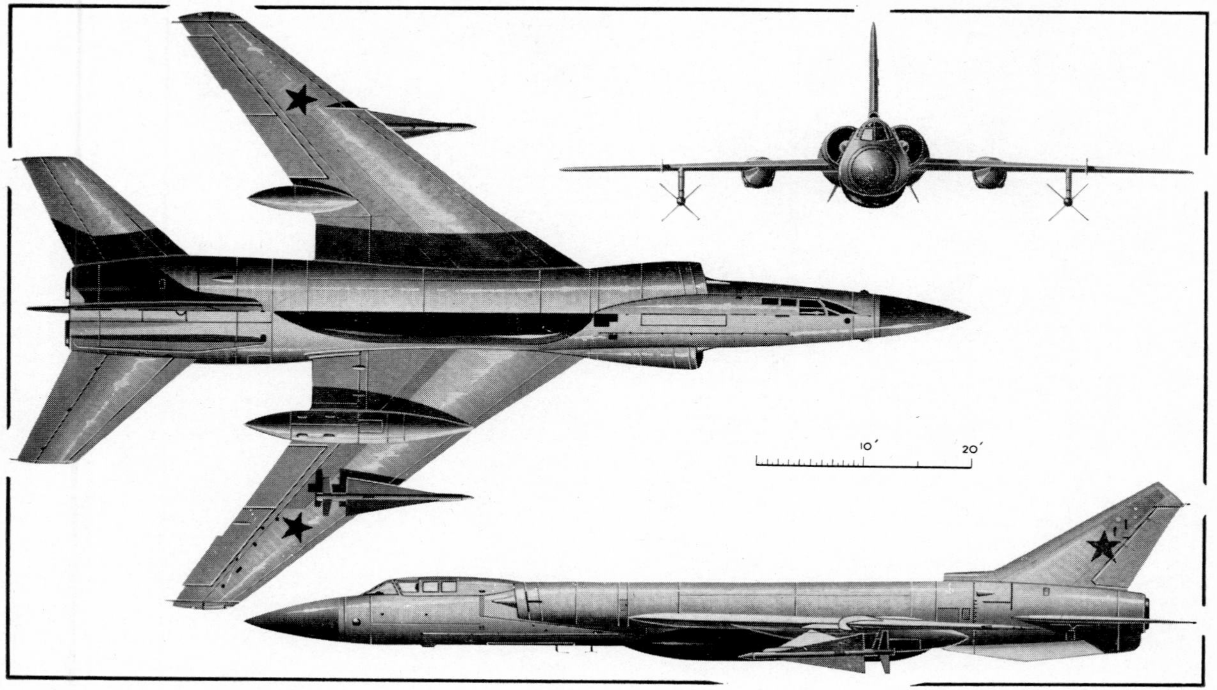
10′
20′

(Left) The "Fiddler", seen with a pair of "Ash" missiles on the underwing pylons, is largest fighter to have attained operational status, and its design has obviously been biased towards economical high-altitude operation. It is not known with certainty how extensive is the operational use of the "Fiddler".

hours with overload tanks, but current intercept armament is uncertain as the two *Ash*-type collision course missiles seen mounted on underwing pylons of examples demonstrated publicly would seem somewhat inadequate for the task for which this fighter is believed primarily intended. One unusual feature of this aircraft is the use of four-wheel bogies for the main undercarriage members, these retracting into bulged housings beneath the wings and extending aft of the trailing edges. It is feasible that these housings act in the manner of Whitcomb bodies. The engine air intakes are mounted well forward, presumably to reduce the risk of ingesting disturbed flow from the fuselage sides at large angles of attack, and in consequence suffer some penalty in wetted area and duct losses.

In the strike role with a pair of small nuclear weapons, the *Fiddler* is likely to have a low-level radius of action of the order of 450 miles, increased by 50–60 per cent with overload fuel, cruising at Mach 0.85, these figures being more than doubled for a hi-lo-hi mission profile, and this product of (allegedly) the Yakovlev design bureau is undoubtedly an impressive aircraft, its only obvious shortcoming being lack of flexibility in ordnance loads. The method of guidance employed by the *Ash* missile is uncertain, but if this weapon is an infra-red homer, being useless against a target flying in cloud, it seriously limits the *Fiddler's* effectiveness in the intercept role.

Power Plants: *Two axial-flow turbojets of* 18,000* *lb.s.t. and* 22,000* *lb.s.t. with afterburning.*
Performance: *Max. speed*, 1,056* *m.p.h. at* 40,000 *ft.* (*Mach* 1.6)*; max. cruise*, 630* *m.p.h. at* 40,000 *ft.* (*Mach* 0.95)*; range* (*internal fuel*), 2,000* *mls.; time to* 40,000 *ft.*, 5* *min.; service ceiling*, 60,000* *ft.*
Weights: *Normal loaded*, 80,000* *lb.*
Dimensions: *Span*, 56 *ft.* 0 *in.**; length*, 85 *ft.* 0 *in.**; height*, 20 *ft.* 0 *in.**; wing area*, 800* *sq. ft.*
*APPROXIMATE

ATTACK AIRCRAFT

It is today extremely difficult to differentiate between the genuine *attack* aircraft and some modern multi-purpose fighters, such as the Northrop F-5. Not only does the operational repertoire of the fighter include close support and strike tasks, these overlapping the regime of the attack aircraft; some aircraft designed specifically for the attack role possess limited intercept capability and thus poach on the preserves of the *true* fighter. A case in point is provided by the A-4 Skyhawk attack aircraft which are based aboard *Essex*-class anti-submarine warfare aircraft carriers to furnish these vessels with some *air defence* capability, and the Skyhawk's intended successor, the A-7A Corsair II, has been designed from the outset for a secondary intercept role.

Design accent in the modern attack aircraft is placed on flexibility. It is intended primarily to carry large and varied loads of air-to-surface ordnance, permitting its weapons to be readily changed to suit a particular tactical situation, and substantial fuel capacity offering a choice of extended range or valuable over-target loiter time is a prerequisite. Adequate fuel is also necessary to offer the attack aircraft, when endeavouring to evade hostile interceptors close to the ground, sufficient endurance to out-last its pursuers in defensive manoeuvres. Avionics and structural design must be such that the attack aircraft can fly in the nap of the earth, operating below the effective capability of radar screens and ground-to-air missiles, and the conflict in Vietnam has stressed the need for a high degree of protection against groundfire for the pilot through cockpit armour, self-sealing fuel tanks in critical areas, and the dispersal of components to minimize damage.

The attack aircraft has no real need for supersonic performance, a fact proven by an extensive evaluation of attack aircraft requirements carried out by the U.S. Navy in 1963. This evaluation determined that for bombing accuracy both supersonic and subsonic aircraft must release their ordnance payload at substantially

The Flug-und-Fahrzeugwerke P-16, originally flown in 1955, was resurrected in 1965 as a private venture attack aircraft, three versions being proposed: the AA-7 with the SNECMA Atar 9C, the AR-7 with the Rolls-Royce Spey 25, and the AJ-7 with the General Electric J79-GE-11A. Full armament load for all three variants comprises two 30-mm. cannon with 125 r.p.g., one retractable MATRA 1000 rocket pack with 44 68-mm. rockets, 24 80-mm. Hispano-Suiza HSR-80 rockets, and four 880-lb. bombs for a total armament weight of 4,820 lb.

the same relatively low speed; vulnerability over the target area is essentially the same for both types of aircraft. In other words, against groundfire, the time of exposure of supersonic aircraft and those capable of high subsonic speeds is approximately the same, and both have an equal chance of survival.

A reasonably high subsonic performance can be provided without the risk of open-ended development costs, and this is the approach adopted by the U.S. Navy in its VAL programme for a replacement for the A-4 Skyhawk. The winning design, the A-7A Corsair II, is now also to be used by the U.S.A.F., and in conflicts such as that being waged in Vietnam, its maximum ordnance load of 10,000 lb. gives it a useful edge over the F-5 with which it was originally in competition. In roughly the same speed category is the Swiss proposal to re-engine the straight-wing P.16 project with a non-afterburning Spey 25, or an afterburning J79-GE-11A or Atar 9C, giving a maximum take-off weight of over 25,000 lb. Like the A-7A, this aircraft (designated AR-7, AJ-7, or AA-7 according to engine) would be subsonic, but it lacks the U.S. aircraft's advantage of a strong home market, and will almost certainly remain a paper project.

The enormous breadth of the attack aircraft category as accepted by the U.S. Navy can be gauged from this service's inclusion of the A-3 Skywarrior with its near-strategic range, primarily high-altitude mission profile, and an *empty* weight of close on 40,000 lb., or almost twice that of the Canberra. At the opposite end of the scale is the veteran A-1 Skyraider which now fulfils what is primarily a counter-insurgency role. As neither machine now comes within the normally accepted definition of an *attack* aircraft, they have been excluded from this section, and appear respectively in the bomber and counter-insurgency sections of Volume II.

DOUGLAS A-4 SKYHAWK

Now entering its eleventh year of continuous service with the U.S. Navy and with newly-placed orders for the updated A-4F model carrying production well into 1968, the Skyhawk bids fair to emulate its piston-engined predecessor, the Skyraider, in achieving remarkable longevity in first-line operational service. A relatively simple single-seat shipboard attack aircraft, the Skyhawk has been relied upon heavily by the U.S. Navy for strikes against North Vietnamese targets, its small size, back-up manual flight control system and basic ruggedness having contributed to an extremely low loss rate, and with radar homing devices and passive electronic counter-measures equipment installed, it has seen extensive use as a lead plane for both U.S. Navy and U.S.A.F. strikes against surface-to-air missile sites.

Scheduled to remain operational until at least 1974, the Skyhawk equips, in its A-4C and -4E versions, more than 30 U.S. Navy attack squadrons and about a dozen U.S.M.C. attack squadrons, and detachments of Skyhawks aboard each of the nine *Essex*-class anti-submarine warfare carriers provide these vessels with a limited intercept and air defence capability. Embodying Korean War experience, the Skyhawk is a simple, straight-forward design stemming from a 1950 U.S. Navy requirement. Contracts to two prototypes and eight pre-production aircraft were placed on June 21, 1952, and the first YA-4A prototype flew two years later, on June 22, 1954. The 7,200 lb.s.t. Wright J65-W-2 turbojet powering prototypes and pre-production aircraft was supplanted in the subsequent 155 production A-4As by the 7,700 lb.s.t. Wright J65-W-4B, but even before the A-4A had achieved operational status with the first Skyhawk-equipped unit, VA-72, on October 26, 1956, a more advanced version of the aircraft, the A-4B, had appeared. Flown on March 26, 1956, the A-4B embodied 28 per cent new structure and equipment. The airframe was strengthened to permit a maximum speed manoeuvring load factor of 7 *g*; a new powered rudder with dual hydraulic control was fitted; a single-point pressure fuelling system was introduced, and a new gun sight and compass, and a navigation computer were installed. The improved J65-W-16A engine, which, like its predecessor, was rated at 7,700 lb.s.t. replaced the J65-W-4B and, later, flight refuelling facilities were provided, with a fixed probe on the starboard side of the fuselage. A total of 542 A-4Bs was manufactured, and these, together with the earlier A-4As, have now been withdrawn from first-line U.S. Navy and U.S.M.C. service. Fifty refurbished A-4Bs are currently entering service with the *Fuerza Aérea Argentina*, although in mid-1966 it was reported that only half this quantity would be delivered, and a small number of A-4As are being delivered to the *Heil Avir le Israel.*

A-4C: The earliest production version of the Skyhawk remaining in first-line service, the A-4C, which first flew on August 21, 1959 and entered service in the following year, embodied some night and all-weather capability, and featured 15 per cent new structure and equipment. APG-53 radar was installed to provide ground mapping, terrain clearance, air-to-ground ranging, and limited air-to-air ranging capability; an AJB-3 all-altitude reference and loft bombing system and a TPQ-10 ground control bombing system were introduced; a Douglas Escapac low-level ejection seat was provided; an automatic flight control system was fitted to reduce pilot fatigue, and the cockpit was revised. These changes increased empty and normal loaded weights from 8,526 lb. and 15,500 lb. to 9,550 lb. and 17,294 lb., and the new model was distinguished externally by its lengthened nose structure. A total of 638 A-4Cs had been completed when this model was succeeded on the assembly line by the A-4E, and about a third of the U.S. Navy and U.S.M.C. Skyhawk-equipped squadrons are still operating this type which was manufactured in larger numbers than any other Skyhawk variant.

A-4E: A major modernisation of the basic Skyhawk was introduced with the A-4E which flew on July 12, 1961. The most important change was the installation of the J52-P-6A turbojet of 8,500 lb.s.t. which permitted further increases in weight and load-carrying ability, and matched by general fuselage and wing strengthening this amounted to 29 per cent new structure. Two additional stores stations were introduced beneath the wings, and this variant of the Skyhawk, production of which was completed for the U.S. Navy and U.S.M.C. in April 1966 with the 500th example, is currently the most widely used model. Current plans call for the A-4E to be reinstated in production in 1967 to fulfil an order for eight Skyhawks of this type for the Royal Australian Navy, but the U.S. Navy's decision in April 1966 to order the updated A-4F as a follow-on to the A-4E renders it probable that the later model will now be supplied to the R.A.N.

The A-4E, deliveries of which began to the U.S. Navy in November 1962, is equipped with APG-53A terrain clearance radar, Doppler navigator, an APN-141 radar altimeter, an AJB-3A low-altitude bombing system, ARN-52 TACAN, and an APX-64 IFF radar beacon. Internal fuel capacity of 800 U.S. gal. (666 Imp.

(*Above*) *The A-4C is the earliest version of the Skyhawk currently in first-line U.S. Navy and U.S. Marine Corps service.*

(Left) An A-4E Skyhawk (Bu. No. 150032) of VA-55 and (below, left), an A-4E (Bu. No.150030) of VA-56. Originally expected to be the final single-seat production version of the Skyhawk, the A-4E is now being succeeded in production by the improved A-4F, the first example of which flew on August 31, 1966.

gal.) comprises a fuselage tank immediately aft of the cockpit and integral wing tanks, and this may be supplemented by two 300 U.S. gal. (250 Imp. gal.) drop tanks on the inboard wing pylons and a 400 U.S. gal. (333 Imp. gal.) tank on the fuselage centreline pylon. An external ordnance load of up to 8,200 lb. may be carried on the five weapons stations, permitting such short-range interdiction mission loads as six 500-lb. bombs on the centreline pylon, and 12 250-lb. bombs plus two AGM-12 Bullpup ASMs beneath the wings. A wide variety of weapons may be carried, such as Zuni launchers each with four 5-in. rockets, 19-shot LAU-3A 2.75-in. rocket pods, AIM-9 Sidewinder AAMs, napalm tanks, and all models have the standard built-in armament of two 20-mm. MK-12 cannon with 100 r.p.g. in the wing roots. However, some A-4E Skyhawks operating over Vietnam have had the port cannon removed to provide space for passive electronic countermeasures equipment, this installation preventing the starboard cannon being fired owing to the risk of damaging the new equipment, and some aircraft now carry the Hughes Mk.4 gun pod housing a twin-barrel MK-11 cannon.

A-4F: Basically similar to the A-4E which it has succeeded in production but powered by a 9,300 lb.s.t. J52-P-8A engine, the A-4F, which first flew on August 31, 1966, is equipped with a zero-zero ejection seat, nosewheel steering, a wing lift spoiler for improved crosswind performance, and up-dated avionics. Performance differs little from that of the A-4E, and for carrier operations take-off weights are virtually unchanged, but for shore-based operations the A-4F will be capable of taking-off at a maxi-

GENERAL ARRANGEMENT DRAWING: *An A-4E Skyhawk (Bu. No. 150032) of Attack Squadron (VA-) 55, part of the U.S.S. Ticonderoga's Air Wing (CVW-5).*

5´
10´
NAVY
NF
2
502
VA-55
150032

mum overload weight of 27,420 lb., maximum external load being, 11,800 lb.

TA-4F: A tandem two-seat trainer version of the Skyhawk embodying a similar J52-P-8A turbojet to that of the A-4F, the TA-4F seats pupil and instructor in tandem Escapac 1C zero-zero ejection seats, the rear seat being raised nine inches above the forward seat. Electronics are basically similar to those of the A-4F with duplication in the two cockpits where necessary, and the cannon armament and five external store stations are retained. The first prototype of the TA-4F was flown on June 30, 1965, the second prototype following on August 2, 1965, and 139 TA-4F Skyhawk trainers had been ordered by the beginning of 1966 when it was expected that procurement would total 152 aircraft. The first three TA-4F trainers were turned over to Operational Training Squadron VA-125 at NAS Lemoore, California, on May 25, 1966.

Power Plant: *One Pratt & Whitney J52-P-6A* (-8*A*) *turbojet rated at* 8,500 (9,300) *lb.s.t.*
Performance: *Max. speed,* 675 *m.p.h. at sea level* (*Mach* 0.88), 614 *m.p.h. at* 35,000 *ft.* (*Mach* 0.92), *high drag configuration,* 576 *m.p.h. at sea level* (*Mach* 0.8), 578 *m.p.h. at* 30,000 *ft.* (*Mach* 0.85)*; combat radius* (*with* 4,000-*lb. ordnance externally mounted*), 334 *mls.,* (*shore-based operation—A-4F*), 380 *mls.; ferry range* (*two* 300 *U.S. gal./*250 *Imp. gal. and one* 400 *U.S. gal./*333 *Imp. gal. external tanks*), 2,527 *mls.* (*A-4F*—2,440 *mls.*)*; service ceiling,* 47,900 *ft.*
Weights: *Empty,* 9,853 (9,937) *lb.; loaded* (*clean*), 16,216 (16,300) *lb.; max.,* 24,500 (27,420) *lb.*
Dimensions: *Span,* 27 *ft.* 6 *in.; length,* 42 *ft.* 10¾ *in.; height,* 15 *ft.* 2 *in.; wing area,* 260 *sq. ft.*
Note: *Specification is applicable to both A-4E and A-4F apart from power plant and weight details in parentheses, and performance details specifically indicated.*

GRUMMAN A-6 INTRUDER

Currently supplanting the A-1 Skyraider in U.S. Navy attack squadrons, the Grumman G-128, or A-6 Intruder, was deployed operationally for the first time over Vietnam in July 1965 with Attack Squadron (VA-) 75 from the U.S.S. *Independence.* Five months later, the A-6A Intruders of VA-85 operating from the U.S.S. *Kitty Hawk* also joined combat, and by the beginning of 1966, a third U.S. Navy squadron, VA-65, had re-equipped with the A-6A, together with one U.S.M.C. squadron, VMA-242, and other units had begun conversion from the A-1 Skyraider.

The G-128 was adjudged the best of 11 designs submitted by eight manufacturers to meet a U.S. Navy requirement formulated in 1956, and calling for a highly sophisticated computerised attack and navigation system capable of flying long distances at low altitude by night and under all weather conditions, finding and attacking its target, and returning to its carrier without reference to outside navigational aids. A development contract for the G-128 as the A2F-1 was awarded in March 1959, this, together with a supplementary contract placed a year later, calling for eight examples for evaluation and development, the first of these flying on April 19, 1960, and subsequently being redesignated A-6A.

A-6A: The production A-6A differed from the evaluation models in dispensing with the swivelling jet pipes (which had been arranged to tilt through 23° to reduce stalling speed by six knots) and in having a fixed flight refuelling probe. At an early production stage the vertical tail surfaces were increased in area. A two-seater with the bombardier seated slightly aft and below the pilot to starboard, the A-6A was initially powered by two 8,500

GENERAL ARRANGEMENT DRAWING: *An early production A-6A Intruder* (*Bu. No.*149942) *of Attack Squadron* (*VA-*) 42, *the "Green Pawns", the Intruder training unit at the Oceana Naval Air Station, Virginia.*

5´
10´
5
AD
VA-42
149942
NAVY
505

(Left) A-6A Intruders of VA-75 from the U.S.S.Independence. VA-75 was the first U.S.Navy unit to employ the A-6A operationally when its aircraft began operations over Vietnam in July 1965.

lb.s.t. J52-P-6 turbojets, these being supplanted by the 9,300 lb.s.t. J52-P-8A late in 1965. The A-6A is equipped with a Digital Integrated Attack Navigation system, or DIANE, the heart of which is the ASQ-61 computer which operates in the take-off, navigation, attack and landing modes. Coupled with Norden APQ-112 tracking and APQ-92 search radar, inertial and Doppler navigators, a communications, navigation and identification package, and an automatic flight control system, this enables the pilot to pre-select a course of action, approach the target, discharge the weapons and leave the target area entirely automatically.

The A-6A is designed to carry both tactical nuclear and conventional weapons on five external 3,600-lb. capacity pylons, maximum offensive load for limited-range interdiction being 15,000 lb. Typical conventional loads include eighteen 500-lb. Mk.82 low-drag bombs on Multiple and Triple Ejection racks, plus two 300 U.S. gal. (250 Imp. gal.) drop tanks, five 1,000-lb. Mk.83 or 2,000-lb. Mk.84 bombs, or four AGM-12 Bullpup ASMs. There is no built-in gun armament, and the proven need for this for flak suppression in the limited-war type mission with conventional warloads over Vietnam has led to proposals to adapt the Mk.4 gun pod with the twin-barrel 20-mm. Mk.11 cannon for use by the A-6A. Internal fuel capacity is 2,400 U.S. gal. (2,000 Imp. gal), endowing the A-6A with approximately twice the endurance of the F-4B Phantom II in the attack role with the same payload. Stressed to 7.5 *g*, it possesses excellent low-altitude manoeuvrability, can hold a 6,500-ft. turn radius, and at 575 m.p.h. and 4 *g*, will turn in an 8,000-ft. radius. Over Vietnam the A-6A has been used primarily for night road interdiction, bridge destruction, and missile site attack over North Vietnam, and as a visually-flown support aircraft over South Vietnam. It was deployed operationally over Vietnam twenty-nine months after officially entering service on February 1, 1963 with the acceptance by VA-42, the Intruder training unit at Oceana, Virginia, of its first aircraft.

A tanker adaptation of the A-6A was flown on May 23, 1966. Stripped of most of its avionics, the tanker A-6A can transfer 21,000 lb. of fuel to another aircraft immediately after take-off, or 16,000 lb. of fuel at a range of 345 miles. The proposed production tanker model would be equipped with air-to-air TACAN, visual attack capability, and possibly an internally-mounted gun armament.

A-6B: A simplified version of the A-6A intended primarily for the day interdiction role with less sophisticated systems and lacking the all-weather capability of the initial model, the A-6B was awarded a production contract in the autumn of 1965, this subsequently being cancelled in favour of the A-7A Corsair II.

EA-6B: An electronics countermeasures version of the Intruder currently under development to replace the EA-1F Skyraider, the EA-6B is intended to accompany A-6As on attack missions, its equipment detecting, locating, classifying, recording and jamming enemy radiation. An earlier ECM version, the EA-6A of which an aerodynamic prototype flew in 1963, was deleted from U.S. Navy appropriations. However, funds for procurement of 13 EA-6Bs were included in the Fiscal 1966 supplemental budget.

G-128NT: A long-range trainer version of the Intruder offered on the European market in 1966 under the company designation G-128NT. Proposal calls for the replacement of the A-6A avionics with off-the-shelf navigational training equipment.

Power Plants: *Two Pratt & Whitney J52-P-8A turbojets each rated at* 9,300 *lb.s.t.*
Performance: *Max. speed,* 685 *m.p.h. at sea level* (*Mach* 0.9), 625 *m.p.h. at* 36,000 *ft.* (*Mach* 0.95)*; max. cruise,* 575 *m.p.h. at* 28,000 *ft.; low-level range cruise* (*high drag configuration*), 345 *m.p.h.; low-level range* (*internal fuel only*), 1,250 *mls.,* (*with five* 300 *U.S. gal.*/250 *Imp. gal. drop tanks*) 1,950 *mls.; ferry range,* 2,600 *mls. at* 28,000 *ft.*
Weights: *Empty,* 24,000* *lb.; loaded* (*max. internal fuel*), 43,000 *lb.; max. overload,* 54,000 *lb.*
Dimensions: *Span,* 53 *ft.* 0 *in.; length,* 54 *ft.* 7 *in.; height,* 15 *ft.* 1¾ *in.*
*APPROXIMATE

(*Right*) *An A-6A Intruder landing with leading edge slats drooped, wingtip air brakes extended, and flaps partly lowered.*

HAWKER SIDDELEY BUCCANEER

Evolved specifically for the low-level strike task from carriers, the Buccaneer entered Royal Navy service in its definitive S. Mk.2 form when No. 801 Squadron became operational on October 14, 1965 at R.N.A.S. Lossiemouth. Conceived initially as a strike aircraft to counter Russia's *Sverdlov*-class cruiser and meeting Royal Navy requirement M.148T, the Buccaneer was designed in 1954, 20 pre-production aircraft being ordered in July 1955, the first of these flying on April 30, 1958 with two 7,000 lb.s.t. Gyron Junior D.GJ.1 turbojets. An initial production order for 50 aircraft followed in September 1959, the first production example flying as the Buccaneer S.Mk.1 on January 23, 1962 powered by two 7,100 lb.s.t. Gyron Junior 101 turbojets. By this time, however, the Gyron Junior-powered aircraft was considered an interim model, studies aimed at improving performance and particularly range having resulted in the decision that the bulk of the Royal Navy's Buccaneers would receive the more economical and substantially more powerful Spey turbofan.

(Below) The 14th pre-production Buccaneer S.Mk.1 (XK530) with four AGM-12 Bullpup ASMs on the underwing pylons.

The first unit to receive the Buccaneer, No. 801 Squadron, was commissioned on July 17, 1962, embarking aboard H.M.S. *Ark Royal* in the following February, and Nos. 800 and 809 Squadrons were also formed on the initial production model, but the S.Mk.1 fell somewhat short of the range requirement and suffered marginal single-engined performance. Power proved critical in certain emergency régimes—specifically, in the event of an engine failure during full-load launching and immediately prior to landing on with full bleed-air boundary layer control operating—but this shortcoming was more than rectified by the introduction of the Spey which was installed for test purposes in two pre-production Buccaneers, the first of which flew with the new power plants on May 17, 1963.

S.Mk.2: An initial production contract for the Spey-engined Buccaneer had been placed in January 1962, and as the Buccaneer S.Mk.2, the first of 100 production examples for the Royal Navy flew on June 5, 1964, following the last of the 50 S.Mk.1s, and deliveries to No. 700B Flight began in the Spring of 1965, this Flight subsequently forming the nucleus of No. 801 Squadron commissioned on October 14, 1965. A second Buccaneer S.Mk.2 unit, No. 809 Squadron, was commissioned at the beginning of 1966, and No. 800 Squadron's re-equipment with the more power-

GENERAL ARRANGEMENT DRAWING: *A Buccaneer S.Mk.2 (XN977) of No. 801 Squadron embarked aboard H.M.S. Victorious.*

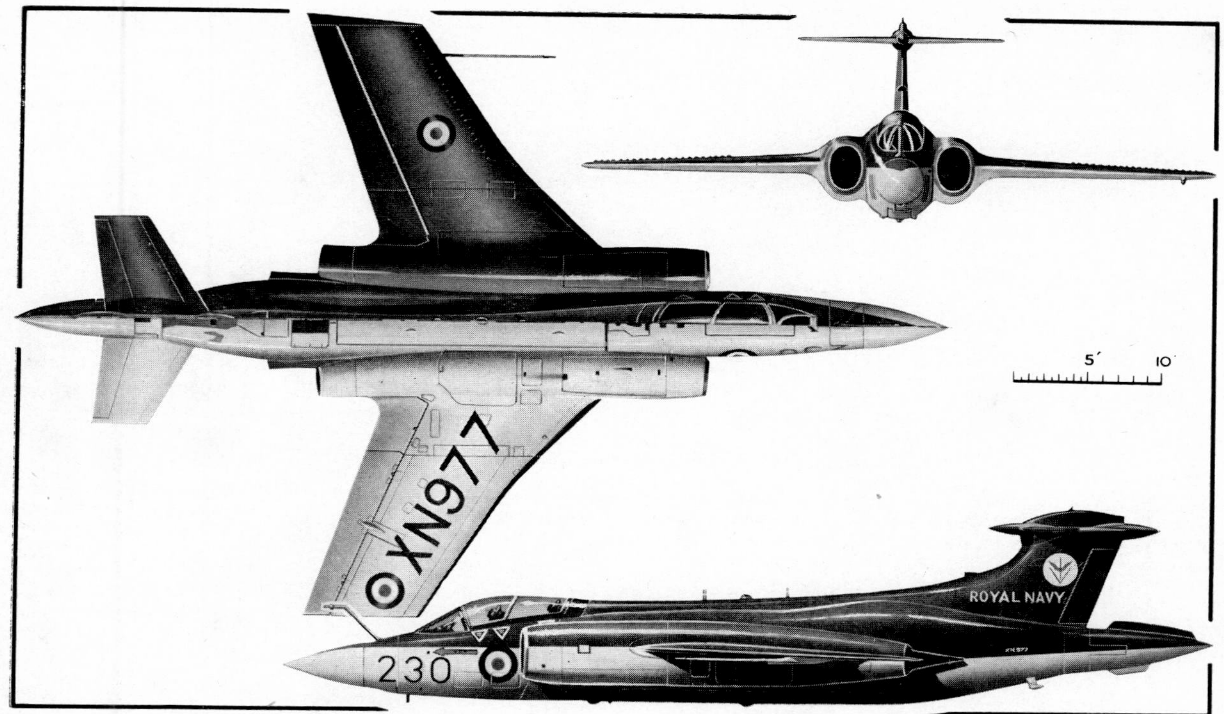
XN977
5'
10
ROYAL NAVY
230

*(Left) A Buccaneer S.Mk.*50, *prior to delivery to the South African Air Force, taking-off with the aid of its Bristol Siddeley BS.*605 *twin-barrel rocket motor. The delivery of* 16 *aircraft of this type to South Africa was completed early in* 1966.

ful version of the Buccaneer had just been completed at the time of closing for press.

The 40 per cent extra power afforded by the two Spey R. Sp.2 Mk.101 turbofans matched with improved range and systems renders the Buccaneer S.Mk.2 an exceptionally potent low-level strike aircraft. By comparison with the original S.Mk.1, the air intakes have been enlarged to accommodate the greater mass flow of the Spey, this being the main airframe change, and the Ferranti Blue Parrot navigation-attack system, which provides ground mapping, terrain warning, and range data for the weapon release computer, embodies some refinements which permit two extra modes of attack. Apart from the master reference gyro and items connected with the Rank-Cintel head-up display, most avionics are located in an aft bay which houses the UHF transceivers, radio altimeter, TACAN, HF, and the Doppler radar and coupler unit for the roller-map display. The two crew members are seated in Martin-Baker Type 5 Mk.1 ejection seats, and piloting tasks are eased by the use of an Elliot autopilot which provides a variety of operating modes, including auto-stabilization for take-off and landing, heading hold for cruise, Mach hold for cruise, climb and descent, barometric height hold and radio height hold for low-level flight.

BLC (Boundary Layer Control) over the wings, flaps, ailerons and tailplane for maximum lift is achieved by bleeding compressed air from the engines, and to produce the substantial profile drag to reduce minimum drag speed and to enable the engines to be run at full power for full BLC in the approach, large clamshell air brakes extend from the rear fuselage. Directly aft of the observer's cockpit and extending throughout the upper centre fuselage is a series of integral fuel tanks which may be augmented by two 250 Imp. gal. (300 U.S. gal.) underwing slipper tanks to provide a total fuel load of the order of 2,000 Imp. gal. (2,400 U.S. gal.), and a take-off weight without weapons of 46,000 lb. of which 16,000 lb. is fuel. For ferry flights or extra-long, reduced-load missions, a special weapons-bay tank may be added to afford a ferry range of 1,800–2,000 miles cruising at Mach 0.83 at 33,000 ft., or 575 m.p.h. A fixed flight refuelling probe is mounted just ahead of the cockpit, and for maximum range operations with maximum warload, particularly in hot climates, the Buccaneer can take-off from the carrier with a full load of weapons and top up its fuel once airborne.

The Buccaneer's weapons bay is situated beneath the fuel tanks and rotated by hydraulic jack at the rear end to expose the bombs for release. This weapons bay can accommodate four 1,000-lb. general-purpose bombs or a single large store. Alternatively, a special reconnaissance pack housing six cameras and flares for night photography may be fitted. The internal bay is supplemented by four underwing pylons each of 1,000 lb. capacity. These pylons may each carry a Martin AGM-12B Bullpup-A ASM, 2-in. or 3-in. rocket packs, or a range of bombs from 1,000 lb. down to 25 lb. An additional weapon will be added to the Buccaneer S. Mk.2's armoury with its adaptation to carry the AJ-168 Martel ASM using television guidance.

S.Mk.50: An export version of and essentially similar to the Royal Navy's Buccaneer S.Mk.2, the S.Mk.50 is serving with No. 24 Squadron of the South African Air Force's Maritime Command. With deliveries to South Africa of 16 aircraft completed early in 1966, the Buccaneer S.Mk.50 is fully navalised although operated exclusively from shore bases, and in order to overcome the principal disadvantage of BLC when operating with full warload and fuel from hot, high airfields, namely, an inordinate runway demand owing to the bleed flow required from the engines reducing acceleration during take-off, a retractable Bristol Siddeley BS.605 twin-barrel HTP/kerosene rocket motor is installed, this affording 8,000 lb. thrust for 30 seconds. Like the S.Mk.2, the Buccaneer S. Mk.50 will carry four 1,000-lb. bombs internally and four similar weapons externally. Alternative external weapons include Nord AS.20 command-guidance ASMs or MATRA rocket packs.

Power Plants: *Two Rolls-Royce RB.*168–1 *Spey R.Sp.*2 *Mk.*101 *turbofans each rated at* 11,030 *lb.s.t.*
Performance: *Max. speed,* 700* *m.p.h. at sea level (Mach* 0.92); *max. low-level cruise,* 665* *m.p.h. at* 5,000 *ft. (Mach* 0.9); *range cruise,* 575 *m.p.h. at* 33,000 *ft. (Mach* 0.83); *tactical radius (without external fuel),* 500–600* *mls. for hi-lo-lo-hi mission; ferry range (with two* 250 *Imp. gal.*/300 *U.S. gal. underwing tanks and auxiliary weapons bay tank)* 1,800–2,000* *mls.; initial climb,* 15,000* *ft./min.*
Weights: *Loaded (clean and without weapons),* 42,000* *lb.; max.,* 54,000* *lb.*
Dimensions: *Span,* 42 *ft.* 4 *in.; length,* 63 *ft.* 5 *in.; height,* 16 *ft.* 6 *in.; wing area,* 508.5 *sq. ft.*
*APPROXIMATE

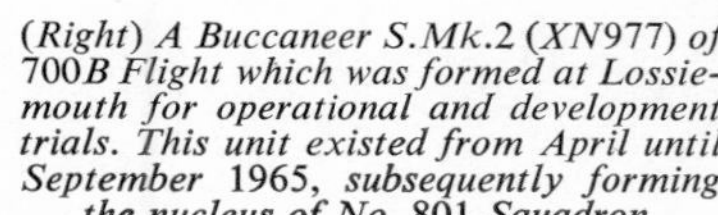

*(Right) A Buccaneer S.Mk.*2 *(XN*977*) of* 700*B Flight which was formed at Lossiemouth for operational and development trials. This unit existed from April until September* 1965, *subsequently forming the nucleus of No.* 801 *Squadron.*

(Left) The fourth A-7A Corsair II (Bu.No.152647) with a "Buddy" flight refuelling pack beneath the port wing. Between September 27, 1965, when the first Corsair II made its initial flight, and June 22, 1966, eight aircraft had flown and had logged 750 flying hours in 500 flights. At that time, the heaviest external load carried by a Corsair II had exceeded 9,850 lb.

LING-TEMCO-VOUGHT A-7A CORSAIR II

To be procured in quantity by both the U.S. Navy and U.S.A.F., and scheduled to enter service with the former during 1967 and with the latter during 1968, the A-7A Corsair II was announced winner of the VAL contest on February 11, 1964, this being intended to provide a single-seat shipboard attack aircraft successor to the A-4 Skyhawk. Essentially a subsonic derivative of the F-8 Crusader series of shipboard interceptors, the A-7A places accent on range and load-carrying capabilities, and ease of maintenance, and the first of seven aircraft for research and development flew on September 27, 1965.

Referred to by the U.S. Navy as a "turbofan-powered state-of-the-art Skyraider", the A-7A differs from the F-8 primarily in having the two-incidence wing feature deleted, sweepback reduced and outboard ailerons provided. It features eight external stores stations, the four outboard wing stations each having a 3,500-lb. capacity, the two inboard wing stations having a 2,500-lb. capacity, and those on each side of the fuselage having a 500-lb. capacity. Built-in armament comprises two 20-mm. Mk.12 cannon with 250 r.p.g., and up to 15,000 lb. of ordnance may be carried in more than 200 possible combinations of external stores which may include virtually any air-launched weapon in the U.S. Navy's inventory. Internal fuel capacity is 1,500 U.S. gal. (1,250 Imp. gal.), and this may be supplemented by four 300 U.S. gal. (250 Imp. gal.) drop tanks on the extreme outboard and inboard wing stations. In-flight refuelling capability is also provided.

The initial production model of the Corsair II has multi-mode Texas Instruments APQ-116 terrain avoidance and following and

GENERAL ARRANGEMENT DRAWING: *The first Research and Development A-7A Corsair II (Bu. No. 152580).*

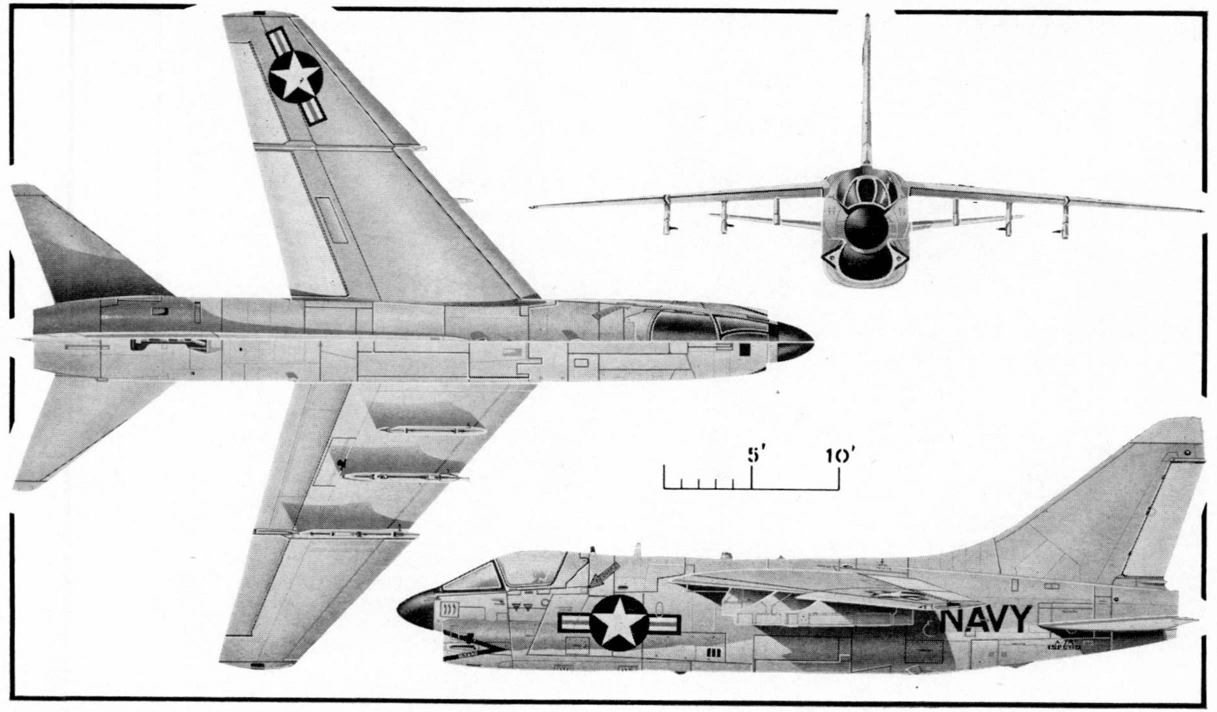
5'
10'
NAVY

(Left) The fourth A-7A Corsair II, and (below, left), the eighth A-7A (Bu.No. 152651) with a Shrike anti-radiation missile under the port and a Walleye television-homing unpowered missile under the starboard wing. In addition to U.S. Navy and U.S.A.F. versions of the Corsair II, Ling-Temco-Vought is currently proposing a two-seat version and a Spey-powered export model.

ground mapping radar. Other avionic equipment includes an APN-154 radar tracking beacon, APX-64 IFF and SIF, General Precision Laboratory's APN-153 Doppler navigation sensor working with an ASN-41 navigation computer and a Lear Siegler ASN-50 all altitude reference system, a Bendix APN-141 radar altimeter, a Servo-Mechanism's air data computer, ARN-52 TACAN, and weapons delivery aids consist of a CP-741 weapons delivery computer, the ARW-77 Bullpup missile command transmitter, an optical sight, and station and weapon selection and arming mechanisms.

The designation A-7B was provisionally allocated to a proposed follow-on version of the Corsair II featuring the ILAAS (Integrated Light Attack Avionics System), incorporating a digital central computer, Doppler-inertial navigation and high-frequency communications, and employing microcircuitry and miniaturization to reduce size and weight. The ILAAS is being developed by Sperry Gyroscope who will deliver the first of four prototype systems for the test installation in an A-7 late in 1967. A further model of the Corsair II is that currently proposed for the U.S.A.F., and for which initial procurement funds are included in the Fiscal 1967 budget. The U.S.A.F.'s variant of the A-7 will differ in a number of respects from that currently being manufactured for the U.S. Navy, one of the principal changes being the introduction of the 14,250 lb.s.t. Allison TF-41-A-1 (licence-built Rolls-Royce Spey 201) turbofan in place of the TF30-P-6. The 20-mm. M-61

Vulcan rotary cannon will be substituted for the Mk.12 weapon, and other proposed changes include the replacement of the CP-741 weapons delivery computer with an analog bombing computer; the provision of a KA-60 strike camera; a switch from the fixed optical sight to a drift-stabilised sight; installation of a boom refuelling receptacle; provision of ECM pods, the introduction of additional armour, and a three-positional wing trailing-edge flap. The current U.S.A.F. procurement programme calls for some 600 Corsair IIs with deliveries commencing early 1969.

Total U.S. Navy procurement of the A-7A is expected to exceed 1,000 aircraft, and initial orders placed by mid-1966 called for a total of 197 machines, including seven aircraft for research and development, eight Corsair IIs having flown by that time. The service's technical evaluation of the A-7A was scheduled for completion by the beginning of 1967, introduction to the Combat Readiness Air Wings of both the 6th and 7th Fleets taking place simultaneously.

Power Plant: *One Pratt & Whitney TF30-P-6 turbofan rated at* 11,350 *lb.s.t.*
Performance: *Max. speed* (*clean*), 679 *m.p.h. at* 5,000 *ft.* (*Mach* 0.9)*; range cruise* (*clean*), 542 *m.p.h. at* 40,000 *ft.* (*Mach* 0.82)*; tactical radius* (*with* 4,000 *lb. ordnance*), 715 *mls.; ferry range* (*clean*), 3,050 *mls. at* 542 *m.p.h. at* 40,000 *ft.*, (*with four* 300 *U.S. gal.*/250 *Imp. gal. drop tanks*), 4,100 *mls. at* 518 *m.p.h.*
Weights: *Empty*, 15,037 *lb.; loaded* (*catapult*), 32,500 *lb.*
Dimensions: *Span*, 38 *ft.* 8¾ *in.; length*, 46 *ft.* 1½ *in.; height*, 16 *ft.* 2 *in.; wing area*, 375 *sq. ft.*

SAAB 32 LANSEN

Originally evolved to meet a *Flygvapnet* requirement for a two-seat all-weather attack aircraft, the Saab 32 Lansen (Lance) has served with the attack *Flottiljer* for 10 years under the designation A 32A, and its service phase-out is not expected to commence until 1970 and the availability of the AJ 37 Viggen. Equipping the four attack Wings, F 6, F 7, F 15 and F 17, each with three *Divisions* of 12–15 aircraft, the A 32A has no direct counterpart in the inventories of other air arms, its nearest equivalent being the twin-engined Russian Yak-28 which possesses a generally similar overall performance but poorer range capability. Manufactured from 1953 until early in 1958, some 260 of the 450 Lansens built being of this model, the A 32A was introduced into service during the first months of 1956 by F 17. Four prototypes of the Saab 32 had preceded the production A 32A, the first of these prototypes having flown on November 3, 1952, and production of the basic design was terminated in the spring of 1960 with an essentially similar tactical reconnaissance variant, the S 32C.

A 32A: Capable of exceeding Mach 1.0 in a shallow dive, the A 32A tandem two-seater is powered by a licence-built Rolls-Royce Avion 100 Series engine designated RM 5A and offering 7,940 lb. s.t. boosted to 9,920 lb. s.t. with an SFA-developed afterburner.

The A 32A Lansen (below) is currently operated by Flygvapnet's four attack wings, and will be phased out during the early '70s.

(*Above*) *An A 32A Lansen of F* 15 *carrying the* 1,390-*lb. Robot* 04*C anti-shipping homing missile which is currently one of the principal weapons of the attack Lansen's armoury. The aircraft is also flying with flush-fitting* 121 *Imp. gal.* (146 *U.S. gal.*) *auxiliary fuel tank.*

Equipment includes L.M. Ericsson-developed PN-50/A and PN-51 navigational radar and PS-43/A reconnaissance radar, a PH-11/A radar altimeter, and a Saab BT9 toss-bombing and rocket-firing computer. Built-in armament comprises four 20-mm. Swedish Hispano cannon, and a conventional gunsight gives range drift and trajectory compensation for cannon or rockets. Fuel is housed immediately aft of the cockpit and in integral wing tanks, total internal capacity being 770 Imp. gal. (925 U.S. gal.), this usually being supplemented by a flush-fitting 121 Imp. gal. (146 U.S. gal.) ventral auxiliary tank.

A considerable variety of underwing ordnance may be carried, including 12 18-cm. or 24 13.5-cm. rockets, or three 1,100-lb., four 550-lb., or two 1,323-lb. bombs. For the anti-shipping role the primary armament comprises a pair of 1,390-lb. *Robot* 04C air-to-sea homing missiles.

S 32C: A tactical reconnaissance derivative of the A 32A, the S 32C currently equips two of the four *Divisions* of F 11 at Nyköping, the other two *Divisions* operating the S 35E Draken. Although intended primarily for the photographic role, the S 32C's *Saturnus* equipment endows it with some electronic reconnaissance capability, and the type will be retained in *Flygvapnet* active in-

GENERAL ARRANGEMENT DRAWING: *An A 32A Lansen of F 6, the Vastgota Flygflottilj, based at Karlsborg.*

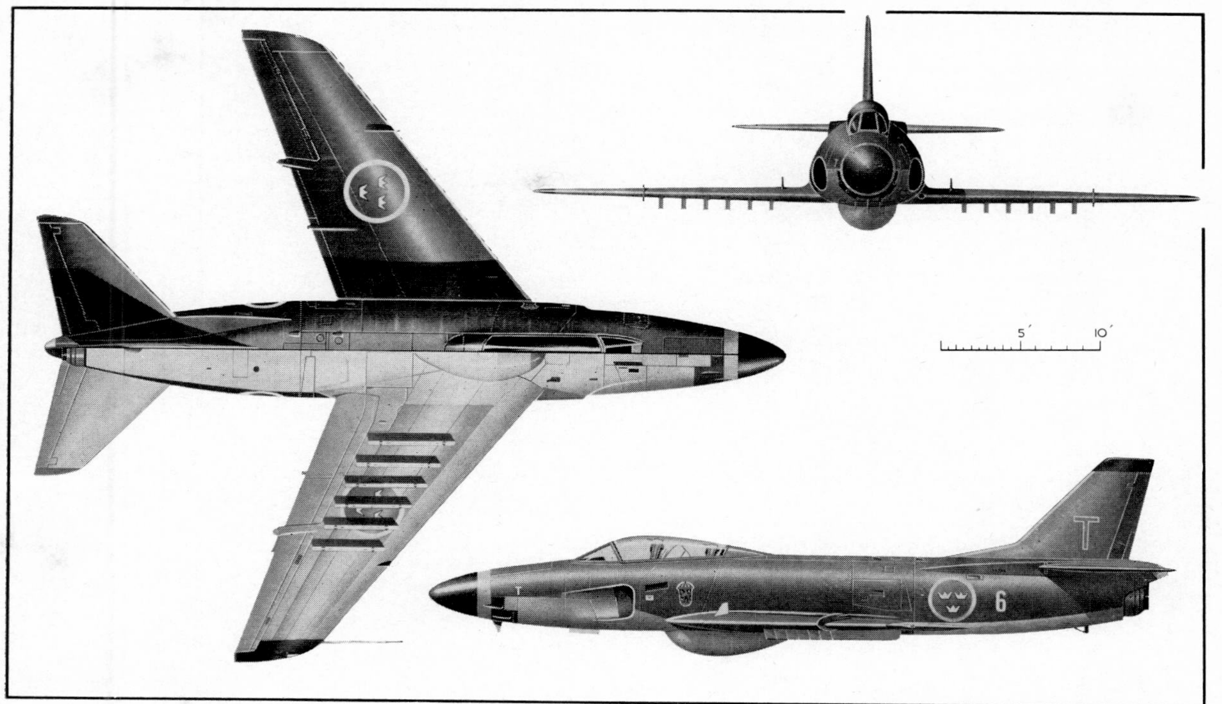
5´
10´
T
6

ventory until supplanted by the S 37 Viggen in the early 'seventies. Equipment is essentially similar to that of the A 32A, including PN-50/A and PN-51 navigational equipment and the PH-11/A radar altimeter, as is also fuel tankage and performance, but empty weight at 16,535 lb. is marginally higher than that of the attack aircraft, and loaded weight at 27,557 lb. is lower. The completely redesigned nose section, from which the cannon armament is deleted, houses the scanner for the PS-431/A reconnaissance radar and five OMERA cameras, these consisting of three SKa 16 side oblique cameras and two SKa 23 (or one SKa 23 and one SKa 15) vertical cameras with a Jungner optical sight. A photo-electric cell is provided for night photography, and 12 165-lb. M/62 flash bombs are carried on underwing racks for nocturnal missions. No armament is normally carried, although the wing, being identical to that of the A 32A, incorporates the necessary strong points for the attachment of stores pylons. The prototype S 32C was flown on March 26, 1957, and a modest number was manufactured during 1959–60.

Power Plant: *One Svenska Flygmotor RM 5A turbojet rated at* 7,940 *lb.s.t. and* 9,920 *lb.s.t. with afterburning.*
Performance: *Max. speed* (*at* 22,956 *lb.*), 685* *m.p.h. at sea level* (*Mach* 0.9), 607* *m.p.h. at* 36,000 *ft.; normal cruise*, 528 *m.p.h. at* 36,000–40,000 *ft.* (*Mach* 0.8)*; range cruise* (*max. fuel configuration*), 490 *m.p.h.* (*Mach* 0.74)*; range* (*clean*), 800–900 *mls. at* 30,000–40,000 *ft.*, (*with* 121 *Imp. gal.*/146 *U.S. gal. ventral tank*), 900–1,000 *mls.; initial climb* (*clean*), 11,810 *ft.*/*min.; service ceiling*, 49,210 *ft.*
Weights: *Empty*, 16,398 *lb.; normal loaded*, 22,956 *lb.; max. loaded*, 28,660 *lb.*
Dimensions: *Span*, 42 *ft.* 7¾ *in.; length*, 49 *ft.* 0¼ *in.; height*, 15 *ft.* 3 *in.; wing area*, 402.57 *sq. ft.*
*APPROXIMATE

(*Above*) *Yakovlev "Brewers" with and without forward radome.*

YAKOVLEV BREWER

A tactical attack and reconnaissance equivalent to the *Firebar* all-weather interceptor (see pages 180–182), the *Brewer*, the Soviet designation of which was unknown at the time of closing for press, is currently serving with the V.-V.S. in several versions. Embodying similar aerodynamic refinements to those incorporated in the *Firebar*, and possessing a similar widely-spaced "bicycle" under-carriage, the *Brewer* serves with the V.-V.S.'s Tactical Air Force, the *Frontovaya Aviatsiya*, and has apparently supplanted the Ilyushin Il-28 progressively since 1961–62. The tactical strike version of the *Brewer* has an internal weapons bay which occupies space in the fuselage presumably taken up in the reconnaissance model by fuel tankage. This reduction in internal fuel capacity is made up by flush-fitting auxiliary tanks carried immediately out-board of the engine nacelles and projecting well forward of the wing leading edge. The weapons bay is positioned well aft of the

GENERAL ARRANGEMENT DRAWING: *A Yakovlev Brewer of the V.-V.S.'s Frontovaya Aviatsiya.*

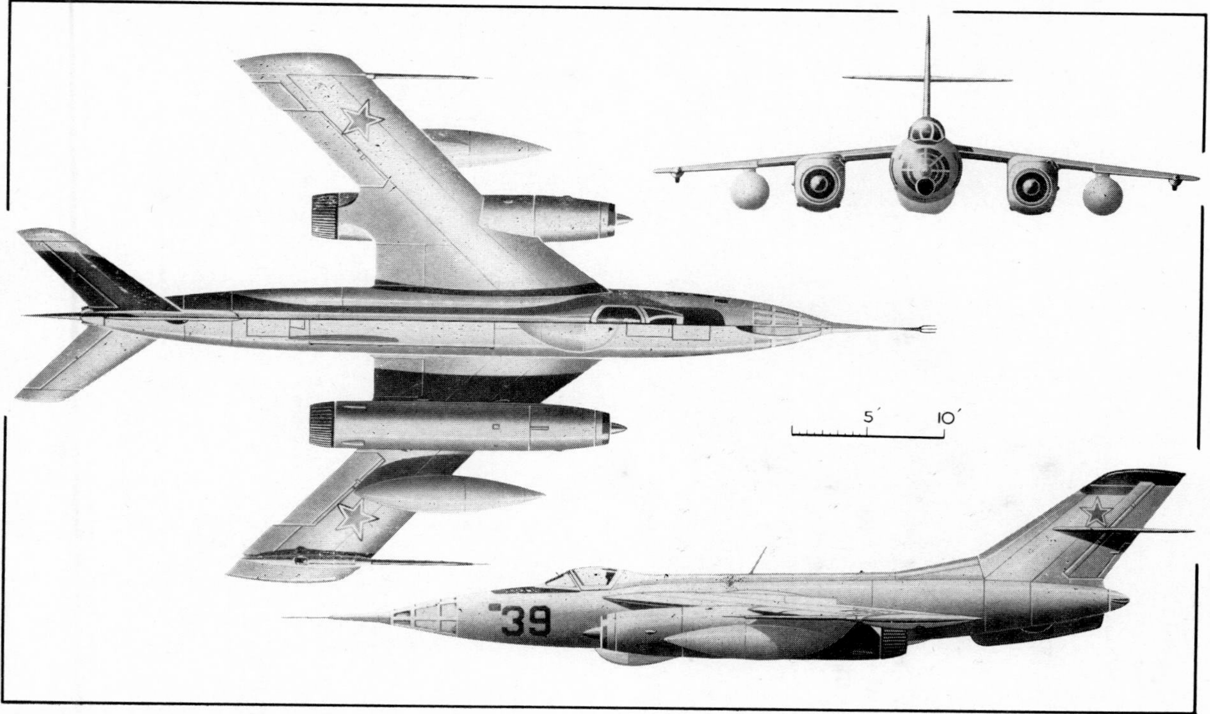
5´
10´
39

The widely-spaced "bicycle" undercarriage of the "Brewer" is clearly shown by these photographs (above and below), as are also the engine nacelles which, larger than those of the Yak-28 (*see Vol. II, pages* 113–115), *help to distinguish this later type.*

c.g. and is presumably intended to accommodate quite modest loads such as a small tactical nuclear store. Its introduction has necessitated some flattening of the lower fuselage contours and the provision of a pair of ventral strakes ahead of the rear undercarriage unit bay. A single 30-mm. cannon is mounted in the starboard side of the forward fuselage, and hard points outboard of the engine nacelles can carry pylons for ASMs, 1,100-lb. or 550-lb. bombs, or rocket pods housing 55-mm. missiles. The pylons, which project well ahead of the wing leading edges, can each carry a pair of 550-lb. bombs or rocket pods in tandem. Smaller stores can be carried on stations between the engine nacelles and fuselage.

The tactical reconnaissance variant of the *Brewer* has no weapons bay in the fuselage, this space being occupied by fuel tankage and non-optical reconnaissance sensors and ECM equipment. Forward- and side-oblique cameras are mounted in the nose which accommodates the second crew member, and the *Brewer* is in service both with and without a radome aft of the forward wheel bay. The radome presumably houses ground mapping and terrain avoidance radar, and radomes of various sizes have been seen on individual aircraft.

Power Plants: *Two axial-flow turbojets each rated at* 10,000* *lb.s.t. and* 13,200* *lb.s.t. with afterburning.*
Performance: *Max. speed,* 735* *m.p.h. at* 35,000 *ft.* (*Mach* 1.1)*;* 725* *m.p.h. at sea level* (*Mach* 0.95)*; tactical radius,* 230* *mls. at* 630* *m.p.h. at sea level,* 575* *mls. at* 570* *m.p.h. at* 35,000 *ft.; initial climb,* 28,000* *ft./min.; service ceiling,* 55,000* *ft.*
Weights: *Loaded,* 35,000* *lb.*
Dimensions: *Span,* 38 *ft.* 6 *in.**; *length,* 59 *ft.* 0 *in.**; *height,* 13 *ft.* 0 *in.**; *wing area,* 400* *sq. ft.*
*APPROXIMATE

AVIONICS FOR COMBAT AIRCRAFT

One of the most significant trends in fighters and bombers since the end of World War II has been the steady increase in the amount of electronics fitted, culminating in the present position where this type of equipment makes up 25–30 per cent of the total aircraft cost. For example, of the approximate £485,000 ($1.36m) production cost of the F-104G Starfighter, the various black boxes making up the autopilot, radio, radar, fire control, and navigation systems account for no less than £125,000 ($350,000), which is more than the entire cost of a fighter of the previous generation such as the F-86E at £78,340 ($219,460), and almost as much as a Hunter at £166,000 ($464,800)! It is obvious that such enormous changes can only be justified in terms of a complete re-appraisal of the role of the manned aircraft, and, in fact, this is exactly what has been taking place. Whereas military aircraft once merely paved the way for an ultimate victory on land, the advent of nuclear weapons gave them the ability to bring an enemy to his knees in a matter of hours. Overnight the decisive service elements became those concerned with the delivery of weapons of mass destruction, while the earlier techniques of blockade, attrition, invasion, and occupation were cast aside. Thus, by 1945, the most vital arm of any country's services was the strategic bombing force, although this has now largely been superseded by ballistic missile commands and tactical air power, thanks to the development of lightweight nuclear weapons.

However, the manned aircraft's dramatic increase in potential could only be used and relied on if weapons could be delivered completely independent of enemy defences and weather. One result was that designers had to aim for much higher performance, especially at low altitude, so as to make the tasks of detection and interception as difficult as possible. The bombing aircraft consequently required various types of flying aid to keep the piloting task within reasonable limits, and to ensure that penetrations could be made safely at night and in bad weather at a height of only a few hundred feet. In addition, highly accurate automatic navigation systems were required to take the aircraft straight to the target, fire control computers to deliver the weapon with precision, and reconnaissance equipment and communications systems that would convey information for succeeding strikes back to base. On the side of the interceptor, similar all-weather flying aids were required, together with effective means to find and destroy the bomber. Further complexity then arose from the bomber's need for counter-measures against the fighter's radar and missiles, and its opponent's need for equipment improvements to circumvent these measures. Thus, by the late 1950s, the combat aircraft's electronics had come to assume just as much significance as its performance and armament, and the idea of designing all this equipment from the outset as a single integrated weapons system had been firmly established.

RADIO EQUIPMENT

Communications are theoretically possible over a broad range of wavelengths, ranging from the 10 km. or more of VLF (very low frequencies), which is used for submerged Polaris submarines, to the 1 cm. or less of EHF (extremely high frequencies), which is a radar transmission under study for use by a data link for re-entry vehicles. However, in practice combat aircraft are normally equipped with UHF, which is used for most communications and supplemented with a stand-by set, and HF, which is used for long ranges and special purposes. Lower frequencies may give transmissions over several thousand miles, but reception can be poor at night, and is subject to meteorological conditions. In addition, there is a general shortage of channels on these longer wavelengths, which further militates against their use for communications, but they are used to some extent for navigation aids (e.g., Decca operates on LF, ADF on MF and DME on VHF).

Prior to World War II, the normal radio operated on HF, and

(Left) A Luftwaffe F-104G Starfighter being checked out by ground personnel. The mechanic behind the cockpit is checking the circuit breakers, aft of which are individual test panels and interchangeable "jeep can" electronics packages, and the mechanic standing on the ground is checking equipment in the high-voltage electrics bay.

this was superseded by VHF, which offered a useful number of channels and far clearer reception because its range was limited to "line of sight" transmission. To be more precise, VHF achieves perhaps twenty per cent more range than the earth's curvature would permit in straight-line transmission, and this waveband is consequently useful out to the region of 400 miles. In other applications VHF is employed for much greater ranges, using reflection from ionised layers in the atmosphere. This is the technique used in the NATO forward-scatter communication chain extending from Norway to Turkey.

In simple terms, UHF might be described as like VHF, but more so. It offers a much greater selection of channels, is strictly limited to line-of-sight range, and gives crystal-clear reception out to the order of 300 miles at medium altitudes. This is naturally excellent for normal purposes, but has a number of drawbacks in the context of modern operational technique. For example, if a low-flying reconnaissance aircraft is to transmit some urgent targeting data back to base from a range of 100 miles or more, then the use of either VHF or UHF would be out of the question. With many current reconnaissance aircraft it might very well be necessary to either climb to transmit, and thereby risk being shot down, or to communicate through a high-altitude aircraft orbiting over friendly territory. A similar problem arises in the case of a V/STOL aircraft at dispersal without support: communication on UHF between two points on the ground is limited to a very few miles, especially in forests and mountain areas, as was found in the early days of helicopter operations. The normal solution to these problems is to carry an additional radio operating on HF, which enables the dispersed aircraft to keep in touch with both its own base and nearby army units, and transmit reconnaissance information back to base irrespective of flight altitude.

AI RADAR

Airborne radar dates from the first few months of the war, when Blenheims were flown with a crude AI (Airborne Interception) equipment. By transmitting short pulses of extremely high intensity, it was possible to measure target range fairly accurately from the time taken for the pulses to return, but at that stage only a rough indication of target bearing could be obtained. Later, with the development of even higher frequencies (i.e., microwave radar), it became possible to focus the radiation into a narrow beam by means of a reflector dish compatible in size with the fighter nose, and to establish the exact bearing of the target by rotating the dish.

A reduction in wavelength had the effect of increasing detection range (assuming a constant transmitter power, dish size, etc.), but it was found that operation became increasingly affected by atmospheric attenuation (i.e., a reduction in signal strength due to absorption of energy). This may be illustrated by the ground-based radars used in long range surveillance and air traffic control: P-band (100 cm) shows no attenuation or reflection from rain, while the shorter end of L-band (25 cm) is markedly affected, although the reflections can easily be eliminated from the radar display. Coming down to the wavelengths used currently in AI radars, water vapour produces its peak attenuation at 1.0–1.5 cm, and consequently most radars of this type employ the longer wavelength of X-band (3 cm), which gives satisfactory performance over ranges of 20-50 miles.

In applications where very little range is required, it is possible to use much shorter wavelengths, namely Q-band (0.8 cm, known in the U.S. as Ka-band), which is the "window" between the peak attenuations of water vapour and oxygen. A Q-band radar might be used as a back-up for a normal X-band AI in case of jamming, but it is more often found on a civil aircraft in the form of storm-warning radar, and it has been developed as a blind-flying aid for helicopters. In the ground-based context, it is used for airfield control, where the high definition produced by short wavelength is essential, and a range of less than five miles is quite acceptable. Turning to electro-magnetic energy of even shorter wavelength, NASA is carrying out tests with a laser mounted in a T-33, the laser producing immensely powerful flashes of red light which are emitted in a narrow beam, permitting target range and bearing to be measured as with normal radar. Some idea of the power involved may be deduced from a typical experimental laser, which absorbs a supply of 2½ kilowatts, and emits pulses of no less than 15 megawatts. This LIDAR (LIght Detection And Ranging) set is intended primarily for detecting clear air turbulence, and is naturally useless in cloud, but it is possible that military applications on the lines of lightweight AI may follow.

Returning to the subject of present-day AI radars, acquisition range varies according to transmitter power, receiver sensitivity, and the effective echoing area of the target, in which the intakes play the predominant part in the head-on aspect. Range can be substantially increased by the use of a radar operator to search for the echo, rather than relying on automatic lock-on at a given signal strength. Probably the longest-range AI in normal service use, the AN/APQ-72 fitted to the Phantom II, is reported to pick up its targets at up to 60 miles range! One of the most significant features of this radar is its CW (continuous wave) target illumination facility, which presumably overcomes the normal pulsed-radar difficulty of detecting a low-flying target against ground return. Originally developed for Doppler navigation radar, CW transmission is basically an unmodulated, non-pulsed wave that enables relative speeds to be detected by the frequency shift of the return. Carried to its logical conclusion, this idea can be developed by modulating the wave in some way, so that the range of the target can be measured, which results in a hybrid, or pulsed-Doppler radar. Typical of recent practice, the F-4B and 4C Phantom IIs have an AAA-4 infra-red Search and Track Set, which probably has a useful search range against supersonic targets, and provides tracking in the presence of jamming, but mixed success with this equipment has led to its deletion from the later F-4D and 4J Phantom IIs. The Hughes infra-red sensor has been standard equipment on such types as the F-102A and F-106A for several years, however, and, more recently, has been adopted by the Saab 35F (see page 193).

AI radars must, of course, be able to recognise the enemy and for this purpose all military aircraft carry some form of IFF (identification friend/foe) equipment, which produces a distinctive blip on the radar screen of any interrogating fighter or ground control. In its simplest form IFF was just a transponder (i.e., it transmitted in response to a radar pulse) which emitted a short burst of energy after a given time delay, but now this type of equipment has become relatively sophisticated, transmitting a coded signal by which particular units can be distinguished. Early IFF was supplied to Russia before the end of the war, and succeeding versions were compromised in Korea, but the latest in service (reportedly IFF Mk. 12) is obviously very different in concept. It is likely that this has been removed from U.S. aircraft flying over Vietnam in view of the virtual absence of air opposition, and the disproportionate risk of it falling into enemy hands.

Just as the bomber needs IFF to declare its allegiance when interrogated by fighters from its own side, so it needs other devices to provide warning of enemy interceptors and to minimise the risk of destruction. Tail-warning radar may be active or passive, the former giving range data (and presumably rough bearing information) on approaching fighters, while passive radar merely in-

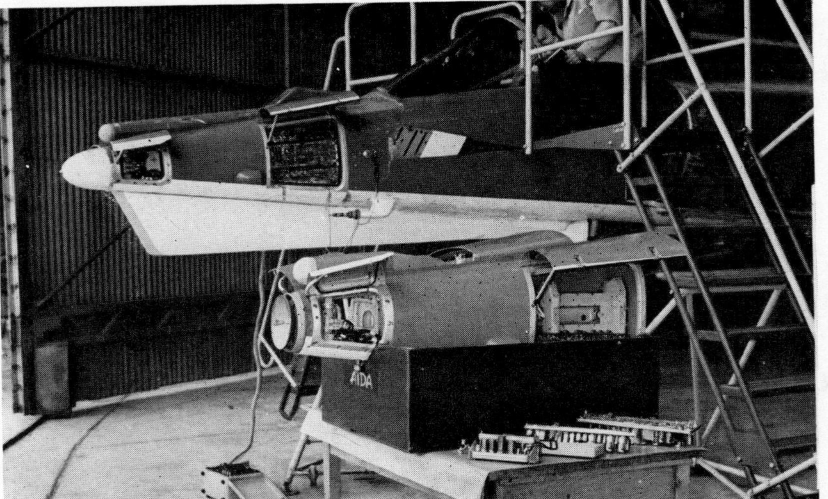

(Left) The Dassault Aïda search and tracking radar installed in the Etendard IVM has separate radomes, one above the other, for the transmitter and receiver units. Its limited-range search capacity was designed specifically for over-water operation.

(Right) The CSF Cyrano Ibis intercept radar of the Mirage IIIC. This provides search, lock-on and ranging modes, and is capable of guiding the semi-active MATRA R.511 and R.530 AAMs. It has no mapping mode but can scan the ground and reveal major surface features.

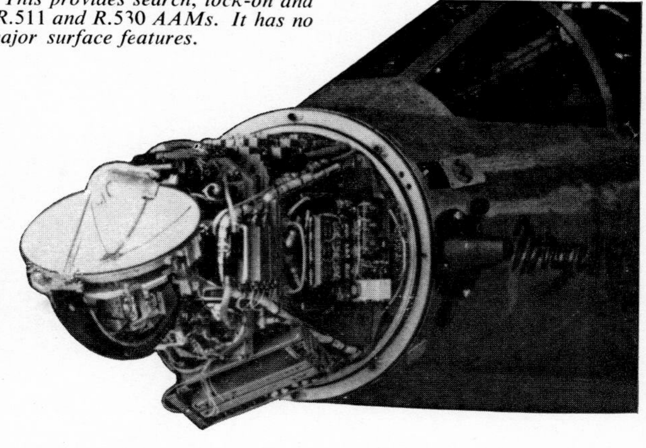

dicates that the bomber is being illuminated by radar. Active radar has the significant advantage that it gives the bomber pilot a clear idea of when the fighter has closed to firing range, and therefore when to take evasive action and to start ECM (electronic counter-measures), but it may also give away the bomber's position. This was happening over Europe late in 1943, when German night fighters were equipped with FuG 227 "Flensburg" AI to home on to the "Monica" tail warning radars of Allied bombers. The obvious solution is for the bomber to carry out a passive watch until the fighter's radar appears to be locked on, then turn to active radar for ranging.

Counter-measures can take many forms, aimed at disguising the bomber's identity, making weapon launch computation as difficult as possible, jamming the missile's guidance, or producing premature fuzing. In any protracted war, it is clear that electronic "ferret" missions would be made with the purpose of interrogating enemy aircraft and analysing their IFF response, so that this could be simulated by friendly bombers. Conversely the bomber might launch decoys which simulate its own response to both ground and AI radars. Jamming in its simplest form is provided by transmitting radar "noise" on the fighter's AI wavelength, thus denying the range data essential for missile firing. Frequency-switching radars were used operationally early in 1945 to overcome this type of counter-measure, and this facility is now doubtless a normal feature of any AI, requiring the bomber to jam over a whole range of wavelengths. In addition, "window" (radar-reflecting strips of metal foil) may be released by the bomber, a move that is probably most effective against a single-seat fighter relying on an automatic radar lock-on.

Provided that adequate warning can be achieved, the missile is the weakest link in the interception chain from a counter-measures viewpoint, since it lacks the cynical detachment of the human operator, and the ability to wait and see, or benefit from a second opinion. First generation homing missiles lack the capability to search for the bomber, once their attention has been distracted, and therefore they must represent easy meat for such measures as "window", flares, or tracer bullets. Warhead detonation is normally triggered by radar or infra-red proximity fuzes, which may be prematurely activated by jamming or spurious heat sources. However, all the counter-measures to be used against missiles rely critically on knowing when firing has taken place, which is an excellent argument for retaining a rear-gunner, who could presumably see the launch flash at normal firing ranges.

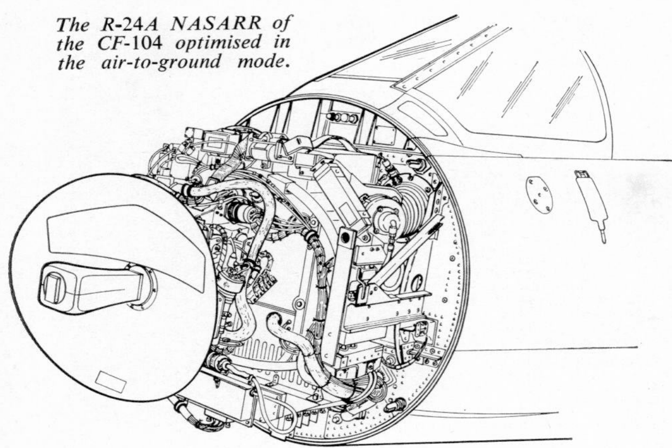

The R-24A NASARR of the CF-104 optimised in the air-to-ground mode.

ATTACK RADARS

Ground-mapping radar came into limited use principally on the Lancaster and B-29 before the end of the war, and developed into massive proportions for the high resolution equipment of bombers such as the Vulcan, B-52 and Tu-20 Bear-B. However, by the late 1950s first generation surface-to-air guided weapons were in widespread service, and realistic intrusions could then only be based on the idea of flying at a height of no more than a few hundred feet. This had the twofold effect of reducing warning time, the bomber being picked up at perhaps 50 miles instead of 300, and of making it virtually impossible to fire missiles against it from the ground. First generation weapons took a considerable time to prepare for action, and could only be launched after locking on to the bomber, so that by this change in tactics the strategic bomber remained a viable system for several years. The U.S.A.F. Strategic Air Command began low level training missions in 1959, and were followed, after a gap of five years, by R.A.F. Bomber Command. The forward-looking radars of these aircraft had been designed to produce a very detailed map of the ground from heights of 45,000–55,000 ft., rather than terrain avoidance facility, yet they achieved a limited all-weather capability at low level, thus holding the fort until American ICBMs had been deployed in quantity.

Notwithstanding the decline of the strategic bomber, ballistic missiles are ill-suited to the rapidly changing needs of tactical nuclear strike, and therefore the combination of lightweight nuclear weapon and high performance fighter-bomber is likely to remain effective into the foreseeable future. When small atomic bombs first became available, they were employed on aircraft such as the F-86H and F-100D, which had no really effective bad-weather capability, although low level flying over fairly flat ground could presumably have been carried out in emergency on radar altimeter. The F-101C Voodoo and A-3 Skywarrior were also allocated to tactical strike duties, but appear to have nothing more than simple ground-mapping radars. As a result of intensive efforts to get the attack aircraft closer to the deck irrespective of weather conditions, a new generation of airborne radars appeared, presenting not only a plot from which the target could be identified, but also a display from which a safe height could be maintained over undulating terrain, and obstacles avoided. The first two aircraft to enter service with this improved equipment were the A-4C Skyhawk and F-105D Thunderchief, both of which might be regarded as having a limited all-weather capability. The F-105D is equipped with Autonetics R-14A NASARR, which has been developed to the F-15A for the F-104G Starfighter, providing both air-to-air and air-to-surface modes.

Although such radars represent a major advance, the task of carrying out a blind strike is by no means easy, and this is particularly true for single-seat aircraft. The map of the ground produced by radar at low level is a vastly different proposition from conventional charts, and the pilot must be very intensively briefed if he is to make real use of this as a navigation aid. Sore-thumb targets such as coastlines, lakes, rivers, mountains, and towns will be seen, but in many tactical situations there are no really distinctive features. A further cause for concern must be that the pilot cannot normally follow a radar map and a terrain avoidance display at the same time. One of the basic forms of avoidance displays is contour-mapping, which shows in plan-form all the ground above a level selected by the pilot, enabling him to divert around mountains in his path. Alternatively the ground along his track may be shown as a plot of height versus distance ahead.

Both of the above systems are rather crude, and are likely to be superseded by an automatic contour-following facility, which was intended for the TSR-2, and will presumably be fitted to the F-111K. At the present moment the only attack aircraft in the world with full all-weather potential is the A-6A Intruder, which is equipped with twin-radar DIANE (Digital Integrated Attack System) to enable it to carry out the entire mission automatically, with the exception of the take-off and landing phases. However, many problems doubtless remain to be solved before blind, low-level operations become an entirely routine procedure: isolated obstacles on hill-tops might give insufficient radar return to activate an automatic system, and ground defences might use radar-reflective balloons to force the bomber to climb and thus make it an easy target.

Once the target area has been reached, then forward-looking radars can be used to feed the co-ordinates of the objective into the bombing computer, or alternatively the attack may be made by reference to an IP (identification point) in the same vicinity. This latter technique caters for a target which has no distinctive radar response, and it also enables the weapon to be launched without radar illuminating the target itself. In the case of a non-nuclear war, electronics play a significant part in an attack with bombs, rockets, or cannon by supplying range information to the fire control computer. Although radar ranging (which has been in use on fighters since 1949, when it was introduced on the F-86A Sabre) is adequate for regular dive attacks, it loses its accuracy at very shallow angles due to the width of the radar beam illuminating a long strip of ground. One means of improvement would be to employ the narrower beam of the laser (mentioned earlier in the AI context), and this idea is now being investigated by the U.S.A.F., this service having evaluated a complete Hughes laser fire control system in an F-4C Phantom II. Fitted in place of the normal infra-red scanner under the nose of the F-4C, the laser emits a beam which is slaved to the optical gunsight. Highly accurate range information is then fed to the bombing computer, where it is combined with height and speed data from the inertial navigator. Most new U.S.A.F. tactical aircraft are currently considered as likely recipients of lasers, including the F-111A with the Mk.2 avionics system, and many existing aircraft may be retrofitted.

Reconnaissance radars differ in several respects from the forward-looking equipment already discussed. One basic difference

(Below) The Gannet A.E.W. Mk. 3 is currently the standard Royal Navy shipboard early warning aircraft. Thirty-eight aircraft of this type were built 1958–61 for No. 849 Squadron which deploys flights aboard the Royal Navy's carriers. Two radar operators are accommodated in the fuselage, the search antenna being housed by the ventral radome.

(Above and below) Grumman E-2A Hawkeye early warning aircraft of VAW-11's Detachment "C", the first operational Hawkeye unit.

in requirements is that in painting a map of the ground, height is of little significance, while a good azimuth definition is essential. The clarity (or definition) is dictated by the ratio of radar wavelength to the effective size (or aperture) of the aerial, so that a narrow beam demands a short wavelength and a large aperture in the appropriate plane. For example, a ground-based height-finding radar needs to be very tall to provide good definition in the vertical plane, and conversely an airborne reconnaissance radar needs to have a large horizontal dimension for mapping clarity. The most straightforward solution is to have a long, shallow rotating dish, as on the E-1B Tracer, which has a 32 ft. by 20 ft. radome housing a 17.5 ft. APS-82 antenna sweeping at 6 r.p.m.

Such gigantic radomes are impractical for high performance aircraft, and this has led to the use of electronic (rather than mechanical) scanning. In this case, rather than directing the transmission at a parabolic reflector dish from a feed horn on the end of a waveguide (a rectangular tube along which the microwave energy is ducted), the transmission is allowed to escape from a series of slots cut into a straight length of waveguide. This slotted waveguide (or linear array) is the basis of SLAR (sideways-looking airborne radar), and the extremely narrow beam that it emits can be scanned from side to side by changing the time delays between the slots so as to incline the wave front. SLAR is frequently produced as a long, cylindrical pod, which can be mounted underneath reconnaissance aircraft. One well known example is the APS-84 SLAR carried beneath the fuselage of the U.S. Army's OV-1B Mohawk, which has been operated in Vietnam to detect night-time Vietcong movements. Looking further into the future, the quest for large effective apertures without correspondingly large aerials has led to intensive development work on synthetic aperture radars, which were originally projected for the B-58, B-70, and U-2, and may eventually reach fruition as a result of a Goodyear contract to produce such a radar for the F-4C. In essence, synthetic aperture achieves the effect of an extremely long antenna by using a pulsed-Doppler transmission and comparing the returns over a period of sampling, so that two points in close proximity on the ground may be distinguished by slightly different frequency shifts over a sample of perhaps seven pulses.

Where the requirement is to produce a radar map of an area for storage or continuous transmission back to base, rather than merely searching for a target, then it is convenient to eliminate beam scanning, and simply use the motion of the aircraft to provide area coverage. In this system (which was developed *inter alia* by EMI for the TSR-2), each pulse of transmission produces a map of a narrow strip of ground abreast of the aircraft, which then moves on to cover an adjacent strip. Each of these linear maps is then recorded on film or transmitted for simultaneous analysis at base, in either case adding up to a normal radar map of the area. Not only does this show natural and man-made features, but also through MTI (moving target indication) it can distinguish objects such as motor vehicles. Aside from the convenience of this method of coverage, it has the advantage that any one point on the ground is only illuminated very briefly, so that the system cannot be homed on to, or jammed. Exactly the same technique can be used on optical wavelengths, when it becomes known as Line Scan. Also developed by EMI for the TSR-2, Line Scan may be applied either passively or actively, the latter night-time mode requiring a spot of light to sweep the ground from side to side, in phase with the scanning of the photo-electric eye.

NAVIGATION

Aside from the search and mapping duties already described, radar can be used to provide a dead-reckoning navigation system which is completely independent of weather conditions and ground installations. In this application use is made of the apparent change in frequency of a wave reflected from the ground, due to the movement of the surface relative to the source, i.e. Doppler effect. In practice this is utilised by placing an aerial system in the belly of the aircraft, and arranging it to produce two narrow beams of CW radiation, which are aimed forwards and toed out lightly. The frequencies of the returning waves are compared with those of the transmissions, and the two beams are then turned until the frequency shifts are identical, when the centre line of the aerial system is pointing down the actual aircraft track, and both the drift angle and ground speed can be fed into a computer. In order to eliminate any errors due to the aircraft pitch angle, a further pair of beams pointing rearwards is sometimes added to produce a Janus system, named after the twin-headed god of time, who had one pair of eyes looking into the future, and the other pair looking back into the past.

Since it eliminates the error in estimating wind strength and direction, a Doppler navigator is naturally far more accurate than a simple air data system, which computes aircraft movement from

(*Above*) *The Grumman E-*1*B Tracer early warning derivative of the S-*2 *Tracker now being supplanted by the E-*2*A* (*see opposite*). *The* 17.5-*ft. antenna housed by the radome sweeps at* 6 *r.p.m.*

(Above) The Douglas EA-1F Skyraider, an electronics countermeasures version of the A-1E, is an early example of a specialised ECM aircraft intended to confuse radar-controlled anti-aircraft weapons and detecting devices. Sensors in external pods analyse signals received and produce active countermeasures. The Grumman EA-6B Intruder is currently under development to fulfil this role.

pitot-static pressures and forecast wind data, but the latter system is probably quite adequate for ground support duties in a non-nuclear war. Where greater precision is essential, a Doppler radar may be used, but navigation accuracy still relies on the compass system which translates the drift angle into the actual track, resulting in errors of perhaps one per cent of the distance travelled, i.e., six miles per hour in a typical low level strike mission. Doppler also has the disadvantage that it may cut out at extreme bank angles and during a loft manoeuvre, and there is some risk that the transmission might disclose the aircraft's position to the enemy. Furthermore, operation may be poor over a calm sea, and over waves there is presumably an error due to their speed.

Radio waves are useful for fixing the aircraft's position relative to known ground beacons, but this type of aid is more applicable to peacetime flying. One of the oldest navaids is ADF (automatic direction finding), which is otherwise known as radio compass, and provides bearings to MF radio stations. An alternative homing aid is DME (distance measuring equipment), which only gives a rough indication of bearing, and is being superseded by TACAN, working on UHF rather than VHF, and giving both range and bearing.

Star tracking, or auto-astro, is an accurate method of navigation for either day or night-time use, but it is clearly not applicable to an aircraft which is to operate below cloud base. It is at present used by the B-52, B-57, and B-58, and operates by tracking a celestial body (in daylight this would be the sun, moon, or Venus), from the altitude of which the computer can deduce the aircraft's heading, although not the actual track. Observation of two bodies produces a position fix. Apart from being used as a primary means of navigation in bombers, missiles, and space vehicles, it is possible that auto-astro will be used in long endurance, high altitude aircraft to monitor compass systems or to align the inertial platform.

Inertial navigation was originally developed to fulfil the needs of the German V-2 ballistic missiles, which had no other self-contained means of measuring velocity, and hence determining the fuel cut-off point. Rather strangely, the present boom in inertial guidance for aircraft applications arises in the main from German demands for a system for the F-104G at a time when none of the major air arms (except that of the U.S. Navy) had any serious interest in pure inertial systems for manned aircraft. The basic principle is that by continuously measuring acceleration (by an inertia weight extending a spring), it is possible to compute velocity, and from this the position of the aircraft. In practice it is complicated by motion taking place in three dimensions over a curved earth; this problem might be overcome by mounting three accelerometers and rate gyros on the structure (a "strap-down" system), but the computation required by the outputs is unnecessarily complex. Instead, the three accelerometers are set on a gimbal-mounted platform (the "stable table"), which is continuously adjusted so that the accelerometer axes point North, East, and vertical, enabling the system to compute movement directly in terms of latitude, longitude and, if necessary, height.

Once the platform has been set up, the re-levelling to allow for aircraft movement is computed from its change in longitude and latitude, this system of control being known as Schuler tuning, after the man who recognised in 1923 that such a system was akin to a pendulum as long as the radius of the earth, giving an 84 minute oscillation. One of the critical points in inertial navigation is the initial alignment of the platform, which is a compromise between delay time and accuracy of computation. Provided that the aircraft is not moved between flights, then reasonably accurate results can be obtained by use of a memory unit, which re-aligns the platform with its attitude at shut-down after the previous flight. By this means the Litton LN-3 in the F-104G can be prepared for flight in approximately 90 seconds. The alternative, starting from scratch, is to use the accelerometers to find the vertical, and then use rate gyros to find East-West by measuring the earth's rate of rotation, a process known as gyro-compassing. This might take as much as 20 minutes to reach the same level of accuracy.

Inertial systems are fundamentally expensive because of the precision with which they must be constructed, requiring close tolerance engineering and assembly in special dust-free plants. Some idea of the advances involved in this field may be obtained from the fact that gyro "drift" can result in a navigation error of up to 70 miles/degree/hour, and that in pre-inertial days a gyro might drift at over 10 degrees/hour! As a result of intensive development, a modern gyro will drift at far less than 0·1 degrees/hour. In spite of the high price involved (the F-104G system costs £35,000 [$98,000], i.e., almost as much as the F-15A radar), inertial navigation is unique in being undetectable, unjammable, fully manoeuvrable, and completely independent of ground beacons and weather conditions.

Following the crude pendulous gyro accelerometer of the V-2, inertial guidance was developed largely at Massachusetts Institute of Technology by a team under Dr. Draper. Thanks to this work at MIT, inertial systems were available for missile applications in the 1950s, but they tipped the scales at around 300 lb., and were in the main only operated for a few minutes. Somewhat lighter equipment that could be operated for longer periods was manufactured notably for the Hound Dog missile and A-5 Vigilante by North American, who are also associated with the SINS (Ship Inertial Navigation System) in the Polaris submarines. Stable tables were produced as highly accurate reference systems for ASW

(*Below*) *The L.M. Ericsson-built Hughes infra-red sensor beneath the nose of a J 35F Draken. This passive, heat-sensitive detector receives infra-red radiation emitted from the target aircraft's engines at ranges of* 12–19 *miles, the signal being processed through the fire control computer to provide an "aiming dot".*

aircraft, and Sperry produced the inertial component of the B-58 Doppler/inertial/astro mix, but the real breakthrough on miniature systems was still to come.

In the late 1950's, when claims of accuracies better than 5 miles per hour were regarded as wild sales talk, the Federal German *Luftwaffe* requested proposals for a miniature system that would give a 50 per cent probability of an error less than 2.3 miles after one hour of flight. After a bitterly fought contest, Litton won the order for over 1,400 systems for the F-104G, their LN-3 weighing approximately 80 lb. and occupying 1.8 cu. ft. To illustrate the progress that has since been made, the same company has proposed for the ILAAS (Integrated Light Attack Avionics System) of later Corsair IIs an inertial navigator designated ASN-44, which weighs less than 40 lb. and occupies only 0.44 cu. ft.!

Keeping step with the complexity of nav-attack systems, artificial flight aids are finding increasing acceptance as it becomes more difficult to produce an aircraft that handles well throughout the ever-widening flight envelope. Many transonic fighters made use of a yaw damper to improve firing accuracy and eliminate Dutch Roll, but their supersonic counterparts mainly employ stability augmentation on all three axes, with some autopilot modes in addition. Typical of Mach 2.0 equipment is the Minneapolis-Honeywell MH-97G on the F-104G, which provides damping in pitch, roll, and yaw, together with height-, Mach-, or heading-hold as required, and automatic pitch control giving stick shaking and stick snatching to safeguard against pitch-up at low speeds.

One result of carrying self-contained navaids and of providing for several modes of attack is that a great deal of computation takes place on board the aircraft, and this is leading to a switch from the previous variety of simple analogue computers to possibly a single all-can-do digital computer. As its name suggests, the analogue computer makes its calculation by using an electrical circuit with characteristics chosen to respond in a manner analogous to a particular dynamic problem, such as computing the trajectory of a bomb. In contrast, a digital computer can be used to store vast quantities of data, and to carry out an infinite variety of calculations, but the price of this impressive capability is in the region of £10,000, or $28,000. The first airborne digital computer is believed to be the Autonetics Verdan which forms part of the REINS (Radar-Equipped Inertial Navigation System) of the A-5 Vigilante. Further applications of digital computers include the DIANE (Digital Integrated Attack System) of the A-6 Intruder and the ILAAS proposed for later Corsair IIs.

One final aspect from which major changes have taken place has been the method of displaying information to the pilot. In earlier years his presentation would have consisted of direct-reading flight instruments, and navigation information shown possibly as a bearing integrated with the compass display, plus a digital read-out of distance. Firstly, servo-operated flight instruments were introduced so that the basic data could be processed more accurately and presented in ways that were easier to comprehend. Secondly, navigation information can now be shown either as a moving strip map (as in the Decca system) or as a moving map display on the instrument panel, produced by optical projection from microfilmed charts. This latter type of equipment was developed by Ferranti for the TSR-2. Thirdly, all basic flight data can be projected from a bright-face cathode ray tube on to a glass screen, or the windscreen itself, so as to minimise the pilot's need to look inside the cockpit during low level flight. One example of this category is the Elliott Head-Up Display, which is used by the Buccaneer, and has been ordered for the Short Belfast and Saab 37 Viggen. One interesting point is that development concentrated on this class of reflective display partly out of a reaction against a much more ambitious American scheme, which envisaged the windscreen as a flat, see-through TV tube, on which various displays could be generated. Perhaps even this system will be practical in time!

INDEX TO AIRCRAFT TYPE

Page numbers in **bold type** indicate primary coverage of the aircraft concerned.